BIRDS of the SHEFFIEL

A

A pair of Black-necked Grebes bred in 1982-84.   P. Leonard

BIRDS of the SHEFFIELD AREA
including the north-east Peak District

---

edited by

Jon Hornbuckle and David Herringshaw

---

contributions by

K. Clarkson, I.S. Francis, D. Gosney,
D. Herringshaw, J. Hornbuckle,
D. S. Marshall, A.J. Morris

---

illustrations by

P.A. Ardron, L. Cornthwaite, P. Leonard,
N.H. Richardson, I.D. Rotherham,
J.P. Smith, F.J. Watson

**SHEFFIELD BIRD STUDY GROUP
& SHEFFIELD CITY LIBRARIES**

ISBN 0 907575 06 4   soft cover
0 907575 05 6   hard cover

First published in 1985 by Sheffield Bird Study Group
in association with
Sheffield City Libraries, Surrey Street, Sheffield S1 1XZ

Phototypesetting, Printing and Binding by
Higham Press Ltd, Shirland, Derbyshire
Text set in 9pt Souvenir

Cover design and illustration by Paul Leonard
featuring Kestrel and Little Ringed Plover
Title-page illustration: Goshawk by Les Cornthwaite

Contents

Foreword

When first invited to provide the Foreword to this book, I was somewhat hesitant, being very aware that I had never even visited Sheffield, quite apart from never having looked through a pair of binoculars in the area to be covered by this book. Now, however, having seen much of the text, maps, histograms and other illustrations, I am quite delighted to have been asked to contribute.

Ornithology everywhere, but perhaps especially in Britain, is based on detailed local studies. Sometimes, especially in the last century and early in this, these were the work of individuals. Nowadays, many birdwatchers have discovered the pleasure to be gained from co-operative work on projects such as atlas surveys, census of individual species, wildfowl counts and so on. It is so much more satisfying to be part of a team and to feel that every piece of information collected is not just pleasurable for oneself but also of value to the team and to posterity. The work summarised in this book is a glowing example of the value of such co-operative studies, and of the collection in one place of the observations made by many individuals. It is difficult, when writing this foreword, not to sound effusive, for the very high standard of work has been matched by the care and attention given by those responsible for its presentation. Not only are the detailed, serious studies described interestingly, but the circumstances of the occurrence of rarities are interestingly outlined and not merely listed in order.

I have no doubt that this book will not only become a classic in the ornithological history of the Sheffield area, but will be very widely referred to elsewhere as a model for other similar local publications. I have, myself, been involved from time to time in both compiling and using works of this sort. My appreciation of the difficulties encountered by the compilers and the strict requirements of the user make me doubly criticial, but this book fills me with admiration.

Even if the purchaser has no scientific interest in birds, the line-drawings in this book are worthy of collection in their own right.

To all those concerned: well done!

J.T.R. SHARROCK

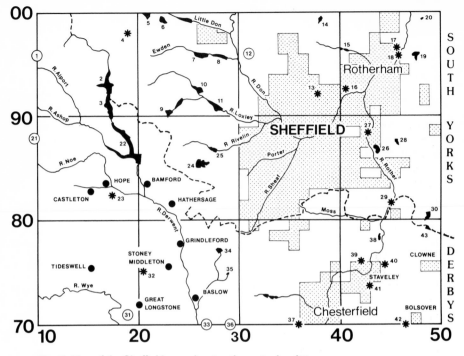

Fig. 1 Map of the Sheffield area showing the major localities.

KEY

1	BLEAKLOW	23	BRADWELL PONDS
2	HOWDEN RESR	24	REDMIRES RESRS
3	DERWENT RESR	25	RIVELIN RESRS
4	MICKLEDEN	26	TREETON DYKE
5	LANGSETT RESR	27	CATCLIFFE FLASH
6	MIDHOPE RESR	28	ULLEY RESR
7	BROOMHEAD RESR	29	ROTHER VALLEY C.P.
8	MOREHALL RESR	30	HARTHILL RESR
9	STRINES	31	MONSAL DALE
10	AGDEN RESR	32	MIDDLETON MOOR
11	DAMFLASK RESR	33	CHATSWORTH PARK
12	WHARNCLIFFE	34	BARBROOK RESR
13	CONCORD PARK	35	RAMSLEY
14	ELSECAR RESR	36	EAST MOOR
15	WENTWORTH	37	WALTON DAM
16	TINSLEY S.F.	38	RENISHAW PARK
17	KILNHURST FLASH	39	BARROW HILL
18	THRYBERGH BANKS	40	STAVELEY S.F.
19	THRYBERGH RESR	41	POOLSBROOK
20	OLD DENABY FLASH	42	CARR VALE FLASH
21	KINDER	43	PEBLEY POND
22	LADYBOWER RESR		

 urban area   - - - county boundary

7

Introduction and Acknowledgements.

The idea for this book was first conceived some eleven years ago, at a time when developments in local ornithology were gaining momentum. It has had a prolonged incubation period, during which time there have been several editorial changes and considerable discussion as to its scope and format. The book's origin lies in the *Atlas* of breeding birds project conducted by the Sheffield Bird Study Group in 1975-80. The survey aimed to map the distribution of all breeding birds in the Sheffield area (Fig. 1) on a 'tetrad' (2x2km or 4km²) basis. It was thought to be unduly ambitious by some, and, indeed, 300 tetrads did seem daunting to the original participants. However, once the end was in sight, it was decided to incorporate the results into a new and complete avifauna of the Sheffield area, principally covering the period since 1960.

Several local ornithologists were invited to write sections relating to their own interests and expertise. Some responded well, whilst others were much slower to complete their tasks. In order to establish some uniformity and to bring the accounts completely up to date, the editors decided to virtually rewrite most of the text. During this process, all published records were checked against the original source and doubtful information reviewed, whilst relevant historical data were also included. The editing process has inevitably been time-consuming, but we believe it to have been worthwhile and take full responsibility for any mistakes which may have occurred.

The art work has proceeded with fewer difficulties, and such was the enthusiasm of the contributors, that we have been able to select the illustrations used from the large number submitted. We must especially thank Paul Leonard for the work he has done with Figures, maps and, of course, his superb art-work, including the excellent front cover. To Derek Watson we owe a special word of thanks, not only for his line drawings, but also for the benefit of his professional expertise on design. Les Cornthwaite was an enthusiastic contributor, as shown by the number of his drawings accepted, and Ian Rotherham gave generously both of his time and artistic expertise. Steve Shaw's contribution to the preparation of the maps and Figures has also been invaluable.

A project of this nature cannot be achieved without a great deal of assistance. Ian Francis put a considerable effort into the chapter on habitats and bird communities, and the wildfowl accounts. David Gosney, who was one of the original instigators of this book, prepared much background material for the accounts, and then wrote the initial drafts for many of the passerine species. Keith Clarkson wrote the chapter on migration studies and most of the original finch accounts. All three commented on many of the original drafts, along with R.A. Frost, P.K. Gill, C. Jacklin and S.J. Roddis. Tony Morris prepared the wader accounts and details of the escaped species. David Marshall, who was particularly active in the *Atlas* project, wrote up nearly all the seabirds and a variety of other species. Geoff Mawson provided the ringing data and comments on certain species such as Black Redstart. Roy Frost and Simon Roddis were particularly helpful, the former largely due to his unparalleled knowledge of Derbyshire birds, and the latter because of his literary ability and knowledge of Sheffield bird records. David Wilson provided useful historical information, and Derek Yalden details on moorland birds.

8

The main brunt of the typing was borne by Mary Bellinger and Trevor Grimshaw with assistance from Jill Lewis, Carol Helliwell, Sue Thomas and Simon Roddis. Assistance in proof reading was given mainly by Steve Shaw, Tony Morris and Simon Roddis.

The following also provided useful comments and information:-
P. A. Ardron, K. Bayes, R.J. Fuller, the late W.E. Gibbs, D.J. Glaves, S.J. Hayhow, S.H. Holliday, M. Limbert, C.R. McKay, T. Marshall, Mrs.B.A. Moore, J. Russell, D.T. Salmon, A.H.V. Smith, J. Lintin Smith, J. P. Smith, K.V. Tayles, D. Whiteley.

We also wish to thank the following bodies for permission to publish their results:-

> Barnsley Bird Study Group
> Derbyshire Ornithological Society
> Doncaster and District Ornithological Society
> Rotherham and District Ornithological Society
> Sheffield Bird Study Group
> Sorby Breck Ringing Group
> Sorby Natural History Society
> Yorkshire Naturalists' Union

Norman Wall of Higham Press was very patient with the Editors and performed an excellent, highly professional job in setting up the pages. Both he and Jon Pyle of Sheffield City Libraries were very helpful on all aspects of the publication. Finally, we must express our gratitude to Dr J.T.R. Sharrock for his Foreword, and to Eve Hornbuckle for assistance in many ways.

The Sheffield region, with its diversity of altitude, climate, geology, habitat and land-use, has considerable ornithological potential. There is much to keep the active birdwatcher occupied for years hence. We hope that this publication will provide a firm foundation upon which future generations of birdwatchers can build.

Jon Hornbuckle
David Herringshaw

Rookery   L. Cornthwaite

CHAPTER ONE

A Brief History of Sheffield Ornithology

Over three centuries have elapsed since Sheffield's first recorded ornithologist, Francis Jessop of Broom Hall, corresponded with the great Francis Willughby. The latter's *Ornithology* (1) was published by his friend John Ray in 1676 and 1678 and contained details of several species submitted by Jessop which were presumably seen by him in the Sheffield region. Since that time the area has nurtured some fine naturalists, several of whom have made major contributions to national ornithology. Renowned ornithologists such as Henry Seebohm, Francis Jourdain, Charles Dixon and Ralph Chislett spent at least part of their lives looking at birds around Sheffield. Many others, perhaps equally talented but not so widely recognised, were active in the region or at least visited it. Some have left the results of their studies in published form; others have left skin specimens, egg collections or diaries; but, sadly, many have left little or nothing and their work is lost forever.

Any avifauna, county or regional, which attempts to assess the changes in status of the birds within an area can only be as good as the foundations laid down by earlier field-workers. There has been much tramping of Sheffield countryside in the past two centuries by birdwatchers of all ages and experience. Interestingly, despite the wealth of accumulated knowledge and the outstanding ornithological prowess of many of our forbears, there was no significant attempt to co-ordinate information about Sheffield's birds in anything other than a cursory form until the last two decades.

In this account we have endeavoured to "set the ornithological scene" in preparation for the main part of the book. Unfortunately, space permits only a résumé of the events which have occurred and the individuals who have made a major contribution to our present knowledge of local birds.

Francis Jessop (1638-1691) is undoubtedly the first ornithologist of any eminence in Sheffield. He inherited Broom Hall at an early age, had private means and a deep interest in natural history. He was a friend of John Ray who stayed with him in 1668, subsequently travelling to north Yorkshire and Westmorland (2). Ray introduced Jessop to Francis Willughby, who was preparing the first account of birds in Britain. This book was later edited and published by John Ray and contains much information supplied by Jessop who also sent him specimens of Dipper, Twite, Puffin, Woodcock and Pied Flycatcher, some or all of which must have been obtained around Sheffield.

In the century following Jessop's death we know little about the birds which occurred in the area. Between 1761 and 1784 the rector of Staveley, Francis Gisborne, collected a large number of bird specimens from within his parish. A detailed account is given by the Rev. Charles Molineux, published in 1892 (3). This provides a valuable insight into the birds present in the south-eastern part of our area before industry radically changed the face of the landscape. The region is next mentioned by Thomas Allis in his important *Report on the Birds of Yorkshire* (4). This was produced in manuscript form only in 1844 but was eventually published by T. H. Nelson in 1907 (5).

During the early years of the nineteenth century Charles Waterton, eccentric squire of Walton Hall, Wakefield, was perhaps the region's most important scientific ornithologist. Famed for his revolutionary ideas on conservation, he did keep a diary and may have ventured into at least part of our area. In 1826 North Derbyshire was visited by the famous American bird artist and ornithologist John James Audubon. He apparently met a Sheffield ornithologist John Heppenstall who bought a painting from him. Heppenstall had a large collection of mounted specimens but his contribution, if any, to local ornithology remains unresolved.

In the middle and later years of the nineteenth century several birdwatchers were undoubtedly active in the area but there is little mention of them in the literature. F. O. Morris gives a report of a Bee-eater from Sheffield in the first volume of his monumental *British Birds* published in 1851 (6). One of the most active ornithologists of the mid to late 1800s may well have been A. S. Hutchinson who was taxidermist for Derby, Sheffield and Manchester City Museums. He lived in Derby but reported a Great White Egret at Clay Wheel Dam, Wadsley Bridge, in 1868, which, together with several other local records, tends to support at least some period of residence in the city. Hutchinson kept detailed field-notes, many of which were used by F. B. Whitlock for his *Birds of Derbyshire* published in 1893 (7). He also corresponded with T. H. Nelson who used Hutchinson's records in his publication (5).

The ornithologist Charles Dixon was also active in Sheffield in the mid 1800s. He lived at Meersbrook for 22 years before moving to London in 1880. Dixon was a most prolific writer and produced at least 19 books, though there was rarely a mention of Sheffield birds, except in *Amongst the Birds in Northern Shires* published in 1900 (*8*).

The Rev. Francis Charles Robert Jourdain was perhaps our most famous ornithologist. Born in the village of Derwent, he became vicar of Clifton-by-Ashbourne in 1894 and remained there for twenty years before moving to Berkshire. Although he spent much of his time in the southern Peak, he undoubtedly visited our area. He wrote many papers and some books, but his most important contribution was as one of the editors of *The Handbook of British Birds* published in 1938-41 (*9*). His diaries are now to be found in the library of the Edward Grey Institute, Oxford and make fascinating reading.

Henry Seebohm (1832-95), a Sheffield steelman, was a contemporary of both Charles Dixon and Francis Jourdain. He lived at a time when Sheffield steel production was at its height and his successful business gave him the financial ability to travel widely in Europe and Asia. He was an ornithologist of great expertise and wrote several important ornithological works, including *A History of British Birds* (*10*) and two volumes about his travels in Siberia, which were subsequently reprinted as one volume in 1901 (*11*). Seebohm supplied information to both Nelson (*5*) and Whitlock (*7*). He was a tireless collector and presented over 16,000 specimens to the British Museum. Sadly, although he must have been active in the Sheffield area, very few of his observations are recorded and the whereabouts of his diaries is unknown.

During the final years of the nineteenth century Sheffield City Museum was expanding and several local taxidermists contributed specimens, including Reuben Webster. Unfortunately, little is known about Webster's activities or indeed those of ornithologists active at this time. Amongst the more prominent of the latter who have left some information in the form of notes or papers in national journals were W. Storrs Fox (who lived in Bakewell, and knew F. B. Whitlock), Edwin D. Doncaster (who lived in Sheffield and also contributed much information to Whitlock) and Elijah Howarth, who was curator of Weston Park Museum from 1875 to 1928. Most of Howarth's published work is related to specimens brought to the museum (*2*). J. B. Wheat, a Sheffield solicitor, collected eggs from 1888-1934 and donated his collection to the museum.

Surprisingly little is known about those birdwatchers active in the first two or three decades of the present century. Prof. C. J. Patten compiled in 1910 a list of the birds recorded in the Sheffield area. This was published in the British Association Handbook for that year (*12*). He also published occasional notes in the *Proceedings of the Sheffield Naturalists Club.* There is little other information available despite the fact that this latter Society was in existence. The Club amalgamated with Sheffield Microscopical Society in 1918 to become the Sorby Scientific Society, which was renamed the Sorby Natural History Society in 1931. During these years two local ornithologists, Charles Wells and Arthur Whittaker, rose to prominence. Both were very experienced birdwatchers who accumulated extensive egg collections and were certainly most knowledgeable about local birds. Wells appears to have published nothing but his notebooks are presently in Exeter Museum. Arthur Whittaker produced useful notes on the birds of the area in 1929 (*13*). He left an extensive egg

12

collection to the City Museum and summaries of his diaries for the period 1900-48 are held in the library of the Edward Grey Institute.

In the period 1930 to 1945 a contemporary of both Wells and Whittaker was Ralph Chislett (1883-1964). He was born in Rotherham and studied birds in many parts of the Sheffield area. He came to be regarded as the expert on Yorkshire birds and ultimately wrote a book of that name in 1952 (*14*), which rapidly came to be recognised as a worthy successor to Nelson's monumental work. Chislett was first and foremost a recorder of birds and edited the Bird Reports for the Yorkshire Naturalist's Union from 1940 to 1959. He was, however, also an accomplished photographer and visited the Peak on numerous occasions to photograph hill birds. Some of his observations were published in 1933 in his book *Northward-Ho for Birds!* (*15*). Many of his bird records for this area lie within the pages of the Yorkshire Bird Reports but others are in his diaries which were never published. Even when he moved to Masham in North Yorkshire in 1945, Chislett retained his ties with the area and returned from time to time.

Amongst a number of egg-collectors active within the Sheffield region prior to the *1954 Protection of Birds Act* was Walter E. Gibbs. He accumulated a small, but historically interesting, egg collection and was an accomplished taxidermist. Many of his skins are in Sheffield City Museum, as well as private collections. Wal Gibbs was a fascinating ornithologist with a wealth of stories about birds around Sheffield from the 1930s to the early 1960s. He climbed for Jourdain at one point in his egg-collecting career and knew many early twentieth century birdwatchers and egg-collectors.

Kingfisher, a species monitored by the Waterways Birds Survey   **I.D. Rotherham**

In the twenty years following the Second World War local natural history prospered. In 1945 membership of the Sorby Natural History Society (SNHS) increased by 46 to 233 and in 1946 an ornithological section was created within it. During these years neighbouring societies were founded: the Derbyshire Ornithological Society (DOS) in 1954 and the Doncaster and District Ornithological Society one year later. At around this time some local birdwatchers became accomplished photographers including Harold Hems, G. R. Pryor and Alan Faulkner-Taylor. During the 1950s David R. Wilson was active within the area; he became Recorder for the DOS in the years 1957-9 and Ornithological Editor of the Sorby Record in 1958. In that year he published a useful résumé detailing the status and distribution of birds within the region (16),and followed this with an update in 1959 (17). At this point he moved on to become Secretary of the British Trust for Ornithology in Oxford, leaving R. G. Hawley as Ornithological Editor of the Sorby Record. In the ensuing thirteen years we owe much to the SNHS in that it provided a vehicle for the publication of some bird records in its journal and, from 1964, as a part of the monthly Newsletter, as well as promoting the interests of ornithology within the area.

The activities of the Sorby Ornithological Section in the 1960s fired the enthusiasm of many young birdwatchers and helped build a firm foundation for the future. In those years Ray Hawley was ably assisted by a number of active ornithologists including John and Douglas Atter, F. N. Barker, A. Critchlow, T. Marshall, Mrs B. A. Moore, Miss H. C. Rodgers, D. Spalding and C. J. Stokes, whose contributions should not be underestimated. By the early 1960s the SNHS Ringing Group was in existence with R. G. Hawley as its Ringing Secretary. A few years later, in 1968, the Breck Farm Ringing Group was established under the careful management of Michael J. Wareing. During this decade a number of studies were carried out by Sheffield birdwatchers including: surveys of certain localities; a survey of diurnal birds of prey; a study of Long-eared Owls, and the initiation of a regular Rookery census.

In Derbyshire there was a similar heightening of activity, with a number of observers, such as Roy Frost and Philip Shooter, very active in the southern part of our area, and contributing to the production of an annual *Derbyshire Bird Report*. Unfortunately, no attempt was made to produce a report for the Sheffield area, although the expertise was available. R. G. Hawley did write a brief summary of Sheffield's birds in 1968 as a part of a SNHS Jubilee publication (18), and co-ordinated local field work for the 1968-72 national *Atlas* of breeding birds (19). He left Sheffield in 1971 to become an RSPB Warden, and the final year of the *Atlas* was organised by D. Herringshaw.

The late 1960s were, in many respects, a watershed for Sheffield ornithology. A new generation of birdwatchers was developing, who were interested in scientific ornithology and less inclined to 'dabble' at their hobby. There was an increasing interest in Common Bird Census work, undoubtedly inspired by the enthusiasm of Betty Moore and Harold Smith, and a growing realisation that a more highly organised recording network was necessary. A new, separate, ornithological organisation was therefore proposed. On 14th December 1972 a public meeting was held in the City Museum, Weston Park, and the Sheffield Bird Study Group (SBSG) came into existence.

In the first few years the new society forged and then strengthened its links with neighbouring societies and national organisations. The first official group projects were launched and included surveys of garden birds, Kestrel, Starling roosts, and waterways birds. Wildfowl on all local waters were counted in the autumn and winter months by a team of observers. A Surveys and Records Sub-committee was set up to co-ordinate all local surveys organised by the SBSG. One of the major aims of the newly established society was to develop an efficient recording network and to this end David Herringshaw became Ornithological Recorder. His responsibilities included adjudication of records, in consultation with other members of the Sub-committee. Such was the volume of records, however, that by 1975 it had become necessary to constitute sub-committees to deal with records and surveys separately. At the same time protection work, local environment pressures and a keen membership led to the establishment of a Conservation Sub-committee. All three sub-committees, with added representation from neighbouring societies, have developed their functions and continue to be active.

The protection work has expanded from small beginnings and now takes up an important part of the SBSG's activities. It first began in 1973 when a Goshawk nest in Upper Derwentdale was wardened. This has continued through to the present time and a substantial number of Goshawk chicks have been reared as a result. Each year the SBSG membership supplies a team of volunteers, ably organised by Betty Moore for the first ten years and subsequently by Vic Gibson. Since the 1970's the protection effort has involved wardening a Peregrine site, in conjunction with the DOS in 1984-85, and Black-necked Grebe in 1982-83.

Ten years after the Group's formation, membership had reached over 230. By the autumn of 1974 a bi-monthly Bulletin was being produced and the first ever detailed report on the birds of the Sheffield area had been published. Production of the *Sheffield Bird Report* then became an annual event and, to date, ten have been published. In 1977 the annual report was supplemented by a journal, *The Magpie*, intended as a medium for publishing the work of Sheffield birdwatchers. By 1985 three issues had been produced, another is in preparation and, as a 'Journal of Ornithology' for the Sheffield Region *The Magpie* now accepts contributions from neighbouring societies and complements the excellent *Sorby Record*.

During the 1970s local ornithology gained momentum and changed almost out of recognition. Two of the most important events occurred in the latter half of the decade. Firstly, in 1975 an *Atlas* of breeding birds project was launched based upon a 2 x 2 km (tetrad) grid system. There were a few who said it should not be done for ethical reasons, and many more who stated that it could not be done. Both camps were proved wrong; the trial year was a success and participants' enthusiasm carried the day. By the end of 1980 the project was finished and ideas were already formulated on how the results should be published. Some suggested a simple atlas of breeding birds, as produced by a number of other societies. In 1978, however, another significant event had occurred, namely the publication of Roy Frost's update of F. B. Whitlock's *Birds of Derbyshire* (7). This new avifauna (20) of the same name as the 1893 publication, was recommended in several national reviews as a good model for future similar productions. We therefore decided to base our publication upon the same format: the atlas results would form an integral part of the new book but it would be an avifauna, detailing the changes in status of Sheffield's birds from 1960. It would also provide a much needed revision of Harold Smith's *Birds of the Sheffield Area* (21), which had been published in 1974. This latter publication had been based upon pre-1970 data and reflected the comparatively few observers who were active at the time.

The 1970s closed in sharp contrast to the way they had begun. Local ornithology was more active than it had ever been before; some sixteen surveys had been carried out; the area had an annual bird report and an ornithological journal. Relationships between allied organisations had never been better; records were co-ordinated; protection work was progressing well and plans had been laid to produce a definitive avifauna.

Goshawk in Upper Derwentdale   **L. Cornthwaite**

The new decade has had a mixed beginning. Sadly, several of the most active birdwatchers have left the area, to the detriment of local ornithology, particularly the survey work. There has also been an upsurge in rarity-hunting or 'twitching', which has undoubtedly occupied the time of many birdwatchers, thereby depleting the active resources engaged in local ornithology. Nevertheless, there was considerable local participation in the BTO's *Winter Atlas* project, from 1981/82 to 83/84. The results were collected on a 5 x 5km^2 basis, but have yet to be evaluated and analysed. One important recent development has been the intensive study of specific sites by several keen observers. This has yielded some valuable results, particularly during the autumn migration period as can be seen in Chapter Three.

In 1981 a guide to birdwatching in the Sheffield Area and the Peak District was written by Roy Frost and David Herringshaw (22). It was a considerable success and, in 1984, was revised and reprinted as a joint publication by the SBSG, SNHS and Sheffield City Museums. The most recent development has been the formation of a separate RSPB Members' Group. Before this the SBSG had acted as the local RSPB Members' Group, but this situation became increasingly untenable and there was an obvious need for a separate group whose aim would be geared to promoting RSPB membership and objectives. This eventually formed in 1982 and has become very successful. It is, as yet, in its early stages but we wish it well and hope that ties will strengthen to the mutual benefit of all three Sheffield sister organisations.

Three centuries have passed and Sheffield ornithology has come a long way since Jessop sent specimens to Willughby. We now rely on the evidence of camera, field notebook and tape recorder, rather than corpses and eggs, to support identification claims. Birdwatchers are numerous today and fully accepted as part of the modern scene. Yet a price has been paid for the progress made. Solitude is difficult to find anywhere in the area; the whereabouts of scarcer breeding birds has to be suppressed for fear of disturbance by egg-collectors and even birdwatchers; and many hours are spent protecting our nesting Peregrines, Goshawks, Merlins and Black-necked Grebes. However, we have at last acquired a good knowledge of the distribution of our bird populations. We can now move on and attempt to understand the overall ecology of the region, by studying the plant and animal communities in which the birds play an integral part.

We hope that when this book is updated in the years ahead and Sheffield's ornithology is once more reviewed, the present era will be regarded as another watershed beyond which further horizons were reached. We should, however, never forget the debt owed to our predecessors. They were at one with wild nature in a way most of us can never be. They laid down the foundations without which our book might never have been written.

Redshanks   **F.J. Watson**

Millstone Grit at Burbage Edge L. Cornthwaite

CHAPTER TWO

HABITATS AND BIRD COMMUNITIES
Ian Francis

This chapter presents an introduction to the Sheffield area, its landscape history, current habitats and bird communities. It is not intended to repeat previous accounts of the area but to outline habitats in the region and briefly describe their characteristic birds, thus providing a background to the species accounts given later in the book. For further details about the area and its birds, the reader is referred to Smith (*21*), Frost (*20*), and especially Herringshaw and Frost (*22*). In addition, Anderson and Shimwell present a much fuller account of the vegetation and landscape history of the Peak District (*23*).

The recording area covers 1,200km², stretching from the high plateaux of the southern Pennines to the flood plains of the rivers Don and Rother. It lies at the boundary of upland and lowland Britain (Fig.2) and this is reflected in the great variety of habitats contained within it. Some species reach the southern-most edge of their range in Britain on the uplands of the Peak District, whilst the south-eastern part of the region holds species near to their western and northern most limits.

Geology and Topography
One of the main controls upon habitat is the underlying bed-rock. The area possesses a range of rock types, broadly orientated north to south, which span an age of 100 million years and vary in their resistance to erosion, so shaping the form of the land. The oldest are those of the Carboniferous Limestone series, which take the form of a flattened dome and are to be found in the south-west of the area (Fig.3). Overlying these are the Carboniferous Millstone Grit and shale sequences (commonly known as 'gritstone') which outcrop in western and central parts, usually in the form of almost flat plateaux, deeply incised by rivers and producing the characteristic 'tors' and edges so beloved by climbers. Above these lie the Upper Carboniferous rocks, the Coal Measure sequences, which have given rise to an undulating landscape of rolling escarpments (cuestas) and deep valleys.

18

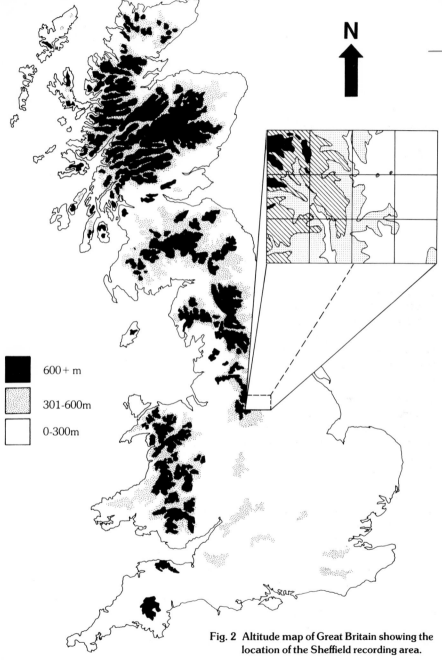

N

■	600+ m
▨	301-600m
□	0-300m

Fig. 2 Altitude map of Great Britain showing the
location of the Sheffield recording area.

19

Lapwing   **L. Cornthwaite**

The Sheffield area forms the eastern half of the Pennine anticline, with the rocks dipping to the east and all the edges (except those controlled by faults) facing westwards. The whole upland Carboniferous plateau reflects more recent earth movements uplifting the area to its present altitude, since followed by erosion dating to the Quaternary or even the Tertiary Eras. The Permian or Magnesian Limestone at the very south-eastern margin of the area lies unconformably over the Coal Measures and forms a relatively low-lying undulating region with numerous small valleys and scarp-slope woodlands.

Fig. 3 Solid Geology of the Sheffield area.

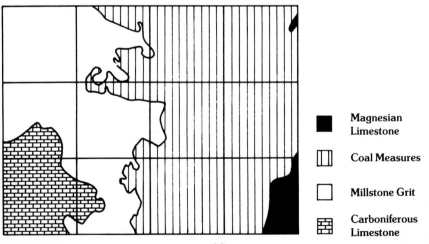

■   **Magnesian Limestone**

▦   **Coal Measures**

□   **Millstone Grit**

▦   **Carboniferous Limestone**

Fig. 4 Maximum and minimum altitude in each tetrad

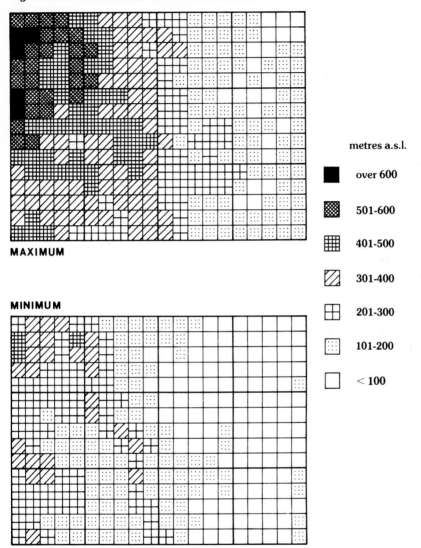

MAXIMUM

MINIMUM

metres a.s.l.

■ over 600

▨ 501-600

▦ 401-500

◫ 301-400

⊞ 201-300

⊡ 101-200

□ < 100

Altitude

The altitude of the land surface ranges from 15m above sea level (a.s.l.) in the north-east to 636m in the north-west. This difference in altitude from east to west has much influence upon the bird distributions shown later in the book, and Figures 4 to 7 illustrate various aspects of this in more detail. The maximum and minimum altitudes in every tetrad are shown in Fig.4, and each can be of considerable importance for the constituents of the

21

breeding bird communities found in them. To illustrate this further, Fig.5 shows the altitudinal range of each tetrad, which is a crude index of the amount of slope or relief present there. In the mid-altitude areas, such as the valleys to the immediate west and south of Sheffield, the high altitudinal range means that species of both upland and lowland inclination can occur, thus increasing the variety of species breeding in a square. Comparison of Fig.5 with Fig.19 (which illustrates the number of species breeding in each square) shows that this is indeed often the case. Fig.6 shows a representative cross-section through the area and Fig.7 is a computer generated 'view' of the area from the south-east, in an attempt to provide a strong visual impression of the contrast from west to east of the region.

Fig. 5 Altitudinal range in each tetrad.

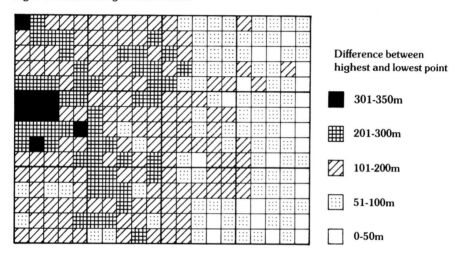

Difference between
highest and lowest point

■ 301-350m

▦ 201-300m

▨ 101-200m

⬚ 51-100m

☐ 0-50m

Fig. 6 West to East altitude transect across the recording area.
         (vertical exaggeration × 10)

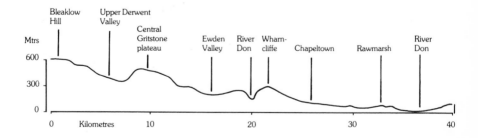

Climate

This great variation in altitude also has a corresponding effect on the climate of the area. The city of Sheffield is well recorded from a meteorological viewpoint and some summary statistics are presented in Table 1.

Table 1: Climatological Statistics, Sheffield, 1951-1980 (by courtesy of Sheffield City Museums).

	Jan	Feb	Mar	Apr	May	Jun	Jul	Aug	Sep	Oct	Nov	Dec	Mean/ Total
Av. Air Temp. (°C)	3.6	3.6	5.5	8.0	11.3	14.4	15.9	15.7	13.7	10.5	6.5	4.8	9.5
Av. Total hours bright sunshine	42	51	95	120	166	182	160	148	119	88	52	38	1258
Av. Total Rain	78	67	64	52	63	56	63	72	63	64	84	82	808

% Wind Direction 1955-67

Calm	North	NE	East	SE	South	SW	West	NW
17.3	11	7	3	8	12.7	15	13.5	14

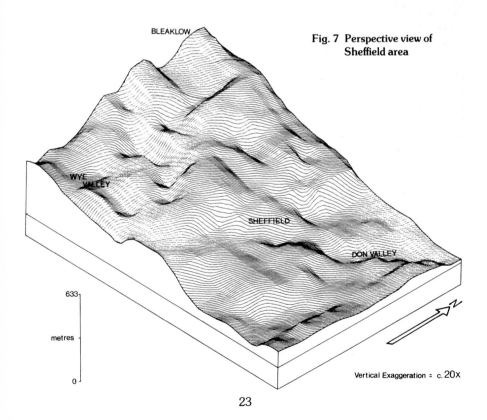

Fig. 7 Perspective view of Sheffield area

BLEAKLOW

WYE VALLEY

SHEFFIELD

DON VALLEY

633 ─┐

metres ─

0 ─┘

Vertical Exaggeration = c. 20x

There is great variation over the whole area, but records for other parts are either patchy or unpublished. The rainfall varies from over 1600mm (63 inches) annually at Kinder Scout and Bleaklow to less than 640mm (25 inches) east of Rotherham, a decrease of some 960mm in 35km, and Fig.8 illustrates the pattern across the area. On the high moors precipitation nearly always exceeds evaporation, but in the east the converse may be true for several of the summer months. Temperatures vary accordingly across the area, and a 6°C or greater difference between the lowlands to the east and the cooler uplands can occur in any season. Wind-speeds are on average higher in the north and west, where there is also less sunshine (Buxton receives on average 100 hours less per year than Sheffield), and snow is much more likely and lies for longer (e.g. in 1978/9 snow lay a month longer on Kinder than in Weston Park). Fig.9 shows a number of climatic variables presented on a 10km square basis, and these emphasise the diversity present over the area.

Fig. 8 Average annual rainfall 1941-70 (from Meteorological Office statistics).

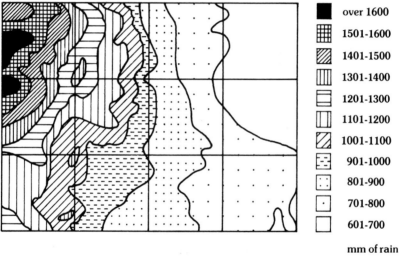

■	over 1600
▦	1501-1600
▨	1401-1500
⦀	1301-1400
⊟	1201-1300
⊞	1101-1200
▨	1001-1100
⦂	901-1000
⸬	801-900
·	701-800
☐	601-700

mm of rain

Land Use

The altitudinal variation has a profound influence on the climate, which in its turn is the primary control on the vegetation communities, either directly through physiological limitations or indirectly through its effect on the strategies humans have adopted over the centuries to utilise the land. The Peak District in particular has been affected by human activities since at least the Mesolithic period (about 8,000 years ago), and this is perhaps the primary reason why tree cover is so low in the national park (5.4% compared with 8% over the whole area). The landscape throughout the Sheffield region is the product of such activity, and there are no completely natural habitats present. Rather they represent the response to varying degrees of interference, be it centuries of deforestation, burning and grazing in the uplands, or tillage, farming and the gradual growth of settlement, urbanisation and industry in the lowlands.

Fig. 9 Climatological maps of the Sheffield area based on 10km squares.

After: White E.J. and Smith R.I. (1982) *Climatological Maps of Great Britain.*
Institute of Terrestrial Ecology (NERC).

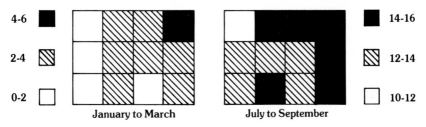

(a) **Mean air temperature (°C) at 09.00 G.M.T. in screen 1.3m above ground.**

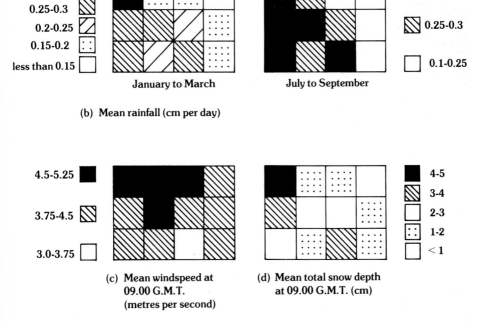

(b) **Mean rainfall (cm per day)**

(c) **Mean windspeed at
09.00 G.M.T.
(metres per second)**

(d) **Mean total snow depth
at 09.00 G.M.T. (cm)**

Table 2 gives the percentage of the area under different land uses and Figures 10 to 18 show the distribution of these and vegetation types by tetrad. There is considerable difference over the area in the percentage cover of these habitats, and this has the most direct influence on the bird communities.

Table 2 Land use in the Sheffield area (%).

WOODLAND			MOORLAND and Rough Pasture	FARMLAND	WATER	URBAN	OTHER
(Conif. & mixd)	(Decid)	Total					
(3.8)	(4.3)	8.1	23.1	46.6	1.5	15.0	5.6

Fig. 10 Percentage of total woodland cover in each tetrad.

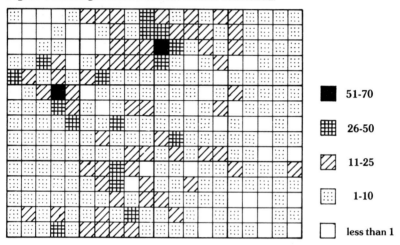

- ■ 51-70
- ▦ 26-50
- ▨ 11-25
- ⸬ 1-10
- ☐ less than 1

Fig. 11 Percentage of coniferous and mixed woodland cover in each tetrad.

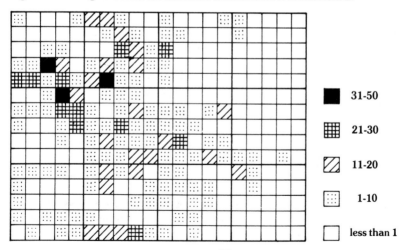

- ■ 31-50
- ▦ 21-30
- ▨ 11-20
- ⸬ 1-10
- ☐ less than 1

Woodlands

Figure 10 indicates that woodland is most predominant in the valleys to the north and west of Sheffield, and is almost absent from large areas of the extreme north-west and south-east. However, a high proportion of this woodland consists of plantations of coniferous species such as Scots Pine, European and Japanese Larch, Corsican and Lodgepole Pines, Sitka and Norway Spruce, particularly in the Upper Derwent Valley and around moorland reservoirs in both the Derbyshire and South Yorkshire parts of the Peak (Fig.11). The predominantly coniferous woodlands tend to be relatively poor in diversity of bird species, the most abundant being Goldcrest, Coal Tit, Chaffinch, Robin, Wren, Redpoll, Woodpigeon and Jay. Blue and Great Tits also occur, although they are not so numerous unless deciduous trees are mixed with the conifers or nest-boxes are provided. The Great Spotted Woodpecker is widespread but seems to prefer mixed woodland. Amongst the birds of prey, Sparrowhawk is widespread in coniferous habitat and its larger relative, the Goshawk, also occurs, though rather more mature trees are needed for this rare raptor. Tawny Owl is common here, and occasionally nests on the ground when suitable disused nests or tree-holes are not available. Long-eared Owl is much scarcer, although it may be found frequenting the denser and younger coniferous plantations. The distribution of certain species, such as Siskin and Crossbill, often reflects that of the coniferous plantations, although the Woodcock, which is commonly found in this habitat, is not similarly restricted. Young coniferous plantations on the moorland fringe are attractive to small passerines including Reed Bunting, Yellowhammer, Tree Pipit, Willow Warbler, Blackcap, Whinchat and occasionally Stonechat or Grasshopper Warbler. Short-eared Owl nest amongst the young trees, presumably attracted by the large Short-tailed Vole population.

Fig. 12 Percentage of deciduous woodland cover in each tetrad.

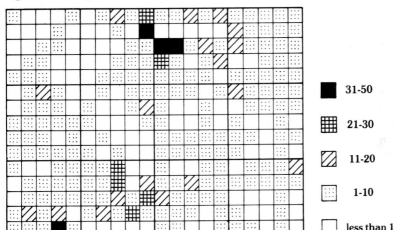

31-50

21-30

11-20

1-10

less than 1

Deciduous woodland is most common in the north around Wharncliffe and Grenoside and in the lower Derwent Valley at Chatsworth (Fig. 12). The presence of trees, and particularly a diverse woodland landscape, is important in influencing the number and variety of breeding birds, as are the tree species present. Northern Oak, Beech, Sycamore and Ash are the commonest trees in the High Peak woods. On the gritstone edges only small areas of 'semi-natural' woodland remain, with that in Padley Gorge being perhaps the best example. Here, amid the Oak and Birch with occasional stands of Beech, is a rich woodland avifauna including Pied Flycatcher, Redstart, Wood Warbler, Nuthatch and Green Woodpecker. Many of the small remnants of former deciduous woodland linger on in moorland cloughs and with them is associated a diversity of birds - Wood Warbler and Redsart are found quite high up these valleys. Where the alien Sycamore is common there are fewer species, although both Sparrowhawk and Goshawk will nest in its well-formed boughs.

In the lush woodlands of the Carboniferous Limestone dales, Northern Oak, Ash, Alder, Hazel, Elm and Field Maple are to be found, and there is an accompanying rich diversity of birds including most of the Sheffield warblers. It is no coincidence that Buzzard occasionally nests in such woodland and Sparrowhawk is widespread, doubtless attracted by the density of birds to be found here. The sparse shelter-belt woods of the limestone plateau are often composed only of Sycamore and so are generally species-poor.

On the Coal Measures there are many small woodlands, although a few are quite extensive - notably Greno and Ecclesall Woods and the Moss Valley woodlands. It is easy to dismiss such areas as being of limited ornithological interest, as they are often close to housing estates, but there is much to be found within them. Most are dominated by English Elm, Sycamore, Beech and Northern Oak, but a diversity of other tree species occurs and the shrub layer can be extensive. As a result birds are plentiful and include all the typical woodland species with the addition of Lesser Spotted Woodpecker. Nuthatch colonised many of these woodlands several decades ago and is still extending its range. The smaller passerines abound, and Stock Dove is plentiful, as are both Woodpigeon and Collared Dove. Carrion Crow may be more widespread here than in many upland woods, and the Magpie is abundant, often nesting at high densities. Interestingly, although these lowland woodlands appear suitable for Hawfinch, it is not recorded in many, the presence of Hornbeam apparently being a critical factor. Sparrowhawk has slowly recolonised its former nesting sites here, even in suburban areas.

Most deciduous woodlands are the result of secondary growth following earlier clearances, but some sites are 'ancient' in that woodland has been present for many centuries, and these are often rich in bird-life. The presence of a varied shrub layer, which includes Yew, Hazel, Hawthorn and Holly, is an important indication of rich woodland. In recent years Rhododendron has become a significant species in the shrub layer in some areas and, although having little value for feeding, this can be of importance to birds for roosting and nesting.

Moorland
One of the most characteristic Peak District habitats is the upland moorland and rough pasture, and the very clear-cut distribution of this is shown in Fig. 13. It is almost completely confined to the Millstone Grit sequences, and adds a unique element to the bird communities of the area. Breeding species such as Red Grouse, Golden Plover, Dunlin and Twite are almost entirely restricted to this habitat. The wetter blanket bogs on the high tops

are characterised by Bog Mosses, Cotton Sedges, Bilberry, Deer Sedge and Cross-leaved Heath. Here, on the wet ground there are few breeding species, but those that do nest are very characteristic and include Dunlin, Golden Plover, Redshank, Teal, the occasional Curlew and the ubiquitous Meadow Pipit. The drier areas grade into the lower grouse moors which are dominated by Ling, Bell Heather, Crowberry, Bilberry and Cowberry. Here Twite, Curlew, Short-eared Owl and, in winter, Hen Harrier can be found, as well as the expected Red Grouse and Meadow Pipit. Short-eared Owl numbers fluctuate annually and in some years birds may also nest amongst the drier parts of the Cotton Sedge communities and on the rough grassland at lower altitudes. Merlin and Kestrel hunt on these moors, the former possibly increasing slightly in recent years after apparently becoming very scarce during the 1970s. The moorland passerines are favoured prey for the Sparrowhawk, especially during the breeding season, and the larger waders and Red Grouse for the Goshawk.

Fig. 13 Percentage of moorland and rough pasture cover in each tetrad.

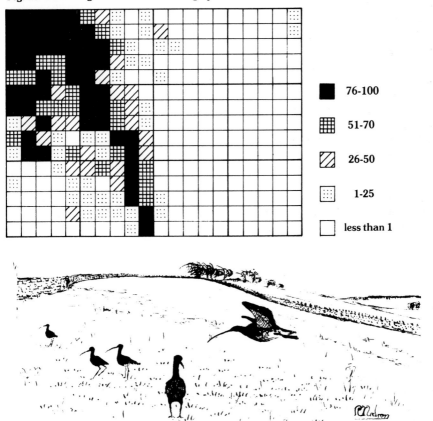

- ■ 76-100
- ▦ 51-70
- ▨ 26-50
- ⦂ 1-25
- ☐ less than 1

Curlew   P.A. Ardron

29

Peripheral regions to the moorlands are acidic rough grazing pastures, often abandoned since the more intensive usage of the last century. Characteristic plant species here are Wavy-hair Grass, Purple Moor Grass and Common Bent. In many areas the cessation of intense pasture management has resulted in the spread of Bracken, which now covers large areas and is a striking Peak District plant, as well as being of significance to nesting Whinchat, Linnet and the occasional Stonechat. Extending from the deep gritstone valleys, such as Derwentdale, are numerous moorland cloughs, often with a rocky torrent in the bottom. Frequently these cloughs finish at higher altitudes where their streams begin amongst the Blanket-bog and Cotton Sedge communities. The clough sides are usually Bracken-covered and it is in such habitat that the Whinchat is especially plentiful. Ring Ouzel may also occur and Wheatear is to be found amongst the rocky screes. Both species are also typical of the prominent gritstone edges where the Kestrel finds suitable nest sites. The Peregrine is now beginning to colonise the major rocky edges as it returns to the Peak after an absence of almost forty years.

Agriculture

The land-use which forms almost a 'negative' of the moorland map is agriculture. Figure 14 shows the cover of enclosed farmland, but does not distinguish between types. The farmland in the western upland regions is generally grazing and pasture land. Perennial Rye Grass is dominant in most fields as a result of ploughing and reseeding, but many enclosed fields on the edge of the gritstone moors may still contain birds characteristic of unimproved pastures, such as Lapwing, Curlew and Snipe, with occasional breeding Redshank in the wetter fields. In winter such areas provide valuable feeding for flocks of Yellowhammer, Tree and House Sparrows and finches including Linnet, Chaffinch, Brambling and Greenfinch.

Fig. 14 Percentage of enclosed farmland cover in each tetrad.

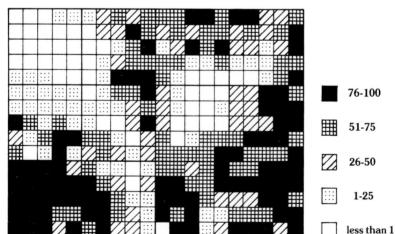

76-100

51-75

26-50

1-25

less than 1

30

Yellowhammer   P. Leonard

In some limestone pastures, more transitional short and tall herb-rich grasslands may be found, with Fescues and Oatgrasses commonly occurring. Hay meadows are present on the plateau and contain plant species which vary according to the base status of the soil. There may be relatively high densities of Yellow Wagtails and Lapwings in these meadows, whilst Common Gulls invariably find them attractive as a food source. Arable cultivation with some grazing is the norm in the south-east, where hedgerows are more common, although gradually disappearing. In these areas, and to the north and east of the region, are found the more typical farmland bird communities. Thrushes, finches, Dunnock and Lesser Whitethroat nest in the hedgerow bushes, whilst both partridge species breed under the hedges and by the field margins. The Grey Partridge is now much more restricted to farmland where hedgerows are plentiful and occasional tracts of wasteland occur. The Red-legged Partridge was once very much an eastern bird, but seems to be increasing rapidly and is now the more familiar of the two species. The open fields hold Lapwing (in decreasing numbers), Skylarks and, in the arble areas, Corn Bunting, although this is much more localised.

Many of the villages and small towns which lie within or on the edge of the farmlands have their own rookeries, the birds using the surrounding fields for feeding purposes at all times of the year. In winter, Rook flocks are augmented by other corvids together with large numbers of feeding Starling, finches, sparrows, buntings, Redwing and Fieldfare. Over much of the limestone and Millstone Grit uplands, where dry stone walls form many of the field boundaries, Little Owls are commonly found, and they also occur in the more traditional farmland communities of the south-west.

Wetlands

There is little standing water in the area (only 1.5%) and almost all the larger bodies are artificial in origin. The substantial and deep reservoirs in the Upper Derwent Valley are the only places where the percentage of any tetrad covered by water rises above 15 (Fig. 15), although there are other large reservoirs scattered down the central gritstone and the Coal Measures. Such reservoirs, especially those in upland areas, appear singularly unattractive to waterfowl, both in summer and winter. Only Mallard and a few Teal, Tufted Duck and Little Grebe nest, although Red-breasted Merganser has recently begun to do so in

31

Derwentdale. The wintering species are equally sparse, presumably because the deep upland reservoirs offer a limited food resource, although a few are important wintering areas for Goldeneye and small numbers of Goosander. Lowland reservoirs, especially Thrybergh, are much more attractive to wintering birds but the latter are, in part, deterred by angling and boating activities. The banks of several of the upland reservoirs are important nesting areas for Common Sandpiper which has its highest density around the Derwentdale chain. The available water is used as stopping-off places for passage waterfowl and, occasionally, wading birds, but such species rarely remain for long. Even so, a long list of rarities has occurred for several of both the upland and lowland reservoirs, Redmires, Barbrook and Thrybergh being, perhaps, the most favoured.

Thrybergh Reservoir — from the south   P. Leonard

Subsidence flashes account for the only other large water bodies and these are mainly in the south-east. The margins of some have been colonised by dense Crack and Goat Willow and Alder Carr. Common Reedmace, and occasionally Common Reed, forms a fringe vegetation, suitable for nesting cover. Waterfowl are numerous, especially in winter, and several species breed, including Great-crested and Little Grebe, Mute Swan (now declining rapidly), Mallard, Tufted Duck and, occasionally, Pochard. Shoveler is a species which has nested in the past and may well have been overlooked. One flash provides suitable nesting habitat for a pair of Black-necked Grebe which first bred in 1982. Coot and Moorhen abound in such areas, whilst the Water Rail is to be found amongst the reedy margins in winter and occasionally nests. Amongst the passerines, Reed Bunting and Sedge Warbler are typical nesting species, whilst Reed Warbler is to be found at only a few flashes. Swifts and hirundines favour the flashes for feeding areas and large roosts may build up in late summer. Similarly the Willow and Alder Carr is used by roosting Stock Dove, Woodpigeon, huge numbers of Starling and the occasional Long-eared Owl.

Fig. 15 Percentage of surface water in each tetrad.

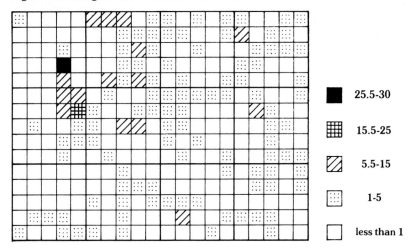

	25.5-30
	15.5-25
	5.5-15
	1-5
	less than 1

Marshland is very scarce in the region, although wet flushes are common in the uplands and may be the only form of wetland in some limestone areas. One or two marshy patches with Common Reed or Reedmace beds hold nesting Reed and Sedge Warbler, and Water Rail occur in winter. Lowland wet meadows attract the occasional nesting Redshank and Snipe (as they do on the uplands) but such habitats are uncommon.

Rivers are generally in the upper and middle courses near Sheffield and few are wide, although flood water to the east of the area can provide large patches of water which attract considerable numbers of wildfowl in the winter months. Many of the upland river systems are characterised by the presence of Dipper and Grey Wagtail, and Common Sandpiper nest beside those with exposed areas of shingle. Kingfisher occurs on both large and small streams but is frequently overlooked. Within the city, the Don has become much more attractive, now holding fish and having a variety of plants in its margins. The Mallard and Moorhen populations are high, Kingfishers nest, Black-headed Gulls abound, and its wintering wildfowl population appears to be rising steadily. It is, unfortunately, rarely examined closely by birdwatchers and is undoubtedly under-recorded.

Urban and Suburban Areas

The area contains three large conurbations - Sheffield, Rotherham and Chesterfield - which, together with a number of smaller towns and villages, bring the proportion of built-up land to over 15%. This is largely concentrated in the central and eastern parts of the region (Fig. 16). The interiors of the large towns are obviously impoverished from an ornithological viewpoint and hold very few species. The Feral Pigeon, Starling and House Sparrow are the most familiar, but are joined by the Black Redstart in industrial Sheffield - a recent coloniser in the 1970s - Kestrel, Carrion Crow and the rapidly increasing Magpie. A very recent feature has been the opening up of the inner and industrial parts of north-eastern Sheffield due to demolition of old housing and the decline of heavy industry. There are now large tracts of wasteland which attract finch flocks in winter and, if left for plant recolonisation, may well bring in birds typical of the suburban and farmland communities.

Fig. 16 Percentage of built-up area in each tetrad.

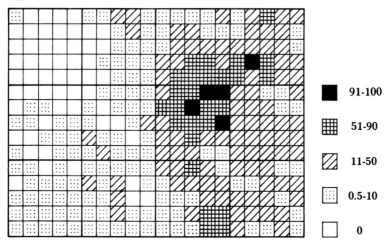

■ 91-100

▦ 51-90

▨ 11-50

⠿ 0.5-10

☐ 0

Fig. 17 Percentage of parkland-type habitat (including playing fields)

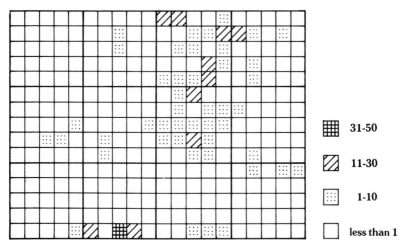

▦ 31-50

▨ 11-30

⠿ 1-10

☐ less than 1

Suburban areas are especially rich, including as they do gardens, allotments, woodlands and numerous parks, playing fields, golf courses and other open spaces (Figs. 17 & 18). Here, the familiar 'garden' bird communities are to be found, including the thrushes, Robin, Dunnock, Blue and Great Tit, Wren, Greenfinch, Bullfinch, Linnet and Goldfinch. Collared Dove and Magpie continue to increase, and Woodpigeon and Jackdaw occur. City parks are a valuable reservoir of wildlife. The grassy playing fields of both these and schools can provide feeding and winter loafing sites for urban and suburban breeding birds and species such as gulls and corvids. They also attract passing migrants including Stonechat, Wheatear, winter thrushes and, in April 1984, a pair of Dotterel!

Spoil heaps in the east and south-east may offer ideal breeding habitat to the Little Ringed Plover. Refuse tips, which, sadly, are declining in number, attract hordes of feeding gulls, including Iceland, Glaucous and, most recently, the rare Mediterranean, during the winter months.

Fig. 18 Percentage of non-urban industrial and waste-land.

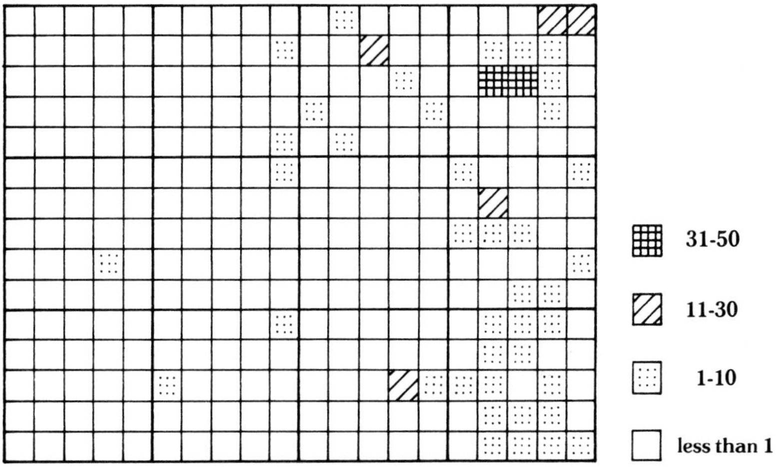

	31-50
	11-30
	1-10
	less than 1

Habitat Diversity and Bird Communities

Individual habitat types are important, and each may provide suitable places for species with specialised requirements, but the most essential element for a rich avifauna is diversity. Areas which have only one type of land use for much of the habitat are often relatively species-poor, whereas those with a small proportion of many different types of cover possess the largest number of breeding and wintering species. In Sheffield, the areas with the most breeding species are found largely in the lower middle-altitudes, which as well as possessing a range of relief are generally too high for extensive cultivation but not too low for the steeper wooded parts to be absent. Habitat diversity and specialisation both influence bird communities in different ways, and information derived from the *Atlas* project provides a good basis for clarifying these relationships.

There are various ways of describing the communities of birds present within an area. The usual approach is to relate communities to regions of similar vegetation and habitat, and this is the method used in the major part of this chapter. A different approach is to divide the area into a large number of small recording units (such as 2 x 2km tetrads) and use the list of species breeding within each to itself generate groupings of similar species or communities.

This latter method is a systematic one for describing community relationships over a large area. It can be sensitive to small differences between areas, but its accuracy depends upon the coverage attained for each tetrad.

In the Sheffield region it is easy to see that certain breeding species characterise similar areas, e.g. Dunlin, Golden Plover and Red Grouse. It would be possible to draw a line round the tetrads which hold all three and make some comment about the area concerned, such as that it was a high altitude moorland region, containing Ling and Cotton Sedges and, perhaps, Sphagnum bog mosses. This can be done for all species and all tetrads using techniques first devised by botanists to describe plant communities and recently used by Fuller in his analysis of the BTO Register of Ornithological Habitats (24).

Using computer analysis,* all tetrads have been put into one of five similar groups which can then be described in terms of both the birds occurring in them and the habitat details that characterise them. This has been done purely on the information contained within the breeding distribution maps, and so is unique to the Sheffield area. In the analysis only 'probable' and 'confirmed' breeding records of 91 species have been included (detailed in Appendix 1); the records relating to locally rare and sensitive species are excluded. One major variable is the number of species found breeding in each tetrad and this is illustrated in Fig. 19. It shows the following pattern.

The upland moorland tetrads in the north-west are the most species-poor, with fewer than eleven breeding species. The next poorest are the bleak upland limestone plateau areas, together with two tetrads which include Derwent Edge and one very impoverished area in the industrial heartland of Sheffield. The third category, holding from 21-30 species,

Fig. 19 Number of species probably or definitely breeding in each tetrad.

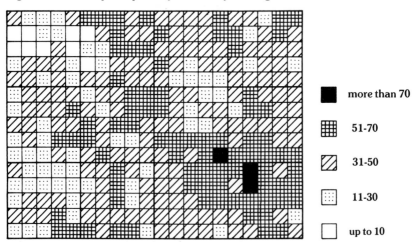

■	more than 70
▦	51-70
▨	31-50
▦	11-30
□	up to 10

* This was carried out by I. Francis and Dr. T.C.D. Dargie at Sheffield University using Ward's method of Cluster Analysis (25a) based upon a Bray and Curtis percentage dissimilarity resemblance matrix (25b).

includes peripheral moorland and limestone areas. Almost half the squares fall into the two categories between 31 and 50 species, and which reflect largely wooded or wetland areas mainly on the lower ground. The next two classes, holding between 51 and 70 species, represent a combination of good observer coverage and high habitat diversity. They are largely tetrads with riverine and mixed woodland species, often with standing water and mixed agricultural land. The richest tetrads in the area are located in the Moss Valley and Renishaw areas, and hold over 70 species. These areas are rich in woodland and aquatic habitats, with suburban influence and agricultural land, and are located in the warmer south-east of the area on better soils.

Fig. 20 Five major bird communities within the recording area.

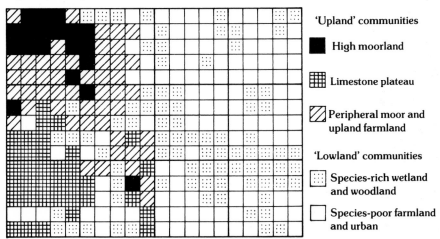

'Upland' communities

■ High moorland

▦ Limestone plateau

▨ Peripheral moor and upland farmland

'Lowland' communities

⠿ Species-rich wetland and woodland

☐ Species-poor farmland and urban

Regions with similar bird communities
Figure 20 shows the location of five classified regions of similar bird communities. The strongest division is between those of upland affinity and those characteristic of lowland. The extent of this division is clearly shown in the diagram, and it coincides almost exactly with the 300m contour. The upland half can be divided into three major component communities:-

1. **'High Moorland'** This community is low in numbers of species, but they are all characteristic of wet blanket bog as described earlier. The major species in this grouping are Red Grouse, Dunlin and Golden Plover. Other birds such as Meadow Pipit may be abundant, but this species is common over much of the area and so is not used to differentiate between communities.

2. **'Limestone plateau'** This community is representative of the bleak upland drystone walled area of the Carboniferous Limestone. It also includes a few tetrads on the central gritstone moors close to the limestone where the species assemblage is very similar. Characteristic species of this community include Lapwing, Yellow Wagtail, Swallow, Carrion Crow and Linnet.

3. **'Peripheral moorland and upland farmland'** This is composed largely of birds with an affinity to uplands not strongly dominated by either of the two previous habitats. In fact a variety of country is to be found in squares included in this group. The woodland area is much larger, the altitude is lower, the area of water is greater and the number of breeding species is higher. Species in this community include Kestrel, Red Grouse, Snipe, Woodcock, Common Sandpiper, Tree Pipit and Whinchat. The group can be split further into one containing the moorland edge and associated farmland, characterised by, for example, Ring Ouzel, and the other containing the reservoirs and woodland, with such denizens as Mallard, Pheasant and Tawny Owl.

The lowland group of communities can be split into major component parts:-

1. **'Species-rich' lowland.** This contains the highest number of breeding species and is characterised by wide habitat diversity. Indeed, the altitudinal range, area of water and wooded area are all greater. Species present in this community include Coot, Turtle Dove, Stock Dove, Little Owl, Garden Warbler and Jackdaw. A further division can be made separating the wetland community which includes all the usual familiar but not common water birds such as Reed Warbler, Sand Martin and Little Grebe, from the non-wetland, and more specifically woodland community with associated Wood Warbler and Goldcrest.

2. **'Species-poor' farmland and urban.** Most of the lower and urbanised parts of the area fall into this community type. The woodland cover is lower; there is relatively little standing water, and the urbanised nature of the landscape and the relatively uniform agricultural system lead to a lower species diversity. Birds characteristic of this community include Carrion Crow, Tree Sparrow, Sedge Warbler, Collared Dove and Grey Partridge.

The bird communities described above have been analysed in more quantitative detail to provide a reference base for future studies. The results are beyond the scope of this book but are important for comparative use in future surveys of breeding birds; e.g. to highlight species which have changed their distribution and areas in which the number of species occurring have changed, for some reason.

The Sheffield region is highly attractive to a wide range of birds, which are understandably influenced by the diversity of habitat types found within it. Sadly, many of the habitats are under severe pressures of one form or another and their constituent bird communities are threatened. Although we have a good 'general' idea of the species composition of the different habitats, detailed knowledge is lacking for many of them. Local birdwatchers can make a major contribution in the field, as our rich, and often unique, bird communities are in urgent need of further study. Only with more detailed knowledge can we hope to retain that diversity of species and habitat which make birdwatching in the Sheffield area so rewarding.

Fieldfares   **P. Leonard**

CHAPTER THREE

Visible Migration Studies
Keith Clarkson

History

Large scale bird movements have long been known to occur in Britain, both along the east coast (*26*) and elsewhere, but it was not until the 1950s that the British Trust for Ornithology attempted to co-ordinate a national network of observers in an effort to determine their true scale and extent. From the River Trent southwards, migrating flocks of Woodpigeons, Meadow Pipits, Skylarks, wagtails, thrushes, Starlings and finches were recorded in varying numbers in autumn during the early hours of daylight (*27*). Unfortunately there were no systematic observations in the Sheffield area nor, indeed, from anywhere in the north of England. Visible passage therefore seems to have gone largely unnoticed in this region until very recently.

Early studies of visible migration repeatedly showed that movement was heaviest in westerly and south-westerly headwinds, since most birds would have been flying on bearings between west and south. Movement was characteristically reduced in easterly or following winds. However, during the 1940s, Dutch ornithologists pioneered a technique for observing bird migration called 'skywatching', which involved staring at a fixed point in the sky through high-powered binoculars. The results revealed large scale movements of birds along broad fronts in following or easterly winds.

The significance of such observations was only fully realised with the advent of high-powered radar in the 1950s. This proved capable of detecting flocks of migrating birds which appeared on the screen as small echoes known as 'angels'. Ornithologists experienced in radar technology were thus able to estimate the area over which bird migration was occurring on any day or night. They also determined the direction and altitude of flight and, in some cases, the type and number of birds involved (*28*). The results confirmed that, in following winds, bird movements were occurring on a vast scale on broad fronts at high altitudes. Furthermore, comparative studies between radar operators and observers recording visible migration demonstrated that these high-level movements were going largely undetected by birdwatchers on the ground (29), whose results were therefore misleading. Radar studies appeared to indicate that most birds prefer to migrate at high altitude in following winds and are likely to be undetected by the human eye. The large-scale recording of visible migration thus seemed to be of little value. However, a number of recent studies have suggested that a sizeable proportion of the migrating population may still be recorded by observing visible migration, at least in certain areas and under particular circumstances. Westerly and south-westerly winds predominate in the British Isles, and since many species appear to have fairly restricted patterns of migration (see below), there is a strong likelihood that headwinds may persist throughout the migratory period (30). Furthermore, it sems possible that some migrants prefer to fly at low altitude, thereby minimising the risk of being blown off-course by wind drift (31).

Observations in Sheffield

The scale of visible movement through the Sheffield region varies dramatically from year to year, even from day to day, and from species to species. Flocks of thousands of winter thrushes are evident to all, but a single Bullfinch or a small party of House Sparrows may prove equally significant to birdwatchers familiar with their local 'patch'.

Redmires Reservoir — top dam   **P. Leonard**

During the 1970s regular observations were carried out at Redmires Reservoir. This locality is situated on the moorland fringe, overlooking the Rivelin Valley, on a ridge which rises from the centre of Sheffield at the point where the River Don turns from a NE-SW axis to a NW-SE axis (see Fig.2). These early observations revealed that in autumn the first two hours of daylight were typified by loose flocks of Meadow Pipits and tight-knit flocks of Linnets flying through to the south and south-west. Since there was no return movement in the evening, it seemed likely that these birds were indeed migrants, perhaps dispersing from local roosts. In an attempt to clarify the picture, daily observations were made throughout the autumn of 1981. The diversity and sheer numbers of migrants exceeded all expectations. Almost 100,000 birds were counted moving through the site, including over 20,000 Starling, 15,000 Meadow Pipit, 10,000 Fieldfare, 7,000 Woodpigeon, 5,000 Chaffinch and Swallow, and 1,000 Linnet and Redwing. Other species moving through in several hundreds included Pied Wagtail, Skylark, Greenfinch, Reed Bunting, Redpoll, Siskin, Goldfinch, Mistle Thrush and Blackbird. Large numbers of waders, duck and gulls were also counted.

The picture is similar elsewhere in the area. Of particular interest are the results from Concord Park on the northern margin of the city, 13km to the north-east of Redmires. This site represents one of the first prominent hills to confront birds moving south-west along the Don Valley. Observations carried out by J.P. Smith have added much to the results obtained from Redmires. In the autumn of 1984, movement through this site alone involved at least 20,000 Woodpigeon, 18,000 Starling and Fieldfare, 8,000 Redwing, 4,500 Meadow Pipit and Swallow, nearly 2,000 House Martin, 1,500 Linnet and 1,000 Chaffinch. These results illustrate not only the difference in numbers between sites but also between years, for in 1984 Redmires also recorded exceptional numbers of Woodpigeon (in excess of 30,000), Fieldfare and Redwing.

Data from other years suggest that different species move through the area along different routes, perhaps following their preferred habitats. Passage of Sand Martins and Yellow Wagtails seems to be restricted almost entirely to the lowland flashes and valleys to the east of Sheffield. Pied Wagtails also appear to show a preference for these lowland sites, whilst Skylarks and Woodpigeons apparently follow the farmland/moorland fringe but rarely cross over open moorland. In contrast, the peak passage of Meadow Pipits traditionally occurs across moorland areas.

The Pennines are almost certainly a key factor in channelling many migrant species not recorded to any great extent on the lowlands. Observations at Mickleden Beck, situated 600m a.s.l. at the southern tip of a north-south moorland valley, annually record a heavy passage of Meadow Pipits and Linnets. To the north-west of this valley, where the Woodhead Pass partially dissects the Pennine range, westerly passage is more pronounced, as shown by the 7,500 Redwings which flew west on the 6th October 1984.

To the south-east of Mickleden, observations from Oughtibridge in the Don Valley have provided little evidence of visible migration in the valley bottom, but it is a different story on the hill tops, where farmland and moorland meet. Woodpigeons, Meadow Pipits, Linnets, and Fieldfares, typically follow the north-south axis of the moorland fringe. On nearby Broomhead Moor, a large Meadow Pipit roost gathers during the spring and autumn, with numbers fluctuating dramatically from day to day. In autumn, evening arrivals are usually from the north and east, whilst in the morning departures to the south predominate. Both observations suggest that the occupants are predominantly transients.

The wave of migrants, so much a feature of visible migration watches, are perhaps partially explained by the passage of birds moving out of different roosts. After a few hours flying, these birds then settle at suitable feeding sites where they remain for the rest of the day, before moving off in the evening to join the nearest roost. More detailed observations at roost-sites may shed further light on this point. It is only with additional information from a variety of sites that we can hope to obtain a more detailed understanding of the effects of altitude, habitat differences and weather conditions upon the scale and form of visible migration.

The timing of migration

The daily observations from Redmires and Concord Park have allowed a more detailed picture of the timing of migration to be built up for many of our diurnal migrants. Each species tends to have a discrete time period during which most individuals move through the area. This may vary from year to year by only a few days for species such as Meadow Pipit, Starling, Woodpigeon, Linnet and Skylark, whereas the peak passage of Chaffinch, Fieldfare, Redwing and Redpoll may vary by as much as a month. It is interesting to note that, with the probable exception of the Starling, the first group consists predominantly of British migrants, whereas the latter group is likely to involve mainly continental birds.

Using this information it is possible to suggest a typical pattern for the timing of largely passerine migration through the area.

JULY - With the exception of gulls, waders and duck, diurnal passage is mainly restricted to Swifts and a small scale westerly movement of Chaffinch and Pied Wagtail. These latter movements may represent the dispersal of young birds.

Redpolls

P. Leonard

AUGUST - A quiet month on the uplands where Swifts often form the only sizeable movement; e.g. 750 flew west at Redmires on 17th August 1982. In the lowlands Sand Martin regularly move through sites such as Thrybergh Resr, where 240 flew south on 13th August 1982. A less striking but nonetheless significant feature is a small but steady southerly passage of Tree Pipits, particularly at Mickleden Beck where 32 flew south on 25th August 1981.

SEPTEMBER - A continuation of the August pattern. Sand Martin pass through in numbers into the second week of the month (max. 300 south at Thybergh Resr on 1st September 1982). In the latter half of September the hirundine passage consists chiefly of House Martin (max. 470 south at Moss Valley on 17th September 1983) and Swallow (1,600 south at Wadsley Common on 27th September 1982).

The last week of September and first week of October invariably provide one of the highspots of the visible migration calendar, with several species reaching peak numbers, as follows:-

Meadow Pipit: max. several thousand south on 28th September 1975 and 2,900 south and south-west on 29th September 1981, both at Redmires.

Linnet: max. 339 south at Redmires on 30th September 1982 and 330 south at Mickleden on 1st October 1980.

Pied Wagtail: max. 203 south-west on 1st October 1984 and 72 south-west on 2nd October 1983, both at Concord Park.

In some years there may be a spectacular influx of Redpoll (350 west at Redmires on 24th September 1980) and Siskin (69 south-west over moorland near Agden on 25th, 1984). These influxes appear to be equally likely in October; e.g. 240 Redpoll flew south-west at Leash Fen on 23rd October 1984.

OCTOBER - Early October usually sees the first large influx of Chaffinch (453 west at Redmires on 3rd, 1982) and Redwing (over 12,000 west at Mickleden, Redmires, Concord Park and Barbrook on 6th, 1984). On a much smaller scale, Goldfinch passage usually peaks in early October (36 south-west at Concord Park on 4th, 1983), as does movement of Reed Bunting (max. 27 south-west at Redmires on 13th, 1981). By mid October the southerly Skylark passage is at its height (max. 650 south/south-west at Redmires on 22nd, 1980) and the first large influx of Fieldfare can be expected; e.g. 1,176 flew west at Redmires on 16th, 1981. The westerly Greenfinch movement also peaks from mid to late October (max. 224 west at Redmires on 13th, 1980). Large movements of Chaffinch (835 west at Redmires on 26th and 27th, 1984), Fieldfare (3,100 south-west at Concord Park on 28th, 1984) and Redwing (1,200 west at Oughtibridge on 29th, 1983) may occur towards the end of the month.

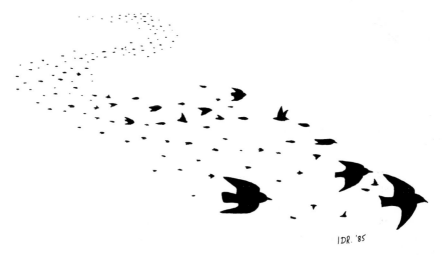

IDR. '85

Starlings   **I.D. Rotherham**

43

The passage of Woodpigeon and Starling provides one of the most spectacular sights of the month. From mid-October onwards both species begin to feature in early morning watches with increasing numbers. The westerly Starling passage peaks in the last week of October, e.g. on 27th, 1984 over 8,000 flew west at Redmires and 6,000 flew west at Concord Park. The Woodpigeon passage extends further into November and is most notable in the clear, calm weather often associated with anticyclonic conditions (max. 4,825 flying south at Redmires on 27th October 1984 and 3,990 south-west on 2nd November 1984). In similar weather conditions both Blue and Coal Tits, on several occasions, have been seen towering up into the sky before flying high over the moors to the south-west. Other occasional migrants at this time include Rock Pipit, Jackdaw, Bullfinch, Tree and House Sparrows, Yellowhammer and Corn Bunting.

NOVEMBER - The diversity of migrants begins to fall rapidly during the early weeks, although this is the most likely time for Water Pipit to occur. Typical migrants include Starling, Woodpigeon, Greenfinch, Chaffinch, Brambling and Fieldfare. Virtually all regular movements have ceased by the end of the third week. In some years small scale movement, especially of thrushes and finches may resume but this depends entirely upon the severity of the weather and availability of food resources.

The Future

The visible passage of large numbers of migrant birds through the Sheffield area is now known to be a regular, annual occurrence. Different species appear to have discrete periods during which movement occurs and to follow preferred routes which include favoured feeding habitat.

However, there are still large gaps in our knowledge. Relatively little is known about return movement in spring. Much of our data is derived from studies at two sites to the north and west of the city and almost no detailed work has been done in the lowlands to the east or the uplands to the south-west. Local weather conditions may play an important part in influencing movement through each locality, but there is relatively little data on this aspect. There are many unanswered questions which will only be solved if more birdwatchers are willing to venture out at dawn to observe migration occurring over the Sheffield region.

Collared Doves   **L. Cornthwaite**

CHAPTER FOUR

Twenty-Five Years On:
The Changing Face of Sheffield's Birds

The last 25 years has been a period of major change within both the Sheffield area and the country as a whole. Gone are the days when one could visit the Peak at any time of year and enjoy birdwatching in relative solitude. The main cause of this has been the increase in recreational pressure resulting from more leisure time and improved road transportation, coupled with a transformation in the interest (and attitude) of the general public towards wildlife and the countryside. This is increasingly affecting the distribution and numbers of birds, although so far to not such a great extent as have the changes in usage of land, water and chemicals. In addition, the populations of some of our local breeding birds have been significantly affected by climatic changes, both in the British Isles, which have led to contraction or expansion of ranges, and abroad. Adverse conditions in winter quarters or on migratory routes (particularly the prolonged drought in parts of Africa) have markedly reduced the numbers of certain summer migrants.

We have attempted, in the Systematic List, to comment on any perceptible change in the status and distribution of individual species. As it is difficult to obtain an overall picture from this, the following account presents a summary of what we believe to have been the major changes in both breeding and non-breeding birds during the past two and a half decades.

The Breeding Species
There has been a slight increase in the number of species breeding annually. Since 1960 six new species have become regular breeders, and a further two are on the way towards

becoming annual breeders, albeit rather tenuously. An additional eight have probably bred at least once or twice, and one more species has recently begun to recolonise its former haunts.

The most spectacular gain has been the colonisation by the Collared Dove which only bred for the first time in 1963 but whose local population must now number several hundred pairs. The Little Ringed Plover first nested in 1960 but did not become established until 1969, since when the population has stabilised at some 15-16 pairs. Goshawks first definitely bred in 1965; the population increased to 17-20 pairs by the late 1970s but since then has failed to expand any further. This is at least partly attributable to pressure from egg-collectors and falconers, and even birdwatchers at some sites. Another important factor may be the deterioration of some grouse moors due to less intensive management for shooting and increasing numbers of grazing sheep.

During the 1970s Black Redstart and Siskin began breeding regularly. The former continues to maintain a precarious hold in industrial Sheffield where availability of suitable habitat is increasing due to the decline of heavy industry. However, this may be only a transient phase as the industrial wasteland, which is currently also favourable to other, commoner species such as Linnet and Goldfinch, is gradually being cleared and landscaped. Siskin have increased substantially within the plantations of the Peak District, aided by maturation of the conifers, and may now number 50-100 pairs, with greater numbers in some years. In addition, the Crossbill has become an annual breeder since 1977, after isolated pairs had nested in 1958 and 1973. Its population tends to fluctuate in response to the success of the cone crop and, although low in most years, reached over 100 pairs in 1981.

Although an annual breeder until 1880, the Stonechat was subsequently only recorded breeding twice (in the 1930s) until the mid-1970s when numbers increased in the winter period and a few pairs began to nest, largely in upland localities. Wintering birds have since shown a marked decline but occasional pairs still nest and the population may be higher since some pairs are undoubtedly overlooked. This species will perhaps join the list of regular breeders, or it may disappear as quietly as it arrived. The Red-breasted Merganser has always been an uncommon winter visitor, but, surprisingly, several pairs now breed at the Derwentdale Reservoirs and have done so more or less annually since 1979. It is possible that this breeding population will increase and that other reservoirs, and perhaps even river systems, will be colonised. The same cannot be said for Black-necked Grebe, even though a pair has bred on a local subsidence flash for the three years 1982-84. This must be classed as a casual breeder, along with Pochard, Goosander, Hen Harrier, Ringed Plover and Fieldfare. Garganey has attempted to breed whilst Raven has nested only twice and the origin of that pair is suspect. Peregrine has successfully recolonised the Peak since 1981, albeit on only a small scale, and was successful for the first time in 1984. If protection measures continue to be effective, it seems likely that this former resident of the Peak District will soon become re-established. Goosander too could establish a small regular breeding population on the Peak District rivers, having bred for the first time in 1982, and other species which might nest in the near future include Ruddy Duck, Hobby, Montagu's Harrier, Redwing and Firecrest.

Goosanders   F.J. Watson

On the debit side, Mute Swan, Merlin, Black Grouse, Black-headed Gull, Barn Owl and Nightjar have undergone a major decline, whilst Corncrake is almost certainly extinct as a local breeding species. Mute Swans still nest on lowland lakes and flashes, but with much reduced success. Black-headed Gulls could re-establish themselves at upland localities, especially since one of the most important former breeding localities still remains. Indeed the species is now a casual, if not necessarily a regular, breeder once again. There seems little hope of retaining the Black Grouse as a local breeding bird as its traditional nesting areas have changed markedly and only a tiny remnant of the original breeding population remains. The Nightjar is in much the same position and at only one site are churring males heard with any degree of frequency. The Merlin, however, seems poised to make a comeback: some three pairs nested in 1983 and 1984, and others may have been overlooked in the recent past. The disappearance of this little falcon from our uplands seems inexplicable, but is perhaps linked with pesticide usage, increased recreational pressure and habitat changes. Barn Owl populations seem to be at a dangerously low level although this too may be a species which has been overlooked. In this case toxic pesticides and changes in farming practice may have been the main reasons for the decline, and it is impossible to predict whether it will survive as a local breeding bird.

There are several species whose small breeding populations have fluctuated during the last decade: Heron, Teal, Redshank and Twite are examples, and no doubt they will continue to do so in the future. The major success has undoubtedly been the Sparrowhawk which had declined dramatically by the early 1960s. There was a slow recovery in the first years of the 1970s - largely in upland coniferous plantations - as a result of voluntary bans on certain pesticides. The recovery gained momentum until, by the early years of this decade, all traditional sites had been re-occupied in both upland and lowland woodlands. It is now regularly seen in built-up areas and is a not infrequent visitor to suburban gardens. However, its expansion has recently slowed in some areas where its breeding success rate is unaccountably low.

There have been variations in the populations of regularly breeding species, but many of these are related either to the winter weather in the region or conditions in the winter quarters of our summer visitors. Thus, for example, Grey Wagtail, Moorhen and Kingfisher have declined markedly since the severe winter of 1979, but should increase if there is a further series of mild winters; Whitethroat, Redstart and Whinchat numbers crashed in the 1970s but have since shown a slight recovery. The numbers of Snipe, Curlew and Lapwing are notably fewer, possibly due to habitat changes such as drying-out of wet moorland (through climatic amelioration) and 'improved' land drainage. The latter has certainly reduced the population of our scarcer marshland birds such as Reed Warbler and Water Rail; the loss of Killamarsh on the formation of the Rother Valley Country Park was a serious blow to such species locally. More recently Swallows and Sand Martins have become much scarcer, presumably due to drought conditions in their wintering quarters or along migratory routes. A few species have continued to expand, however, the most notable being the Nuthatch in deciduous woodland and Reed Bunting in dry habitats, although the latter appears to have suffered a marked reverse since the 1981/82 winter.

Roosting Herring Gulls   F.J. Watson

The Non-breeding Species

There have been 34 new species recorded in the area since 1960, of which nine first occurred in the 1960s, twelve in the 1970s and a further thirteen in the last five years. It can be seen from the list (Appendix 3) that 20 have occurred on only one or two occasions, mainly at reservoirs or subsidence flashes. It seems highly likely that such vagrants have visited the area on occasions prior to 1960 but have gone unrecorded. The lengthy list of new species since 1960, and especially since 1970, is doubtless related to increased coverage of suitable sites and the much greater number of observers frequenting most parts of the area. It can be safely predicted that new vagrant species will continue to be found, and it would not be too surprising to find the addition of several more, particularly North American birds, in the next few years. The most likely of the latter are species such as Long-billed Dowitcher; Pectoral, White-rumped and Spotted Sandpipers; Ring-billed and Laughing Gull.

The other 14 species can be divided into three categories:-
1. Expected to occur occasionally, namely Fulmar, White-fronted Goose, Long-tailed Duck, Black-tailed Godwit, Little Gull and Lapland Bunting.
2. Expanding winter or summer populations within the British Isles, i.e. Greylag Goose, Ruddy Duck, the three 'white-winged' gulls, Bearded Tit and Golden Oriole.
3. Irruptive species such as Parrot Crossbill.

The likelihood of more species in these categories occurring in the near future is not great, but possibilities include Cetti's Warbler, whose population in southern England has expanded rapidly, and Nutcracker, which has not 'irrupted' into Britain since 1968.

Records of passage migrants have increased dramatically in the last decade, but this may simply be the result of increased observer coverage. Many wader species, e.g. Grey Plover, Sanderling, Little Stint and Turnstone, previously considered to be scarce or irregular visitors, have been found to occur annually. Regular monitoring of local reservoirs has shown that the rarer ducks such as Scaup and seabirds such as Kittiwakes are commoner than was previously realised.

Numbers of winter visitors tend to vary markedly from year to year, and it is therefore difficult to detect trends. It is hoped that the *Winter Atlas* data, when analysed, will provide a good basis for the determination of population changes. There is no doubt that the larger gull species increased greatly in numbers in the 1970s with the formation of roosts on local reservoirs. Also in this period Hen Harrier, Rough-legged Buzzard, Firecrest and Great Grey Shrike were first found to occur regularly, although towards the end of the decade the last three species were much scarcer. The only noted change in wintering wader numbers has been for Jack Snipe which has recently become scarce. Blackcap and Chiffchaff have regularly over-wintered during the last decade, with the former the more numerous. Large flocks of Hawfinch have been reported during this time, with up to 30 feeding in a suburban woodland and up to 50 roosting in the Peak District, but these may have occurred undetected in the past.

Hawfinch   P. Leonard

Conclusion

It is inevitable that a review of ornithology over a period of 25 years will identify many aspects that have changed, with new pressures affecting our birds, particularly the breeding species. The years since 1960 have been no exception and, indeed, the bird-life of the Sheffield area has had to show perhaps a greater degree of resilience than at any other time even to maintain the *status quo*. Not every species has been able to cope with the pressures of the late twentieth century, but this review indicates that the losses have been outweighed by the gains of some species whose populations have increased and others which have started to colonise the area.

We now know far more than we did 25 years ago about the density and distribution of breeding birds, and the numbers and species migrating through the area or visiting in winter. However, the need for careful monitoring of population levels can never be overstated, so that we can detect significant changes in sufficient time to take appropriate action wherever possible.

Turnstone

Snipe and Black-headed Gull are common winter and passage visitors but numbers of breeding birds have declined substantially.

The Systematic List

The following Systematic List considers all bird species recorded in an apparently wild state in the Sheffield area from 1960 to 1984 and includes species which, although originally introduced by man, have now established a regular feral breeding population in Britain. Nomenclature and sequence are those of Dr. K.H. Voous' (1977, *List of Recent Holarctic Bird Species*).

The bird's name is followed by a summary of its status and habitat preference. Definitions of status terminology are as follows:

Resident breeder	All or part of the local population is present throughout the year and breeds within the area.
Migrant breeder	Breeds within the area but all or most of the breeding population departs in autumn or winter.
Casual breeder	Has bred irregularly in the area since 1960 and is likely to do so again.
Winter visitor	All or part of the population breeds outside the area, but either spends the winter here or has visited the area on at least 25 occasions in the winter months.
Passage visitor	Has occurred on 25 or more occasions as a migrant in spring and/or autumn.
Infrequent visitor	Has occurred on more than 12 but less than 25 occasions as either a passage or winter visitor.
Scarce visitor	Has occurred on 12 occasions or less.
Vagrant	Not normally to be expected in the area, occurring well outside its breeding and/or migratory range.
Escaped species	Records may refer to birds which have escaped from captivity.

The accounts for most breeding species are accompanied by a distribution map which is a representation of the results of the *Atlas* project carried out in 1975-80. All data for each map are plotted using the tetrad system (i.e. 2km x 2km squares based upon maps produced by the Ordnance Survey).

The largest dots show that breeding was confirmed in the tetrad; the medium dots that breeding probably occurred but was not confirmed; the smallest dots that birds were present during the breeding season and may possibly have been breeding. There are four pairs of data alongside the maps. The first is the total number of tetrads occupied, i.e. with breeding records, followed in brackets by this number expressed as a percentage of the 300 Sheffield tetrads. The other three pairs are the numbers of tetrads in each category of breeding, followed by their percentages of the total number of tetrads occupied.

Each species account includes details of habitat, status and distribution, with estimates of numbers or densities where known. Typical and extreme dates are given for migrant birds. Full details are given for all species recorded on fewer than six occasions in the period under review. Ringing recoveries of particular interest or relevancy are noted, as is any other information such as the occurrence of flocks or visible movement which helps to build up a picture of that species within the area.

Records are also included for neighbouring areas just outside the strict boundaries of the *Atlas* survey, namely the southern part of Chatsworth Park, and in the north-west, the Langsett area including Swinden plantation.

Records of all nationally rare species have been accepted by the *British Birds* Rarities Committee and the County Records Committee of Yorkshire or Derbyshire, unless otherwise stated. All available records from 1960 to 1984 are included together with material for early 1985 when considered to be especially relevant. Reference is made to pre-1960 records if they are of particular significance to the review period.

The scientific names of species other than birds mentioned within the list are given in Appendix 7. Observers' initials are stated only when species have been recorded on less than six occasions; for first breeding records; where hitherto unpublished information is used; and for records considered to be exceptional in some way, such as early or late migrant dates or large flock numbers. The names of all initialled observers are given in Appendix 8.

The following abbreviations are used in the text in addition to standard abbreviations such as e.g. and km.:

Brit.B	*British Birds*
BTO	British Trust for Ornithology
CBC	Common Birds Census
DDOS	Doncaster and District Ornithological Society
DOS	Derbyshire Ornithological Society
RDOS	Rotherham and District Ornitholical Society
RSPB	Royal Society for the Protection of Birds
SBSG	Sheffield Bird Study Group
SBRG	Sorby Breck Ringing Group
SNHS	Sorby Natural History Society
WBS	Waterways Bird Survey
YNU	Yorkshire Naturalists' Union
a.s.l.	above sea level
c.	*circa* - approximately (this has been omitted for round numbers of 50 or more)
C.P.	Country Park
max.	maximum
Resr	Reservoir
S.F.	Sewage Farm

The names of the artists illustrating the species are listed in Appendix 1.

RED-THROATED DIVER *Gavia stellata*

Scarce visitor.

Although Allis (4) records in 1844 that young Red-throated Divers were taken several times near Sheffield, there is little mention of the species in historical records. Chislett (*14*) quotes a bird found in the yard of a Sheffield hotel in The Wicker on 17th February 1947 which was released on the Humber, but there were few subsequent records prior to 1960. Since then there have been only nine records, involving eleven birds at six localities, and so the status has probably remained unchanged. All reports except one were in the period December to early April. Thrybergh Resr seems particularly favoured by this and other diver species: two were there from 12th March to 2nd April 1961, one probably of this species on 14th February 1966 and one on 24th December 1972. Three birds have been seen on Damflask Resr: a single on 30th March 1968 and two on 24-25th February 1979, one remaining until 18th March. The latter two birds were part of a nationwide influx prompted by hard weather and the dates conform exactly to the main period for Britain as a whole (*32*).

All other records relate to single birds, on: Strines Resr from 3rd-10th December 1972 (found dead on 12th), Underbank Resr on 26th March 1973, Dale Dike Resr in full breeding plumage on 30th July 1973, and Derwent Resr on 10th January 1982.

BLACK-THROATED DIVER *Gavia arctica*

Scarce visitor

This species was not recorded until 1938 when one stayed on the relatively small Beauchief Dam in February and March. After one was seen at Staveley on 3rd April 1947, the next record was not until 1976 when one was present on Thrybergh Resr from 1st-15th February. The only other winter records occurred in 1979, during the main hard-weather influx period for Britain (*32*), and in 1985. In 1979 singles were seen on Ladybower Resr from 18-24th February, the River Derwent at Calver on 21st February, and Damflask Resr from 25th February to 18th March in the company of up to two Red-throated Divers. It is possible that only one or two different birds were involved. One stayed on Thrybergh Resr from 9-17th January 1985.

There have been four spring birds, three of which were seen in the first four days of May. The first, in summer-plumage, was on Howden Resr from 1st-3rd May 1978, followed by singles at Thrybergh Resr on 23rd April 1981 and 3rd May 1982, and a summer-plumaged bird at Barbrook Resr on 4th May 1981.

GREAT NORTHERN DIVER *Gavia immer*

Scarce visitor

This is the area's scarcest diver with only six confirmed records involving six or seven birds, all but one occurring since 1960. The first record was of a young female picked up exhausted on 1st August 1899 between Tideswell and Peak Forest. The next was of two present at Thrybergh Resr from 4th December 1960 to 26th Febuary 1961, with one remaining until 4th April. Eighteen years later, one was on Ladybower Resr from 8-15th December 1979. A summer-plumaged bird was present at Redmires Resr on 29th September 1980 and what was probably the same bird was seen on Thrybergh Resr on 12th October. In November 1982 an adult in winter-plumage arrived on Thrybergh Banks on 5th and remained until 27th. In 1984 an adult flew onto Barbrook Resr in heavy rain and northerly winds at 5 p.m. on the early date of 3rd September, and was seen to leave to the south at 7 a.m. the following morning.

LITTLE GREBE *Tachybaptus ruficollis*

Resident/migrant breeder; lakes, reservoirs, flashes and rivers.

The Little Grebe has been seen at over 60 localities since 1960, including six city parks and four sites on the industrial River Don. It breeds throughout the area, mostly on reservoirs, lakes and ponds, although the rivers Derwent and Wye are also important - up to nine territories have been recorded on 6km of the Wye. The number of sites occupied in any one year is probably about 25, the total population not exceeding 50 pairs, but occupancy varies from year to year.

The status of the species outside the breeding season seems to have changed little from that described by Wilson (16). There is an influx in autumn, the maximum count being 99 in September 1984, followed by a decline in winter until migration swells the numbers in March to approximately a third of the September population (33). Neither this pattern nor the numbers involved were affected by the severe winter of 1981/82, but hard weather can cause birds to move to city parks and rivers and even out of the area. The lowest numbers recorded on Wildfowl counts were in January 1978 and 1982 when only three birds were located.

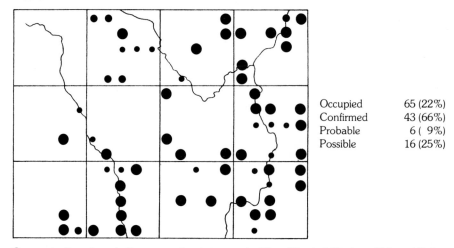

Occupied	65 (22%)
Confirmed	43 (66%)
Probable	6 (9%)
Possible	16 (25%)

Concentrations form in three areas in winter: on the River Wye in Miller's and Monsal Dales (with up to 35 and 20 birds, respectively), at Poolsbrook, and in the north-east at Catcliffe, Treeton Dyke, Thrybergh Banks and particularly Wentworth. Wentworth used to be the single most important wintering area, with peak counts of 60 on several occasions (21), but in recent years the maximum has been approximately 20.

Single birds are often recorded in spring and autumn on upland waters and in city parks remote from the usual breeding and wintering areas.

GREAT CRESTED GREBE *Podiceps cristatus*

Resident/migrant breeder; lakes, reservoirs and flashes.

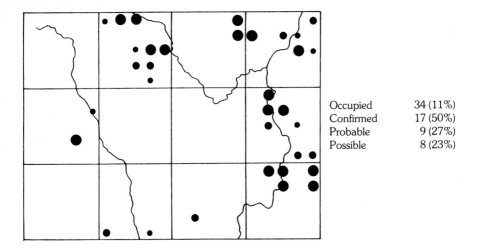

Occupied	34 (11%)
Confirmed	17 (50%)
Probable	9 (27%)
Possible	8 (23%)

The Great Crested Grebe was quite a rare breeding bird during the last century but is now found mainly to the east of Sheffield, nesting at relatively eutrophic lakes, reservoirs and subsidence flashes. It has also bred at five sites to the west, though at none higher than 200m a.s.l. Records come from an average of 17 localities each year, and breeding has been reported from 13 sites. No more than ten localities are usually occupied in any year, with a probable total breeding population of less than 20 pairs. Comparison with the national map (19) shows little substantive change. Numbers have increased in both spring and autumn, probably reflecting higher populations elsewhere (34), as the size of the local breeding population has not increased. Breeding success is often low: for example, at Wentworth it is rare for more than two broods to be raised although an average of six pairs are present.

Numbers peak during migration periods, with March totals sometimes higher than those in September. The maximum count was 70 on 13th March 1984. Wentworth is the most important locality, with a maximum of 27 on 17th September 1978. Numbers decline after September, with the lowest totals in December and January. Over-wintering birds have been recorded at Catcliffe, Elsecar, Morehall and Renishaw but, more often, birds are sighted irregularly at a number of sites throughout the winter. Hard weather can result in a complete exodus from the area, and none was recorded in February 1979 or December/January 1981/82. The main arrival period in spring is late February and early March when some may be recorded from even the highest waters in the area.

RED-NECKED GREBE *Podiceps grisegena*

Scarce visitor; reservoirs, flashes and rivers.

Traditionally very scarce in the area, the Red-necked Grebe has occurred only seven times at five localities since 1960. The first was a bird at Langsett Resr, which arrived in gale force north-westerly winds on 28th October 1972. The next was six years later at Harthill Resr on 17th December 1978. In 1979 there was a major influx related to the onset of hard weather. One bird was seen on the River Loxley near Damflask Resr on 31st January and 1st February, and on 18th February three were on Ladybower Resr despite almost total ice cover. One of these birds was subsequently found dead on 25th February and a second on 1st March. In March one was present at Treeton Dyke from 19-30th. Chandler (*32*) shows that the main influx period in 1979 for the north midlands was 12-25th February when most of the large numbers of dead birds were found. The above records correspond closely to this, and the March bird conforms to a smaller March peak also described (*32*).

SLAVONIAN GREBE *Podiceps auritus*

Scarce visitor; reservoirs.

This species is the rarest of the divers and grebes recorded in the area. The first was a live bird picked up at Edale in November 1953, followed by one seen at Damflask Resr on 3rd January 1960 (RGH). The only other records were in January 1979 - singles at Broomhead Resr on 2nd (PM) and Ladybower Resr on 7th (DM & JJ). These were undoubtedly associated with the hard weather influx from the continent (*32*), although they arrived before the main period in February.

BLACK-NECKED GREBE *Podiceps nigricollis*

Infrequent visitor, casual breeder; reservoirs and flashes.

A Black-necked Grebe in breeding plumage at Thrybergh Resr on 10-30th June 1956 would seem to be the first definite record this century. It was followed by one at Barbrook Resr on 9th December 1958.

From 1960 to 1981 there were eleven records involving 24 birds, becoming more frequent in the late 1970s. Most were in the period August to December, particularly October and November, with singles in January, March and May. In 1962 three were seen on Redmires Resr on 13th October, followed by singles in 1964 on Broomhead Resr on 6th December and in 1965 on Barbrook Resr on 2nd November. Eight birds, the largest party ever seen in the area, were on Agden Resr on 13th October 1973 (DG,DH), and in 1975 there was one on Barbrook Resr on 3rd August, ten years after the first. There were three records in 1978: two birds in full summer-plumage at Tinsley S.F. on 1st May, and singles at Barbrook Resr on 3rd September and Ladybower Resr on 26th November. In 1979 two were at Ulley Resr on 26th January and another there on 18-20th March, was only the second occasion a bird stayed for more than a day. Three were on Howden and Ladybower Resrs on 8th November 1981.

In 1982 breeding occurred in the area for the first time. A pair was first seen at the site, a subsidence flash, on 3rd June (RDW), and although the nest was apparently destroyed by rising water due to heavy rain, the pair re-nested successfully. Two young hatched (on 11th or 12th July) but one died in early August. The immature remained in the area until 7th October. In this year 11-12 pairs were reported breeding in the British Isles and at least 25 young hatched. Breeding was again successful at the site in 1983, when three young were raised, and in 1984 when two young hatched although it is not known whether they survived as the birds were much more secretive.

FULMAR *Fulmarus glacialis*
Vagrant.

There have been only six records, involving seven birds, three of which were in July. The first ever was on 16th January 1974: two birds spent ten minutes flying low over the water at Walton Dam, Chesterfield (LO) in unexceptional weather. Strangely, there was another record at the same place in the same year: a single on 6th July, following strong west-north-westerly winds. An adult was picked-up at Staveley on 3rd July 1978 and released in Pembrokeshire, and in 1980 singles flew south over Poolsbrook on 12th July and west from Langsett Resr on 14th September. In February 1984, during a cold and windy spell, a corpse was found in a conifer plantation in Upper Derwentdale (RC,DH).

MANX SHEARWATER *Puffinus puffinus*
Vagrant.

There have been only five records this century, all presumably of storm-blown vagrants. One was picked-up alive near Rotherham on 24th August 1908; a second live bird was found at Crookesmoor, Sheffield, in 1918 and yet another in a Sheffield street on 7th September 1944.

The only record since September 1950 (when a juvenile was recovered at Chesterfield, having been ringed at Skokholm four weeks earlier) is of an adult which died at Eckington on 7th September, 1963 (FNB). This bird had been ringed 310km away at Copeland Bird Observatory, Northern Ireland the previous day! The journey does not appear to be attributable to the weather as the winds were light north-easterly veering to south-westerly. Another was found eight days later only 20 km away at Conisborough, just outside the north-eastern corner of the Sheffield area.

STORM PETREL *Hydrobates pelagicus*
Vagrant.

Thomas Allis (4) quotes an early nineteenth century record of a Storm Petrel, from John Heppenstall, which was apparently swimming in a river in Sheffield and was subsequently shot. Since that time the species has been recorded only three times. In 1967 an exhausted female was found at Damflask Resr and later died (WEG). In 1979 one was found alive but injured at Bernard Road incineration plant, near the city centre, on 22nd October but it too died. On 20th October 1983 a dead adult bird was found at Edale (per DH) following a period of strong westerly winds.

LEACH'S PETREL *Oceanodroma leucorhoa*

Vagrant.

There have been only six records, all in this century. In 1909 one was picked-up at Grimesthorpe, Sheffield, on 13th November, and another was found exhausted at nearby Brightside on 22nd September 1924. In 1952 birds were reported from Wentworth and Clowne; both were part of a nationwide 'wreck' of Leach's petrels. The next record occurred in 1977 when a bird was found exhausted on Broomhead Moor (AHa) on the unusual date of 24th April during a period of strong south-westerly winds. The bird subsequently died and is now in the Sheffield City Museum. In 1982 one was found on Ulley Resr on 16th September (PB *et al*) in calm foggy conditions. This was followed in 1983 by another September record : at Thrybergh Resr on 7th (AR, WD) when the winds were not exceptional although had been gale-force west-south-westerly earlier in the week.

GANNET *Sula bassana*

Scarce visitor.

Although only rarely recorded before 1960, there have been twelve records of single birds since that date. All are from localities scattered predominantly throughout the western half of the area. Eight were in September and October, with single reports in November, February, March and May, which differs from the pattern for Derbyshire where only five of the 17 records occurred in September and October, but seven were in March and April (*20*).

The majority of birds have been immatures, but some were full adults, including two at Eckington in 1977: the first mobbed by Crows on 25th May, and the other found dead on 25th September. Four immatures were found exhausted, all during the period 7th September to 3rd October, but were revived and later released on the coast.

In the 1970s the Gannet was almost an annual visitor, being recorded in five of the years up to 1977. However, only one has been seen since then - an exhausted immature at Stocksbridge in September 1983.

CORMORANT *Phalacrocorax carbo*

Passage/winter visitor; reservoirs, lakes and flashes.

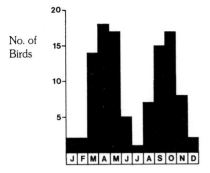

Fig. 21
Monthly distribution of Cormorant
(1960-83)

There have been 88 records involving 219 birds in the main review period, thus establishing the Cormorant as a regular rather than an occasional visitor (*16*). Birds have been seen in every month (Fig. 21) but approximately 45% of records have occurred in March to June and 45% in mid-August to November, with April the peak month. At least 45% have involved flying birds, the predominant direction in spring being north. Three-quarters were singles or twos and only 4% of records were of flocks exceeding eight birds. The largest movement seen was 42 over the city on 10th June 1979, which included one flock of 32.

Most birds remain in the area only a few hours, and the only wintering record is of two on the River Don near the city centre, surprisingly, from 25th November 1978 to 15th January 1979. Both the number of localities and birds seen are twice as high in the upland west than in other parts of the area, suggesting that Cormorants fly high when moving overland. Possible sources are colonies in south-west Scotland, the Farne Islands and north Wales (*35*). Many records refer to first year birds, as for eastern Britain as a whole (*36*), but the majority do not appear to be of this age.

Birds in breeding plumage showing the characters of the Eurasian race *P.c. sinensis* have been recorded on several occasions, e.g. two on Ladybower Resr on 21st March 1982 and one on Strines Resr on 13th March 1983.

SHAG *Phalacrocorax aristotelis*

Scarce visitor; reservoirs and rivers.

Prior to 1960 the Shag was only rarely recorded in the area. One was at Chapeltown on 29th March 1954, and in 1958 two were at Rivelin Dams for some weeks from 24th April whilst another was in Monsal Dale for several days around 27th May. Since 1960 there have been eleven records, all outside the breeding season. The only report in the 1960s was one at Bamford Millpond in February 1967 (CEE). In 1972 one was at Thrybergh Resr on 23rd March, and in 1974 an exhausted bird was found at Chapeltown on 28th October. An immature was at Damflask Resr on 5th October 1977; this bird is presumed to be the one found dead near Castleton seven days later. There were two records in 1978: one at

Treeton Dyke on 13th September and another flying along the River Don in Rotherham on 20th December. An immature stayed at Rivelin Dams from 16th December 1979 until 27th January 1980 when it was found dead under ice.

In February 1984 one was seen on Ulley Resr on 19th; another was on the River Don at Aldwarke on 26th and a corpse of a sub-adult was found at about the same time 5 km south-west on the river at Rotherham, the finder reporting a second bird alive on the river. These records were the local evidence of a wreck of Shags which occurred along the east coast of England, following several weeks of storms. The only time a party was seen occurred on 12th October 1984 when three stayed on Redmires Resr for 15 mins before departing to the west.

Most of the birds were probably immatures originating from colonies in north-east Britain (*20,36,37*).

BITTERN *Botaurus stellaris*

Scarce visitor.

Bitterns are certainly seen in the Sheffield region much more rarely than they were during at least the early part of the nineteenth century when Allis could describe several occurrences near Sheffield (4). In the latter part of that century they were present only in severe winters. One was shot near Agden in the winter of 1889/90 and another at Chatsworth on 20th January 1892.

This century, however, Bitterns have occurred on only nine occasions, eight of them since 1937 when one was at Damflask, and three of these were in the 1984/85 winter. A corpse was found at Ringinglow in November 1953. A bird flushed near Swinton on 31st August 1960 was the only one seen outside the winter period. Two years later one was recorded at Treeton Dyke on 20th November.

The only bird known to have stayed was at Renishaw from 16th January to 11th March 1971. One was flushed by wildfowlers at Poolsbrook Marsh on 18th December 1983.

Hard weather on the continent in December 1984 apparently caused an influx into Britain. In Sheffield the first bird was noted at a pond near Hassop on 8th December. An emaciated individual was picked up at Bradwell Ponds on 31st January 1985 and died two days later (per FJW). Finally, one was present at Old Denaby from 17th to at least 23rd February. All the recent records are subject to acceptance by the Records Committee.

LITTLE BITTERN *Ixobrychus minutus*

Vagrant.

The first record was from the Rivelin Valley in 1870(5). The only other occurrence was on 24th August 1967 at Catcliffe Flash when an adult male flew from reeds beside the road, across the pond, and alighted in the top of a Willow (CJ). It was not seen subsequently, but a local person had apparently seen it the previous day.

NIGHT HERON *Nycticorax nycticorax*

Vagrant.

The only record is of an adult which stayed on the ornamental lake in Graves Park, Sheffield, from 3rd-9th July 1978 (RPB). There were four records of adult Night Herons in the southern half of the country in June 1978 but no other adults in July (Brit.B).

GREY HERON *Ardea cinerea*

Resident/winter visitor, casual breeder; margins of lakes and reservoirs, rivers and wetlands.

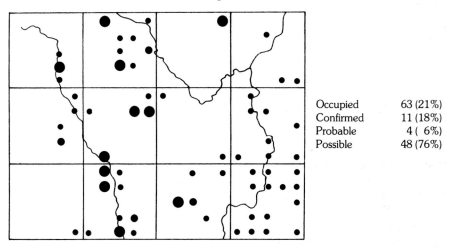

Occupied	63 (21%)
Confirmed	11 (18%)
Probable	4 (6%)
Possible	48 (76%)

Although the Heron may be seen at many localities throughout the year, it is erratic as a breeding species. Up to six birds have been present at more than 20 localities from April to July, but there has been only one recent regular nesting site since the demise of the Wentworth heronry in the 1940s. There was no evidence of breeding until 1969, but up to six pairs have bred annually since 1975, mostly to the west and south, in conifers in river valleys below 300m. A colony built-up to five nests with young by 1982 but was subsequently destroyed by shooting, probably because of fears for the interests of a nearby trout farm. In some years there have also been instances of suspected breeding where adults have been seen with juveniles but no further evidence obtained. This represents a substantial improvement from the national *Atlas* (19), and it is also possible that breeding pairs go undetected as few records involve more than two pairs and they tend to be in secluded areas of woodland. The change in breeding status is probably linked with an increase in the population nationally. Reynolds (38) showed that numbers of Herons in Britain have been healthy since 1975 and that an increase in the number of smaller heronries (2-10 nests) indicates a general trend towards colonisation of new areas.

Nomadic movements and juvenile dispersal bring larger numbers of birds into the area in autumn and winter. Indeed, some of these may be of continental origin as Frost (20) details the recoveries in Derbyshire of four birds ringed in Europe, and one found near Rotherham in December 1952 had been ringed in Sweden in June 1951. They can be seen almost anywhere where there is water, and are often recorded flying over farmland and even urban areas. Certain localities seem preferred as roost sites, and winter gatherings of 10-14 birds have been noted at Wentworth, Agden, Bradwell, Morehall and Orgreave, mainly between October and January. Hathersage attracted the highest numbers in the 1960s and early 1970s, with a maximum of 26 on 13th October 1968, but since then the largest counts have been at Chatsworth, with 27 there on 17th January 1976.

Reports have come from several city gardens, upland reservoirs such as Barbrook and Redmires in June, and on the River Don in Sheffield city centre in April 1978 and September 1980. Records from moorland areas are scarce, but two adults were seen on Featherbed Moss on 27th June 1974.

SPOONBILL *Platalea leucorodia*

Vagrant.

A sub-adult at Rivelin Dams on 6th and 7th June 1975 (DG,DH) was the first record. There was a pronounced drift of eastern migrants on the Yorkshire coast at that time, e.g. three Greenish Warblers on the same two days (YNU). The only subsequent report was of one in flight near Grenoside on 2nd May 1983 (AP), which was presumably the bird seen at Fairburn Ings on 30th April and Broomhill Flash on 1st May, departing on 2nd.

MUTE SWAN *Cygnus olor*

Resident breeder, winter visitor; lakes, reservoirs, flashes and ponds.

Mute Swans have been recorded at an average of twelve breeding sites a year and pairs have been regularly present at six. All breeding sites are to the east of Sheffield, except for Chatsworth and Miller's Dale, with Catcliffe, Clowne, Old Denaby, Pebley and Wentworth the most regularly used. Some changes in distribution have occurred since the national *Atlas*, but not in range as the same number of 10km squares were occupied. However, since 1979 the number of active sites has seriously decreased, so that the Mute Swan has virtually ceased to be a breeding species. In 1982 only one pair succeeded out of three that attempted and no nests were found in the following years.

Although the reason for this is not clear, lead poisoning and human interference are probably significant (*39*).

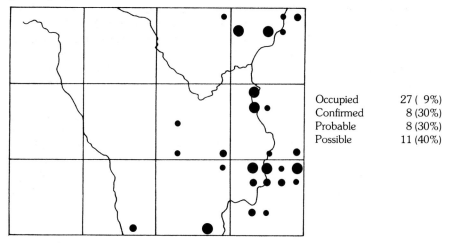

Occupied	27 (9%)
Confirmed	8 (30%)
Probable	8 (30%)
Possible	11 (40%)

There is usually a small winter influx which is attributable to small-scale movement of adults and juvenile dispersal (*40*). Evidence of interchange with populations in south Derbyshire has been provided by sightings in the east of birds colour-ringed in the Trent Valley. The winter population is never more than 25 birds and there is evidence of a recent decline; e.g. there were four records of flocks exceeding 20 birds in the period 1960 to 1975, but since then the maximum number has fallen from 14 in 1978 to six in 1983. Birds may wander in winter, and have been seen at 29 localities, twelve of which are not in the east.

Any upland bird is noteworthy, as high ground is generally avoided (*41*). Eight on Ladybower Resr on 13th June 1970 were unusual, as were four flying west (with four Bewick's Swan) at Barbrook on 31st October 1980 and one flying east at Langsett on 1st February 1976.

BEWICK'S SWAN *Cygnus columbianus*

Winter/passage visitor; reservoirs, flashes and lakes.

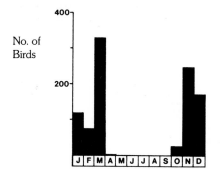

Fig. 22
Monthly distribution of Bewick's Swan (1960-83)

Bewick's Swan is recorded between October (earliest 15th, 1982) and March, and a single bird stayed until 7th April (1974). It has been seen at 28 localities, 17 of which lie to the east of Sheffield, but many records come from the uplands, including most reports of flying birds. Numbers vary greatly from year to year, with less than ten in 1965, 1967 and 1971, and over 100 in 1969 and 1976, the average being 38 per year. The monthly distribution is shown in Fig. 22: there is a distinct peak in March and most of the other birds are seen in the period November to January. It is likely that the majority are moving to and from wintering grounds, as the peak months for the British winter population are January and February (42).

Many birds are seen flying over the area and few stay, although there have been some substantial periods of residence. For example, in 1976, 18 birds remained on the south Pennine reservoirs from 29th January to 21st March, and were joined by a further 39 from 10-18th March. Birds were seen on four of the reservoirs at various times, in keeping with the habit of this species of wandering between local wintering sites (42). The biggest single herd was 65 - in 1969 at Staveley on 25th March, the month in which the largest flocks are usually seen.

WHOOPER SWAN Cygnus cygnus
Winter/passage visitor; reservoirs, flashes and lakes.

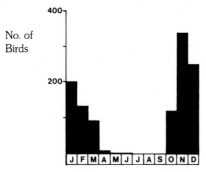

No. of Birds

Fig. 23
Monthly distribution of Whooper Swan
(1960-83)

Small parties and occasional larger herds of Whooper Swan were recorded irregularly at a number of localities, largely to the east, prior to 1975. However, since then small parties have tended to spend several months in the area. Thrybergh Banks and Renishaw have both held wintering herds of four to six birds, with the former locality possibly more important in late winter and the latter in autumn and early winter. Although there has been an increase in the annual number of birds, 1975 and 1976 stand out as peak years, with over 140 recorded in each, compared to the average of 50 per year.

The monthly distribution of birds is shown in Fig. 23 (excluding one which spent five years on Treeton Dyke and Catcliffe from 1970). The major influx is in October, earlier than in Bewick's Swan, with the earliest record on 5th (nine at Thrybergh Banks in 1981). Numbers peak in November and gradually decline until early April, when most birds have departed. The only May record was a single on Ladybower Resr on 4th in 1979 (A & BH), and one bird spent three days on Elsecar Resr in June 1973, an interlude in a five week stay at Broomhill Flash just outside our area.

The Sheffield area is at the extreme south-eastern edge of the Icelandic population's wintering range (43), and therefore most records probably do not relate to passage but to birds actually wintering here. Sheffield birds are possibly linked to small numbers in eastern and central Yorksire, as further south in Derbyshire the Whooper Swan has remained an irregular winter visitor, very rarely staying (RAF pers. comm.). There is evidence that many birds move from Britain to Ireland during the winter (44), and since almost all of the 30 or so flocks seen over the area have been moving westward, Ireland may have been their principal destination.

Records have come from 43 localities throughout the area, with greater numbers in the east but most reports of flying birds from the uplands. Average flock size is less than for Bewick's Swan (85% under ten birds), the largest being 40 at Totley on 28th October 1970.

BEAN GOOSE *Anser fabalis*

Vagrant.

The extraordinary number of 32 alighted on the edge of Redmires Resr in heavy rain on the morning of 2nd January 1976, and moved up the bank to feed as visibility deteriorated (AS). Wallace (45) notes that Bean Geese appeared in 15 widely scattered places in Britain during that month.

PINK-FOOTED GOOSE *Anser brachyrhynchus*

Passage/winter visitor.

Most records are of birds flying over in skeins, although on rare occasions they alight on local reservoirs, mainly in the west. Skeins are often reported as 'grey geese' and these are highly likely to be Pink-footed, if in the period October to March. The sightings probably relate mainly to the regular movement of this species from wintering grounds in south-west Lancashire to those on the Wash. Since 1960 there have been over 270 records involving a total of well over 20,000 birds.

An analysis of the 1970-79 records gave the following results (46):-

87% of sightings were in the period November to January with peaks in late November/early December and late December/early January. Most flocks (70%) contained fewer than 100 birds, although mean flock size peaked in December. Only eight flocks exceeded 300, the largest being 900 and 1,000. Movement was largely south and east in autumn, and north and west in spring; 97% when the wind was 30k.p.h. or less, and 82% on days of high pressure (greater than 1,000 mb), numbers moving correlating significantly with the strength of the anticyclone.

The earliest sighting was of 54 at Midhope on 25th September 1983 (strangely, flying north-west) and the latest, three at Langsett on 3rd April 1985, but 25 geese flying north up Derwentdale on 9th April 1973 which were not specifically identified were likely to have been Pink-footed. There were far fewer records in the 1960s compared with the 1970s, and as numbers wintering in England are increasing (47), it is likely that birds will be seen more frequently in the future.

WHITE-FRONTED GOOSE *Anser albifrons*

Scarce visitor.

Although seven records of this species were originally accepted, only three are now regarded as being without doubt. The first was on 17th January 1970 when two birds were seen to fly off to the north-west at Staveley (JP). In 1979 an individual of the Greenland race *A. a. flavirostris* was in the Renishaw/Barrow Hill area from 12-29th April (SBRG), which corresponds to the main period of return movement for this race (40). On 9th October 1982 two birds flew over Thrybergh Resr, arriving from the west and departing to the north (AR).

A recent record awaiting review concerns a first year bird (carrying no rings) at Harthill Resr from 23rd February to at least 4th March 1985 (AJM *et al*).

GREYLAG GOOSE *Anser anser*

Infrequent visitor/escaped species; lakes, reservoirs and flashes.

There have been at least 32 records since 1967, involving 450 birds, with none before, although Allis said that it was "obtained about Sheffield", and there was a feral bird at Pebley Pond with Canada Geese from 1957-59. Nine in the months May to August almost certainly relate to birds of captive or feral origin. Most records are of single birds and only three flocks numbering more than six birds were reported before 1982: 18 at Wentworth on 15th October 1967; 54 south at Swinton on 8th January 1978 and 75 west at Langsett with 200 Pink-footed Geese on 30th November 1975. However, in 1982 there were five such records: in February 23 were at Carr Vale from 7th to 9th, 90 flew west at Harthill Resr on 14th and 15 were at Rother Valley C.P. on 20th, whilst in December 38 flew east over Howden Moor on 6th and 60 flew east over Sheffield Parkway on 13th.

As there are no major wintering grounds south of the Solway Firth (47) and many feral birds are at large in the country, it is difficult to comment on the origins of the Greylag Geese seen in the area.

CANADA GOOSE *Branta canadensis*

Resident breeder, passage/winter visitor; lakes and reservoirs.

The Canada Goose is an irregular breeder at a handful of sites, with further pairs summering in most years. Large flocks may be seen at certain eastern localities, particularly in the autumn, and smaller parties move over the area, most often in the summer months. Even so, in some years, such as 1976 and 1977, there are very few records.

Historically, British Canada Geese have remained in discrete populations centred upon areas of introduction (48) and the nearest of these are at Wentworth in the north of the region and the Dukeries to the east. Pairs probably originating from these areas have bred at Chesterfield, Clowne, Pebley Pond and Renishaw as well as Wentworth. Since 1975, following a trend recorded in North Yorkshire, pairs have begun to stay on several upland reservoirs such as Agden, Barbrook, Broomhead, Midhope, Ramsley and Redmires during April and May, but the only evidence of successful breeding was at Redmires Resr in 1983, when a pair reared five young. These changes have resulted in two additional 10km square records of confirmed breeding and four of possible breeding since the national *Atlas* (19).

The moult migration to Beauly Firth (Highland) started by birds from North Yorkshire (49) is being increasingly taken up by birds from further south (20,50,51). In Sheffield, flocks of up to 40 birds have been seen in early June, many of them moving north. Few birds are seen in July and early August, although on 10th August 1984 at Middleton Moor 48 arrived from the south at dusk (PAA). Two which remained on Barbrook Resr from 18th June to 27th August 1977 would have moulted there. From late August, sightings become more frequent and up to 55 birds moving in a variety of directions have been reported. Most are from the north-east of the area, but there have been records from the western moorlands.

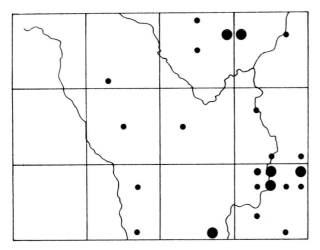

Occupied	23 (8%)
Confirmed	6 (26%)
Probable	1 (4%)
Possible	16 (70%)

The influence of populations outside the area can also be detected in the winter months. The most important site is Wentworth, where over 100 were recorded in every year from at least 1965-79, with a maximum of 156 on 12th October 1969. However, these numbers occur mainly in September and decline rapidly thereafter (33). Movements to Wentworth are probably linked with disturbance at Bretton Park (20km away) where there is a large introduced population, and possibly the more leisurely return of birds from Scotland.

Since the late 1970s there has been an increase in the numbers recorded in the south-east, particularly at Harthill Resr and Pebley Pond. Birds remain longer than at Wentworth but again peak in autumn: maxima at Harthill Resr in late September and early October have increased annually from 74 in 1981 to 262 in 1984. These may well be linked with the Dukeries population, as one ringed at Clumber Park in 1975 was shot at Renishaw in 1977. During the late winter relatively few birds are recorded, although sightings can occur at many localities during this period. The decline in the winter population noted by Francis (33) appears only to have been temporary, as numbers have increased since 1977.

BARNACLE GOOSE *Branta leucopsis*

Scarce visitor/escaped species.

Barnacle Geese have been recorded occasionally since 1971 at most times of the year, generally as single birds. Most, and possibly all, of these birds will have escaped from wildfowl collections. Since a Spitzbergen-ringed bird was present at Wath Ings (South Yorkshire) to the north in April 1982, the following two records of singles could conceivably relate to wild birds: at Ulley Resr on 27-28th December 1975 (KC,WJS) and at Thrybergh Resr on 19th January 1982 (AR *et al.*) Five birds present at Thrybergh Resr from 13th-23rd October 1980 (AR,SHH *et al*) could have overshot Scottish wintering areas, as passage birds are regularly recorded in Northumberland and Gloucestershire, but are more likely to have been of feral origin.

BRENT GOOSE *Branta bernicla*

Vagrant.

An immature seen on Thrybergh Banks on 7th November 1982 (AR,SB,KL) was the first record. The second, if accepted by the Records Committee, was of three Brent Geese on Derwent Resr in late January 1985 during thick fog (RC), and was followed by a single seen flying over nearby Ronksley moor on the late date of 29th May (SBe).

EGYPTIAN GOOSE *Alopochen aegyptiacus*

Vagrant/escaped species.

The first record was of one shot near Staveley in 1906 (*20*). The species was not seen again until two birds occurred at Middleton Moor from 11-14th August 1979 (PAA). Then in 1983 two flew east at Pebley Pond on 25th January (JWW) and a single adult was on Thrybergh Resr on 7th March (SJH). As the very small British feral population is resident (*40*), a captive origin for all these birds seems very likely.

RUDDY SHELDUCK *Tadorna ferruginea*

Escaped species/scarce visitor.

One flew onto a lagoon at Tinsley S.F. for ten minutes before flying east, on 2nd August 1978 (RT,PL,PG). A recent status review (*52*) concluded that no record in Britain during the past fifty years has definitely related to a wild vagrant.

SHELDUCK *Tadorna tadorna*

Passage/winter visitor; reservoirs, flashes and sewage farms.

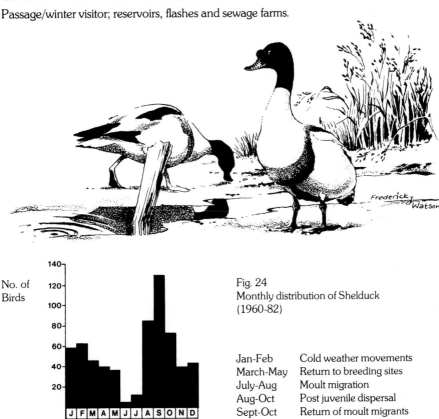

No. of Birds

Fig. 24
Monthly distribution of Shelduck
(1960-82)

Jan-Feb	Cold weather movements
March-May	Return to breeding sites
July-Aug	Moult migration
Aug-Oct	Post juvenile dispersal
Sept-Oct	Return of moult migrants

The Shelduck occurs frequently, with an average of 40 birds a year, and has visited 33 localities throughout the area. However, most records are from the uplands and relate to small numbers which remain briefly. The monthly distribution is shown in Fig. 24 with an explanation of regular movements across the area (53). Although very few are seen in July, the majority of Shelduck from the Dee and Mersey estuaries are known to cross the Pennines then, through Longdendale on their way to moult in the southern North Sea (54). Therefore they should cross the north-west corner of our area north of Bleaklow. There is a sharp increase in records in August, due to post-juvenile dispersal and possibly moult migrants, peaking in September when many of the moult immigrants retun to the west coast, especially the Dee. Sightings then decline slightly to the year end, with some birds remaining for several days during this period, return passage being often longer and more leisurely (55). The secondary peak in January and February may be associated with cold weather movements in the southern North Sea where many Shelduck spend the early winter. Records tail off towards June as birds return to their breeding grounds.

73

Although there has been a slight increase in the number of birds per year, this is overshadowed by peak years such as 1974, 1981 and 1982 when double the average number were seen. Graves and Grieve (53) show that there was a fourfold increase in records in the southern Pennines between 1950 and 1980, the increase being particularly marked from the early 1970s onwards. Although most records are of fewer than five birds, there have been at least seven reports from upland localities of flocks greater than ten birds in the period mid-July to mid-October. The largest was seen in 1964 when 35 flew east at Barbrook on 19th August, and in 1982 there were 25 birds on Redmires Resr on 11th September.

MANDARIN Aix galericulata

Scarce visitor/escaped species.

Male Mandarins have been recorded in six years from 1973, particularly on the River Derwent during 1983 and 84. However, it is unlikely that any of these birds originate from the feral population in southern England.

WIGEON Anas Penelope

Passage/winter visitor; reservoirs, lakes and flashes.

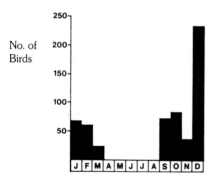

No. of Birds

Fig. 25
Monthly distribution of Wigeon
(1973-83) - wildfowl counts only

The status of the Wigeon does not appear to have changed substantially in the last two decades. Birds are seen mainly during the period late August to April, with a pronounced peak in mid-winter (Fig. 25) as is usual for northern England (56). Most spring and autumn records relate to passage birds and are from upland reservoirs, but occasionally birds are seen at unusual localities such as six on the River Derwent (31st March 1974), three at Birleyhay Dam (24th September 1977) and one on the River Don in Sheffield (28th September 1981). Winter records are largely from eastern localities, particularly Thrybergh Resr, and some birds may stay for up to several weeks. The December peak is attributable to local movement of some of the many birds found at major floodwater sites further east of the area, such as Derwent Ings.

Between five and 15 birds are seen on most wildfowl counts, and records are received from 15-20 localities each year. The largest flock was 49 at Thrybergh Resr on 3rd January 1977, and there have been three other counts in the 40s all from Thrybergh or Renishaw in December and January. Most records are of less than five birds but some large flocks have been seen on the upland reservoirs, particularly in the autumn, and 52 flew west at dusk on 8th August 1984 at Barbrook. These reservoirs are also the sites where small numbers of birds have been seen during the summer. There have been at least 15 records during the period May to early August, many involving immatures or males. Most do not stay, but a male on Langsett Resr from 22nd May to 23rd June 1974 was an exception. Presumably these sites are favoured because of the predominantly upland distribution of the small British breeding population.

GADWALL *Anas strepera*

Winter/passage visitor; reservoirs, lakes and flashes.

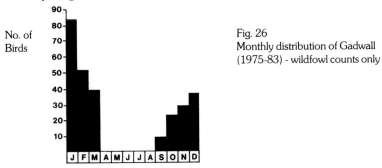

No. of Birds

Fig. 26
Monthly distribution of Gadwall
(1975-83) - wildfowl counts only

The Gadwall is the most localised of the ducks regularly recorded in the area. Although seen at 19 localities, Renishaw has been predominant as a home for this species since it was first recorded there in December 1975. Numbers peaked at between 8 and 12 there every subsequent year until January 1981 when 27 were present, and then in 1983 on 15th January there were 52, falling to 22 by mid-February. Elsewhere, numbers are much smaller and sightings irregular, usually at lowland sites with Thrybergh Resr and Banks the most favoured. Occurrences at upland localities are unusual and often coincide with times of passage, such as two reports of two birds on Barbrook Resr in August 1973 and 1974. Five birds on Derwent Resr on 31st December 1977 (DVH) and two on Morehall Resr on 12th November 1978 were exceptional.

Although the Gadwall has not yet bred in this area, it is likely to do so as occasional pairs have been seen in spring since 1982. The only summer records were of singles at Chatsworth on 29th July 1979 and at Renishaw on 17th June 1981. The earliest autumn arrivals are usually at the end of August; numbers then build to a peak in January and decline to April (Fig. 26).

The population has increased markedly in the past two decades, as in Derbyshire (20) and Doncaster (57). The origin of the birds is uncertain but is likely to be a combination of local movement of English breeding birds, which are mainly feral and increasing (58), together with Scottish, Icelandic and continental immigrants (40).

TEAL *Anas crecca*

Resident breeder, winter visitor; moorland pools, marshes, flashes, lakes, reservoirs and sewage farms.

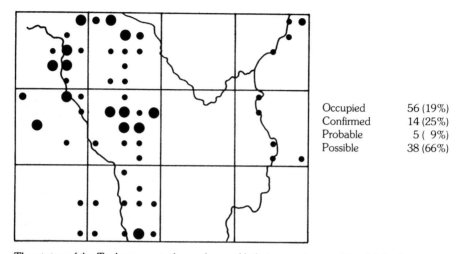

Occupied	56 (19%)
Confirmed	14 (25%)
Probable	5 (9%)
Possible	38 (66%)

The status of the Teal appears to have changed little in recent years. All published accounts refer to a widespread but not numerous breeding population with an influx of birds in the autumn and winter, and the current situation reflects this. There appears to have been a slight increase in the number of upland breeding pairs in the early 1970s: in SK29, where there was no evidence of confirmed breeding in the national *Atlas*, 30 young were counted in 1973 and more than ten pairs bred in 1974. A similar increase was noted in Doncaster but Frost (20) states that in Derbyshire the Teal is less widespread than formerly. Although nesting mainly on the moors, most confirmed records refer to sightings of young on upland reservoirs, as it is only when the birds move to open water that they become easily visible - e.g. at Redmires where eight pairs were seen with young in 1978. Most lowland *Atlas* records came from the Rother Valley, although breeding was not confirmed until 1981 when three young were seen at Tinsley S. F.. The population in any one year probably lies between 10 and 50 pairs. In the mid-1970s it may have been in the upper half of this range but the population declined later in the decade and is now in the lower half.

During the winter, Teal may be found at many sites, but only Thrybergh and Redmires Resrs regularly hold over 50 birds. Aldwarke was the most important locality until 1978 when the habitat was destroyed (17). Other sites such as Wentworth, Harthill and Old Denaby have held large numbers of birds on occasion, and since 1981 Middleton Moor has held over 100 in the autumn. It is possible that birds moult at Redmires, and perhaps Barbrook, as numbers peak here in August and decline thereafter. Most birds winter in the east of the area, regularly at sites with permanent water and more erratically on areas of floodwater, such as at Barrow Hill where there were 475 on 30th January 1975 and 450 on 16th January 1983. The population can fluctuate markedly from year to year, to some extent in response to changing water levels, but there is little evidence of movement away from the area in periods of hard weather. Most British wintering birds are from the Continent (40), and the two local ringing recoveries are of birds found dead near Staveley which had been ringed in Holland in September and Denmark in April. Birds flocking in the area in August and September are probably of British origin.

MALLARD *Anas platyrhynchos*

Resident breeder, winter visitor; lakes, reservoirs, flashes and rivers.

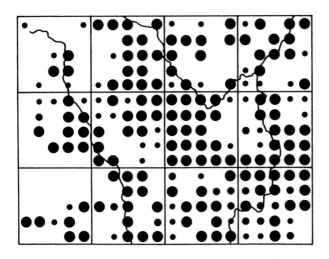

Occupied	200 (67%)
Confirmed	38 (69%)
Probable	15 (7%)
Possible	47 (24%)

This is the commonest duck in the area throughout the year. It is a widespread breeder, needing only small wetlands and streams, and even nesting well away from the water. The major 'blank' areas on the map relate to the rather dry limestone plateau and the bleak tops of the gritstone Pennines. Other areas where breeding was not recorded, especially to the east, may have been inadequately covered.

77

The Mallard breeds in many habitats, including the main conurbations; its population has increased on several stretches of the industrial River Don in recent years. Approximately 150 territories are recorded annually in the WBS, every stretch having breeding birds, with the average annual density on the River Derwent being 42 pairs/10 km. From this data and records such as 30 pairs (rearing 100 young in 1974) at Wentworth, 12 - 20 pairs at Broomhead Resr and 8 pairs at Langsett Resr, the breeding population is estimated to be of the order 500 - 1,000 pairs, which is twice the national density (*19*). Two interesting records are of a female incubating 12 Mallard and 4 Pheasant eggs, at Totley in April 1971 (HJR), and one nesting 15m up an oak tree in 1977 (PT), which is much higher than normal (*40*). Over the ten years 1975-84, an average of 8.3 females were seen with young on 5.6 km of the River Noe (JH).

Numbers are at their lowest in the breeding season but increase as the young hatch. A wildfowl count organised in July 1979 totalled 873 birds and 904 were counted in June 1984. The population peaks in October/November with the advent of continental migrants. The maximum count for the area was 2,429 in October 1983 and for a single locality, 740 at Chatsworth in October 1982. Birds were particularly numerous in the 1973/74, 76/77, 79/80 and 82/83 winters, as nationally, but there were very few in 1981/82. The population decreases rapidly after January.

Mallard tend to avoid the most exposed waters, but nevertheless some upland reservoirs are important as day-time roosts, e.g. 621 were on Broomhead on 13th October 1974. In the early 1970s Broomhead and Thrybergh Resrs held the most birds, but were superceded by Chatsworth and Wentworth lakes, particularly in the 1980s. Floodwater in the south-east can also be important, e.g. Breck Farm held 400 on 27th September 1976. Birds can be found almost anywhere in winter, including city parks (particularly in hard weather) and the River Don near the city centre where 49 were counted in December 1981.

PINTAIL *Anas acuta*

Passage/winter visitor; reservoirs, lakes and floodwater.

Although not common in the area, the Pintail is an annual visitor with an average of 18 seen per year. The number of records has increased over the years, but this is probably related to improved observer coverage. Peak years were 1973, and 1981-83, which follows the trend nationally, but numbers were low in 1977/78 which was a good year over Britain as a whole (*35*). Birds are not seen in the summer until late August, after which numbers rapidly peak in September/October, decline slightly in November/December, and then are much lower in the new year (Fig. 27). The apparent peak in December is caused by a flock of 40 at Breck Farm, on 24-27th December 1981, which moved into the area during hard weather.

Most records relate to movement through the area during autumn. The strength of this has become particularly apparent since migration watches began; e.g. from 14th September to 16th October 1983 there were nine records at four localities involving 44 birds in flight. As expected for a passage migrant, most are seen at upland sites, with 17 of the 26 localities involved lying to the west. However, there is no evidence of a prominent return passage.

No. of
Birds

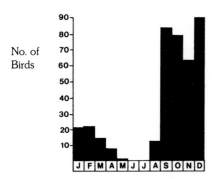

Fig. 27
Monthly distribution of Pintail
(1960-82)

Most birds do not remain in the area, exceptions being a male which spent a month from mid-December 1970 on Broomhead Resr and a pair resident on Thrybergh Resr in the first two months of 1974. The average number recorded is only three birds. Unusual reports include six at Longshaw on 7th October 1973, one in Monsal Dale on 13th January 1979 (presumably related to hard weather at that time), the only May record - one flying west at Rivelin on 9th in 1981 (RH) - and one at Catcliffe on 7th July 1985

GARGANEY *Anas querquedula*

Passage visitor; flashes, reservoirs and lakes.

The Garganey is an uncommon migrant visitor with 25 records in ten years during the period 1960 to 1981, involving 36 birds. Its status appeared to have changed little until 1982, although numbers had fluctuated with no sightings in three of the four years 1977 -1980. However in 1982, there was a pair at Thrybergh Banks and a male at Kilnhurst Flash in June, and a pair at Carr Vale Flash from 28th April until the end of June. The latter pair were seen displaying and probably bred, but were unsuccessful due to flooding (AA, RAF). This was a 'good' year for Garganey nationally with between ten and 94 pairs breeding. Pairs were seen at three sites in the spring of 1983, but for no more than six days at a time.

The species has been recorded at twelve localities, all lying to the east other than Redmires and Barbrook Resrs. The earliest date is 23rd March (1969) and the latest 11th October (1975), with most records in August. The only breeding season reports in the *Atlas* years were of a pair at Catcliffe for twelve days in 1976 and a male at Old Denaby on 14th May 1975. The majority of sightings are of single birds, with the largest party five on Redmires Resr on 12th September 1975 (SJ).

SHOVELER *Anas clypeata*

Passage/winter visitor; reservoirs, lakes and flashes.

The Shoveler is largely a passage migrant to the area, although the presence of a small wintering population and a handful of birds during the summer means that sightings are received from every month (Fig. 28). The main period of passage is in the autumn. Numbers build from late July, to peak in August, probably due to British breeding birds passing through the area (40). After a lull in September, the population remains high until December, due to passage of Continental migrants (59). Thereafter numbers are low, with little evidence of return passage. Similar numbers occur each year, although 1974 and 1982 were peak years.

Through the autumn and winter an average of two to seven birds is recorded on each wildfowl count, but much larger parties are occasionally seen, such as 33 at Renishaw on 30th September 1961 and 32 on Thrybergh Resr on 23rd October 1973. In the 1980s there have been up to 20 birds at Old Denaby and Middleton Moor for several months in autumn, with a maximum of 49 at Old Denaby on 20th October 1983 (YNU). The species is most regular at sites in the Rother Valley such as Catcliffe.

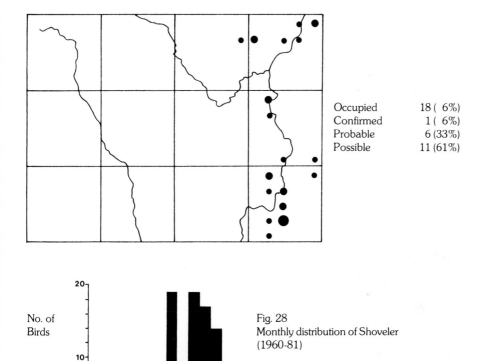

Occupied	18 (6%)
Confirmed	1 (6%)
Probable	6 (33%)
Possible	11 (61%)

No. of
Birds

Fig. 28
Monthly distribution of Shoveler
(1960-81)

The only confirmed breeding occurred at Staveley, in the early 1960s and in 1976, although the Shoveler does breed outside the area, to the north and east. Summering birds have been present in most years at, for example, Old Denaby, Thrybergh Banks, Wentworth and Catcliffe, and there have been records of small parties at upland sites. Eight males on Barbrook Resr on 20th June 1970 (RAF) was exceptional.

F

81

RED-CRESTED POCHARD *Netta rufina*

Vagrant/escaped species.

At least seven Red-crested Pochard have been seen in the area but most, if not all, are likely to have been of captive origin. Three females were on Redmires Resr on 10th November 1957 (DRW). In 1970 a male was on Thrybergh Resr on 15-16th February; after several days at Potteric Carr near Doncaster, it spent a month at Catcliffe and Treeton Dyke, before moving to Killamarsh on 11th April where it was last seen. In 1974 a female was on the River Loxley on 29th October, and in 1976 a female spent a month from 31st October at Thrybergh Banks, and possibly the same bird returned on 6th February 1977. A female seen at Pebley Pond on 21st September 1980 (DJG,PMG) is the most likely candidate for a wild bird, as this species is a scarce but regular autumn migrant to the south and east of England.

POCHARD *Aythya ferina*

Casual breeder, passage/winter visitor; lakes, reservoirs and flashes.

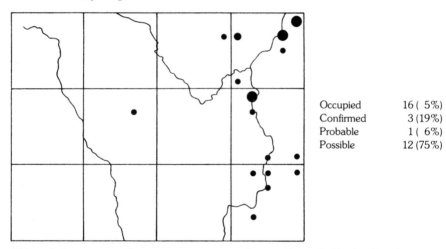

Occupied	16 (5%)
Confirmed	3 (19%)
Probable	1 (6%)
Possible	12 (75%)

Although characteristically an eastern species at all times of year, the Pochard can be seen at many localities in the region. However, in the breeding season it is confined to the north-east of the area. Breeding was not confirmed until 1979, when a female was seen with two young at Old Denaby on 8th August (RDOS). It subsequently occurred at Catcliffe in 1980 and 1981, when two and three young were reared, and at Thrybergh Banks, with a probable breeding record from Wentworth. Birds have been present in suitable habitat during the breeding season at several other localities in the Rother Valley. Although the British breeding population has been slowly increasing (60), the sites around Sheffield are not ideal as the species requires large areas of open water with substantial emergent vegetation. Thus it seems unlikely that more than a few pairs could breed in the area, and indeed breeding has not been confirmed since 1981.

Small numbers are recorded each year during the summer months at a variety of sites, with eleven at Langsett on 4th July 1976 and up to 15 at Thrybergh Banks in June and July 1976 being particularly notable. It is possible that these birds are linked to either the presence of moulting flocks or movement to them, as a considerable British summer population exists and moulting occurs at several sites.

An increase in numbers begins in late August and accelerates between September and October. Peak counts are usually in November/December and February, with fewer birds present in December, and the numbers fall off rapidly to April. The maximum wildfowl count total was 264 in February 1981, with 262 in February 1983, and there were 253 at Thrybergh Resr on 16th February 1978, and 204 at Wentworth on 15th February 1970. The largest numbers probably relate to times of passage, with the wintering population lower than the maxima would suggest, at around 100 to 500 birds. Hard weather can cause these patterns to be altered, however, and the January population was much reduced in 1979 and non-existent in 1982. Numbers wintering in the area increased after the 1950s (21), but since then the population appears to have stabilised. Males are usually present in greater numbers than females, in common with the country as a whole.

During the winter the major concentrations are found in the north-east, with Thrybergh Resr, Catcliffe and Ulley Resr regularly holding between 10 and 50, and Wentworth over 50. Although the wintering populations are inversely related to altitude, there is always a small number of birds present at a few western sites such as the Derwentdale and Redmires Resrs. These numbers have remained fairly constant, except at Morehall Resr where 40 birds were regular in 1977 but then declined substantially.

Records have come from over 40 localities including rivers, such as the Derwent and Wye, and mill ponds, e.g. in the Moss, Sheaf and Limb Valleys.

RING-NECKED DUCK *Aythya collaris*

Vagrant.

An adult male on Pebley Pond on 9-10th February 1982 was the first record of this Nearctic species for the area (DHu *et al*).

FERRUGINOUS DUCK *Aythya nyroca*

Vagrant/escaped species.

One on a small mill pond at Herries Road, Sheffield on 1st October 1957 (RGH) was the first record for the region. In 1973 an immature male was on Langsett Resr on 4th September (KC, WJS, TP) and at Treeton from 20-25th October (RAF). It is possible that the same bird was involved. An adult male was seen on Pebley Pond on 13th December 1982 (DHu). A captive origin cannot be ruled out for all these records.

TUFTED DUCK *Aythya fuligula*

Resident breeder, winter visitor; reservoirs, lakes, flashes and rivers.

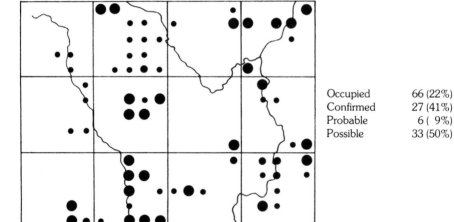

Occupied	66 (22%)
Confirmed	27 (41%)
Probable	6 (9%)
Possible	33 (50%)

Although introduced onto Wentworth lakes in the latter years of the last century, the Tufted Duck probably did not begin breeding with any regularity until the 1920s or 30s. It is found on many waters throughout the area at all times of year. It breeds at a variety of wetlands with still and slow-flowing water. Wentworth, Chatsworth, Redmires Resr and the Rivers Derwent and Wye are the most important breeding localities, and another twelve sites are probably occupied each year. Wentworth holds an average of seven breeding pairs annually, but the rivers are a particular stronghold : on 4.4km of the Derwent densities of upto 30 territories/10km have been recorded in the WBS, the highest in the country (*61*).

84

Breeding has also been recorded at smaller isolated sites such as moorland reservoirs, upland rivers and at Tinsley S. F.. Taking these into account, the annual breeding population is estimated to be c. 40-50 pairs, which accords with the density nationally (*19*) and appears to have remained constant over the two decades.

At Redmires Resr there is an influx of birds during the late summer, reaching a peak from early August to September and declining thereafter. This is unique in the area and is attributable to the use of Redmires Resr as a moulting ground (*62*). Numbers peaked at 172 in August 1975 but rarely exceeded 100 after this until 1983 when there were 126 on 2nd September with 125 on 4th September 1984.

Elsewhere there is relatively little change in the non-breeding population except for a slight mid-winter maximum, presumably related to some movement of the largely resident southern-British birds and a few continental immigrants (*40*). The total population is c. 150-200 birds, with several counts over 200, the maximum being 500 in September 1984. Hard weather movements occur, as in January 1979 and 1982 when the population was respectively 15% and 10% of the normal level.

Although the Tufted Duck has been recorded at almost 50 localities, only 19 hold regular numbers. Wentworth was the most important with over 50, but its population declined in the early 1980s, with corresponding increases at Thrybergh Resr, Catcliffe and more recently Rother Valley C.P. Shallow sites are preferred and so the winter distribution is largely confined to the east, although less so than for the Pochard. Occasionally western waters can hold upto 50 birds.

SCAUP *Aythya marila*

Passage/winter visitor; reservoirs, lakes and flashes.

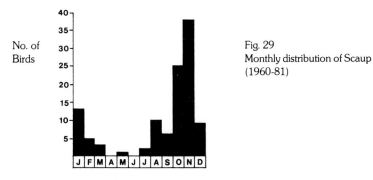

No. of Birds

Fig. 29
Monthly distribution of Scaup
(1960-81)

The Scaup has occurred in 19 out of the 24 years since 1960, with an average of four per year. However, the number of birds has increased during the period, being most numerous in the years 1973 and 1974, when the wintering population peaked at several British sites (*46*), and in 1976 and 1978. However, since 1979 few have occurred.

There is a small passage centered upon August, the source of which is unclear, but the main period for records is October and particularly November, when continental migrants move through. After that, sightings decline with a small peak in January and very few reports after March. This pattern suggests that Sheffield records are composed mainly of passage birds in the autumn, and a smaller number of birds present inland during the winter. There is no sign of a return passage, which apparently begins in late February to March (40). The average sighting is of two birds and only two flocks of more than five have been recorded: 11-12 females on Thrybergh Resr from 18th October to 6th November 1965 (YNU) and five males with four females on Langsett Resr on 24th November 1978 (PM). Most birds do not stay, but single females were on Barbrook Resr from the beginning of 1973 to the 31st March, and on Broomhead Resr from 14th November 1973 to the year end, and an immature male stayed at Rother Valley C.P. from 14th October to 24th November 1982. Most Sheffield birds are females or immatures; of 80 sexed birds, only 30% were definitely males.

Although Scaup have been seen at 22 localities scattered over the area, most records come from the upland reservoirs, with Barbrook, Broomhead, Midhope and Redmires particularly favoured. This accords with its main status as a passage migrant, as upland reservoirs feature strongly in the occurrence of migrant wildfowl. There is no evidence of any hard weather influxes, as mentioned by several authors (14,20). One unusual record was of two females at Tinsley S.F. on 23rd October 1973 (CRM).

There have also been a number of records of Aythya hybrids, i.e. birds showing the character of more than one Aythya species. For example, in 1983 single Scaup x Tufted Duck hybrids were suspected at Renishaw in March and Redmires Resr in November, and an apparent Tufted x Ferruginous Duck hybrid was at Redmires Resr in December.

EIDER Somateria mollissima

Scarce visitor.

There have been four records of this species, which is less regular inland than other marine ducks. The first was on Wentworth Lakes on 15th December 1968 (JIM), and no more were seen until a male appeared on Treeton Dyke on 23rd and 24th December 1979 (RP et al). A female and two males were on Broomhead Resr on 8th November 1980 (PKG, DH), a time when large numbers were seen on the Yorkshire coast and one other bird was seen inland in Yorkshire. In 1982 an immature was on Thrybergh Resr on 4th December (AR), which was the starting date for an influx into the Trent Valley in Derbyshire involving at least eleven birds.

LONG-TAILED DUCK Clangula hyemalis

Scarce passage/winter visitor; reservoirs and lakes.

The Long-tailed Duck has occurred eleven times at nine localities, since first recorded at Barbrook Resr in November 1963, although only twice since 1975. All records relate to single birds, except for two involving two birds, and have been in the period 21st September to 3rd January, excluding a male on Barbrook Resr on 28th May 1973 (RAF) and the Thrybergh bird detailed below. Most have been seen in November and on only one day. However, a female stayed on Elsecar Resr for eight days from 22nd October 1970 before moving to Wentworth until 3rd January 1971; two were on Ulley Resr on 4th November

1980, an immature male staying until 18th; and an immature female was on Thrybergh Resr from 18th February to 16th March 1984, returning for one day on 19th March. A bird at Rother Valley C.P. in November 1984 had apparently been released there after being found exhausted outside the area, and so is excluded from the above figures.

COMMON SCOTER *Melanitta nigra*

Passage visitor; reservoirs and lakes.

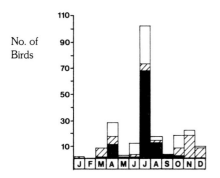

No. of Birds

Fig. 30
Monthly distribution of Common Scoter
(1960-81)

Key — Solid black = Ad ♂
— Hatched = ♀/immatures
— White = Sex unknown

The movement of Common Scoters over Sheffield reflects the situation in much of central and northern Britain. An average of eight birds per annum occurred in the period 1960 to 1981, with peak counts of 34 in 1971 and 32 in 1974. 1982 and 1983 were also good years, with 29 and 27 birds reported. The pattern has remained stable and there is no evidence of any long-term change. Most records are of singles or small parties, the average being three birds. There have been only four records involving more than seven birds, three of which were in July and referred to mainly males, namely 28 on Howden Resr on 26th (1971), 18 at Strines Resr on 21st (1974), and c. 20 flying west at Orgreave on 18th (1982). Most recently there were 19, mainly females/immatures, on Ladybower Resr on 12th November 1983. Common Scoters have been recorded at 18 localities, only five of which lie to the east, and there have been only ten records away from the upland reservoirs.

There are three peaks in the monthly distribution (Fig. 30) - in April, July and November. The main peak in July probably corresponds to east-west movements of birds from the Irish Sea, related to moult (*63*); the later peak to movement of other birds from moulting areas in the North Sea to winter quarters further west (*40*); and the April peak to return passage. There are distinct differences in the proportions of males and females/immatures (Fig. 30): males predominate in July and August, and to a lesser extent in the spring, females/immatures in October to January. This corresponds to the situation for Derbyshire (*64*), West Yorkshire (*65*) and nationally (*63*).

87

VELVET SCOTER *Melanitta fusca*

Scarce visitor.

The only record of Velvet Scoter prior to 1962 was of nine immature males on Redmires Resr on 8th October 1941 (JPU). There have been five records subsequently, involving eight birds, in October, November and January. Single males were seen on Ulley Resr on 10th November 1962 (RAF) and on Ladybower Resr on 6th October 1963 (RGH), and a female was on Wentworth Lakes on 17-24th November 1963 (JIM). In 1976 a male flew south-south-east at Old Whittington S.F. on 11th January (RAF, MET).

The only record involving more than a single bird occurred in 1979 when four alighted briefly on Langsett Resr on 7th January (MT, SD). This falls within one of the main hard weather influx periods described by Chandler (*32*).

GOLDENEYE *Bucephala clangula*

Passage/winter visitor; reservoirs, lakes and flashes.

Frederick J Watson

The average population of Goldeneye wintering in the area is only 14. The mean arrival date in autumn is 6th October, with the earliest sighting of a definite migrant 26th September 1978. The major influx, however, occurs towards the end of October. Numbers increase to a peak in November/December, when the area maxima are often recorded, then fall later in December as birds move to coastal areas (*58*). Numbers peak again in February as return passage begins, and the population declines thereafter, with the average last date being 8th May, although birds have been seen as late as 25th May. Display is often noted in the spring.

There is evidence that the departure date has become later in recent years, and 'last date' records are spread over a five week period. No such trend is evident for arrivals, which are usually within a three week period. There have been two summer records: an immature male remained on Redmires Resr from July to October 1981 and two were seen at the same locality on 1st August 1982. Numbers of wintering birds increased during the 1960s, but there has been little overall change in status since then, although 1975 and 1976 were peak years in the 1970s.

In winter most birds are found at upland localities, Broomhead, Redmires and Barbrook Resrs being particularly important, although birds have occurred more frequently at eastern sites in recent years. The number of localities visited has remained similar throughout the 1970s and totals 38. Most records are of singles or small parties, although the largest counts were 25 on Redmires Resr on 9th January 1984, and 21 on Langsett Resr on 7th December 1975 and on Dale Dyke Resr on 20th October 1976. The last record was part of a major movement at the time, with several large parties sighted. Twenty-six were present in three parties on Underbank, Midhope and Langsett Resrs on 21st October 1972. In late November/early December 1983 there were 19 on Redmires and 18 on Linacre Resrs.

There have been several sightings on rivers, particularly the Derwent, which may have been linked with hard weather. However, a male on the River Don at Tinsley on 27th December 1981 was unusual, as were three sightings in Monsal Dale in 1974 and 1982. Other interesting reports have been from flashes in the Rother Valley in 1981 and 1982, and of one on a small pond in the Loxley Valley in November and December 1974. The majority of Sheffield birds are females/immatures, which accords with the fact that adult males migrate less far and predominate in northern wintering areas (66).

SMEW *Mergus albellus*

Scarce winter visitor.

A female/immature on Langsett Resr on 7th December 1975 was the first record for the area, apart from one which was shot at Staveley in 1774. There have been five subsequent records, all of singles in the mid-winter period. A male was on Thrybergh Resr from 31st January to 7th February 1976 and on 25-26th January 1984. There was also a male on the River Don near Thrybergh on 23rd January 1982. Females/immatures were present on Elsecar Resr on 3rd February 1981 and Thrybergh Resr from 22nd-24th December 1981.

RED-BREASTED MERGANSER *Mergus serrator*

Migrant breeder, passage/winter visitor; reservoirs and lakes.

Prior to 1978 there were no records of Red-breasted Merganser for the period May to August. In July 1978 a 'redhead' (female or immature bird) was seen in Upper Derwentdale and a male was on Broomhead Resr. Then in 1979 a pair bred at Ladybower Resr; eight young were first seen there on 19th July. In 1980 upto four birds of both sexes were evident on Ladybower and Derwent Resrs; no young were seen but a female was found dead on a nest. A female was also seen on the River Noe near Hope throughout May. In 1981 three pairs were present on Ladybower and Derwent Resrs from 2nd May to 13th June, and a male was ween with five 'redheads' upto 21st June but there was no definite proof of breeding. There was also a 'redhead' on Barbrook Resr in June. However, successful breeding did occur from 1982 onwards, as a female was seen on Ladybower Resr with two young in 1982, 14 in 1983 (indicating more than one brood), and 11 in 1984. The establishment of apparently regular breeding is somewhat surprising, as the nearest major population is in north Lancashire, although the species did breed in the Goyt Valley (Derbyshire) in 1973 (20).

There have also been three lowland summer records in this period: one at Tinsley S.F. on 23rd June 1979, two there on 28th May 1980, and two on Thrybergh Resr on 23rd June 1982.

Outside the breeding season the Merganser can be seen in any month, with peaks in September, November and April suggesting passage through the area. However, the average is only three birds per year and none was recorded in nine years. Most birds do not remain, although the largest party recorded (five 'redheads' on Underbank Resr) was present from 25th November to 7th December 1972, and a female stayed at Thrybergh Banks from 1st January to 19th February 1976. There was no evidence of the hard weather influx in 1979 described by Chandler (32). Sheffield records may be attributable to birds moving to and from coastal wintering areas, as 14 of the 21 localities are upland reservoirs which are favoured by other migratory wildfowl.

GOOSANDER *Mergus Merganser*

Winter/passage visitor, casual breeder; reservoirs, lakes and rivers.

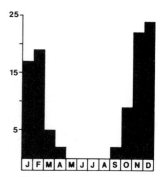

No. of Birds

Fig. 31
Monthly distribution of Goosander (1960-81)

Although the Goosander can be seen in any month from September to April, the main population, which consists largely of females and immatures, is present from November to February (Fig. 31). The November influx is likely to involve continental migrants, as most British breeders move west and north in winter (67).

In the 1970s birds tended to arrive earlier and depart later than previously, and there have been several September and late April records in recent years. However, these must be viewed along with records of 'redheads' on Barbrook Resr in June 1980 and August 1981, on the River Noe in June 1981 and on the Derwent Resrs on single dates in the latter half of May 1982-84. Nesting first occurred in 1982 and again in 1984 when a duck was seen with young on the Derwent at Chatsworth. This is perhaps not surprising in view of the species range expansion in Britain (68).

The wintering status has changed as Wilson described the Goosander in 1957 as an occasional visitor, more frequent to the east (16). The present situation is similar to that described by Smith (21), but the population has increased substantially since the 1960s. Most records are of fewer than ten birds, with only five flocks exceeding ten. The largest numbers occurred in January 1979 on the River Derwent at Chatsworth, the maximum being 16 on 14th, and 17 were seen on Ladybower Resr on 13th. These dates correspond to the main hard weather influx to Britain from the continent (32).

Goosanders have been recorded at 28 localities, with 19 to the west. Most upland reservoirs are visited during the winter as birds move from site to site. Records are scarce from the east, with Thrybergh Resr the only site regularly used. Unusual records are of singles on a mill pond near Wortley on 25th April 1976 (R and NW) and at Tinsley S.F. on 31st January 1981 (CRM).

RUDDY DUCK *Oxyura jamaicensis*

Infrequent visitor; reservoirs and lakes.

Frederick J Watson

The first record was of a male at Morehall Resr on 14-15th September 1979. Two were reported in 1980: an immature at Treeton Dyke on 3rd September and one at Pebley Pond on 4th November. None was seen in 1981 but two males were on the River Don near

Thrybergh from 17-20th January 1982. There was an explosion of records in 1983: ten from seven localities. The first was an adult male, seen 'bubbling' at Thrybergh Resr on 21st April, before possibly moving to Wentworth where one summered from 8th May until 1st October. At least one immature was in the Rother Valley from 15th August to 14th October, visiting successively Staveley, Pebley Pond, Treeton Dyke and Thrybergh Resr where one was also seen on 7-8th December. Single females were reported in September at Barbrook Resr on 6th and Midhope Resr on 15th.

Very few reports were received in 1984 but in the spring of 1985 c. 10 birds were present on lowland waters, from Harthill to Old Denaby. In view of the rapid range expansion of this introduced species (69), its status is undoubtedly changing and it is likely to become a resident breeder within the decade.

Postscript — at least five young were reared at Wentworth in 1985.

HONEY BUZZARD *Pernis apivorus*

Scarce visitor.

A pair shot in Wharncliffe Wood in 1833 and one obtained at Renishaw ten years later may be an indication that Honey Buzzard bred in deciduous woodlands within the region during the nineteenth century. This is supported by the capture of an immature near Middlewood Hall just prior to 1875. There is, however, no evidence that breeding has occurred this century, although the bird may have been overlooked. There have been only eight acceptable records since 1960, all, apart from one, occurring in autumn and undoubtedly involving birds on passage. The exception was a Honey Buzzard seen at Redmires on 20th June 1976 (KC,KK).

Passage records have all been of single birds and include one found injured at Swallownest on 21st October 1969 which is the latest report. Others were at Hassop on 12th September 1970, Lodge Moor on 16th September 1976, Owler Bar on 2nd August 1977, Derwentdale on 27th September 1980, Staveley on 1st September and Thrybergh on 10th October 1982, and Redmires on 21st September 1984.

RED KITE *Milvus milvus*

Scarce visitor.

Ralph Whitlock (7) suggests that the Red Kite's Derbyshire headquarters was 'in the wooded portions of the Peak', and there is no doubt that the bird was, at least in the early nineteenth century, widespread in the region. It may have persisted within the wooded Dales until the mid-1800s and possibly even later. Dixon (8) certainly notes that it had totally disappeared from the region, presumably by the time he left Sheffield in 1880.

Since 1960 there have been only six acceptable records. One remained in Coombs Dale from 22nd August to 1st September 1971. In 1975 one flew east at Walkley, Sheffield on 1st August and was later seen over Wincobank, Sheffield, whilst another was at Elmton on 26th August. A Red Kite flew south-south-west over Grindleford on 13th April 1981, and in 1985 one was seen on several dates in the Dark Peak in May and June, including at Broomhead Hall on 23rd May (CT) and Alport Dale on 9th June (SBe).

MARSH HARRIER *Circus aeruginosus*

Scarce visitor.

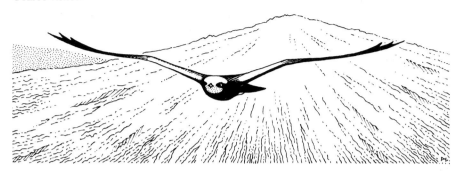

Thomas Allis commented that the Marsh Harrier 'sometimes visits moors near Sheffield' (*4*). Although it may formerly have bred on upland mosses until the early 1800s and perhaps on the lowland marshes in the even more remote past, it has certainly not done so for very many years. The bird appears to have been a scarce passage migrant through much of the nineteenth century and up to the present. Unfortunately few historical records remain other than that one was at Strines in the summer of 1891 and another was shot near Bradfield in 1895.

Chislett (*14*) mentions a Marsh Harrier seen at Redmires on 26th November 1941 but all subsequent records date from 1967. This is perhaps surprising since the British breeding population slumped dramatically, after a peak of 19 pairs in 1957-58, to a maximum of only six pairs in 1963-66 (*70*). Most reports have been in the spring, from 16th April to 15th June. An immature was seen on Eyam Moor on 28th May 1967, but the next report was not until 1975 when one was present on Langsett-Midhope Moors from 31st May to 2nd June. Since that date records have been almost annual: singles were on Langsett Moors on 8th May 1976 and 10th May 1977; a female was reported from Ramsley Moor on 30th April and East Moor on 15th May 1977. An adult male at Upper Rivelin on 11th April 1983 follows the trend of a spring passage across upland areas, as perhaps does a late individual at Big Moor on 15th June 1980. The only spring record in lowland areas was one at Thrybergh Banks on 3rd June 1979.

There have been only three 'autumn' records, all of single juveniles in 1982-83: at Thrybergh Resr on 13th August and Harthill Resr on 10th September 1982 and at Middleton Moor on 6th August 1983.

HEN HARRIER *circus cyaneus*

Passage/winter visitor, casual breeder; moorland and farmland.

The High Peak is undoubtedly very suitable habitat for Hen Harriers and they must presumably have once been widespread on the uplands. Even by the nineteenth century, however, they were scarce in the Sheffield region and there are few reports for the whole of the 1880s. Whitlock (*7*) mentions a pair shot while attempting to nest at Strines, perhaps

F.J.Watson

some time in the mid-to-late 1800s, but this is one of the very few reports. Indeed, there are no acceptable references during the present century until 1956 when a male was at Langsett on 27th May, and they do not become of annual occurrence until 1963.

Since the species was increasing in both Yorkshire and elsewhere during the 1900s, it seems likely that occasional birds did pass through the region but went unreported. The great scarcity of observers undoubtedly accounts for the fact that there was no evidence of long-term over-wintering until 1970/71. Even so, the Hen Harrier was a relatively scarce bird throughout much of the 1960s, and each individual report was considered by County

94

organisations to be worth publishing. During the period 1955 to 1970 there was a steady increase in the number of Hen Harriers reported, but there were rarely more than a few sightings per winter through the whole of that period. Almost all reports came from the East Moors, which were presumably better watched than other upland areas to the north. There were relatively few reports from the moorlands to the north and east of Derwentdale.

The unprecedented number of records of Hen Harrier in the 1973/74 winter, when at least six individuals remained throughout the winter months, perhaps attracted by the large flocks of Woodpigeons which were present on the moorland fringe at that time, was the beginning of what was to become the normal pattern. Most birds arrive in late September or early October (earliest, a pair on Big Moor on 18th September 1976) and leave in mid-to-late April, although some remain into early May (latest, at Langsett on 11th May 1974). The numbers passing through in autumn and again in spring are usually much greater than those which winter. However, in most years, depending upon the severity of the weather, some four or five individuals over-winter on the northern gritstone moorlands, with most reports from Howden, Langsett, Midhope and Broomhead Moors. Two or three birds similarly winter on the East Moors of the central gritstone plateau. A total over-wintering population of some six to eight birds on the entire gritstone plateau has thus been the norm since the winter of 1973/74.

The discovery of three small communal roosts has helped the accurate monitoring of numbers in the area. These are the only regularly used roosts known from the whole Pennine chain (R. Clarke, pers. comm.), and sadly their continued existence is threatened by moorland open access proposals. The main one on Broomhead Moor was first located in 1975, and provides a good indication that the gritstone plateaux of the Southern Pennines are regularly used as a migratory route. Late autumn and early spring numbers at this roost are often quite high, e.g. seven on 16th November 1980, nine on 3rd March 1976, and a marked passage through in April 1983 with up to five birds seen, including two males, on several dates. The other two roosts, on Big Moor and East Moor, usually hold only one or two birds, and latterly, the former has rarely been used (probably due to deterioration of the heather). The East Moor roost has held as many as four males and two females - in stormy weather on 27th December 1979 (71). The largest number of Hen Harrier ever recorded was eleven, including nine in the air together, on Derwent Moor on 11th November 1982 (DHu).

Herringshaw and Gosney, in a review of Hen Harrier status (72), point out the discrepancy between the number of reports of adult ('grey') males on the central gritstone, compared with those on the moorlands in South Yorkshire (i.e. the northern gritstone plateau). Up until 1976 the ratio of 'ringtails' (females and immature males) to 'grey males' was approximately 3:1 on the East Moors, where males have over-wintered on several occasions, compared to 8:1 in South Yorkshire, where males seem to occur only on passage in September/October and April/May. This situation is still largely true, although a single male has wintered on the northern moors in the last two years, and may well be related to prey preferences. The smaller males are more likely to feed on small passerines and voles, which will be more numerous during the winter months at lower altitudes such as on East Moors and adjoining farmland. The larger females are able to tackle larger birds and can thus survive on the higher northern moorlands. Very severe winters, with a prolonged

95

period of cold weather, result in a great reduction of Hen Harrier numbers, or even their complete departure such as occurred in early 1979.

There have been a few records from lowland areas in recent years. Females were seen in the Moss Valley on 11th December 1978, over Hillsborough on 12th February 1979, at Gleadless on 19th December 1981, and Thrybergh Resr on 13th October 1982. Adult males have been reported from Cordwell Valley on 1st March 1981 and Thrybergh Resr on 13th November 1983.

Summering birds, usually females, have occurred in a few years, and a pair was present in 1975 but nesting was not proven. However, in 1976 after frequent display in the spring, a nest was built but failed, possibly because the eggs were removed. Despite rumours to the contrary, no other breeding attempt has been substantiated, although it is quite likely to occur in the future.

MONTAGU'S HARRIER *Circus pygargus*

Scarce visitor.

A Montagu's Harrier which was 'obtained' on Hallam Moors by the taxidermist Sam Gardiner in the years immediately prior to 1875 is the first definite record for the area and the only one during the nineteenth century. In 1903 one was shot on Big Moor in late April, and another was at Derwent in May 1947. In 1953 a male and two females frequented Hallam and Burbage Moors and by 15th June one of the females was incubating five eggs and the other, four eggs 300m away, both in old, low-hanging heather. One of the clutches was removed by a local egg-collector, but the eggs of the other hatched on 28th June. The female of the robbed nest laid a repeat clutch which had four eggs by 30th June and hatched on 3rd August. Both females reared the young successfully with the help of the polygamous male. Although birds were again present in 1954 they did not breed (WEG pers. comm.).

Since 1956, when a female summered at Derwent, there have been only six fully acceptable records. A male was on Big Moor on 27th May 1961; a 'ringtail' on East Moor on 12th May 1966; an immature male at Ladybower on 9th August 1969; another 'ringtail'. at Ladybower on 13th August 1971 and an immature male on East Moor from 10th June to 18th August 1982. A male maintained a territory on Broomhead Moor for over three weeks in May 1983, during which time it was seen displaying, carrying nesting material and even mobbing a Peregrine.

In addition there have been several records of 'ringtail' harriers thought to have been Montagu's, including singles near Beighton on 21st September 1958 (RGH), near Langsett on 18th July 1959 (JSA) and at Alport Castles on 16th May 1982 (JH).

GOSHAWK *Accipiter gentilis*

Resident breeder; woodland and moorland.

On 22nd May 1965 a nest was located in a large Beech in a mainly coniferous plantation in the northern Peak (FNB, D & JWA *et al*). It held four eggs and was the first definite evidence that Goshawk was nesting within the Sheffield area. With hindsight there has been some evidence that the species may have bred as early as 1957, when a large nest containing a clutch of bluish-white eggs was located by D.R. Wilson. These were thought to be Buzzard but the adults were never seen. This nest, and another found two years later at a nearby site, could have been those of Goshawk.

The 1965 nest was unsuccessful, but another pair in Derwentdale the following year reared two young. By the end of the decade, at least four and probably five pairs of Goshawks were known to be present, and a total of seven young had been reared. This small population has steadily increased, despite the severe deprivations of egg-collectors, falconers and some local gamekeepers. The increase may also have been retarded by disturbance through birdwatchers visiting some of the nest sites. For these reasons we have had to refrain from publishing the *Atlas* map.

In the period 1965-85 the population has increased to between 18 and 20 pairs, and at least 120 young have been reared successfully. There would seem to have been a fairly considerable juvenile (and probably adult) mortality over the years, with birds found dead or dying on at least eight occasions. An adult female at a nest site in 1975 was almost certainly poisoned.

Most nests are located in coniferous plantations along the moorland fringe. The population is at a high density in some areas and less so in others; much seems to depend upon prey availability. In recent years coniferous trees have been preferred, usually Larch or pine, but in the early years of colonisation, deciduous trees were used more freely. Four is a typical number of eggs, although five has been recorded on at least two occasions, and three fairly frequently. Analysis of prey at nest sites has shown almost 33% to be game-birds and some 28-30% pigeons. The remainder consists of a variety of species including Grey (and even Red) Squirrel, Rabbit, Mountain Hare, corvids, thrushes, waders and gulls. Occasionally other birds of prey are taken.

There is little doubt that the small breeding nucleus which developed in woodlands within the northern Peak originated from escaped or deliberately released falconers' birds. It seems there may have been further releases in recent years but most of the present stock are fully wild. Considerable effort has been made to protect the breeding nucleus within the Peak, initially by local volunteers, and latterly by the RSPB. These have, in part, been moderately successful, but determined efforts by egg-collectors and falconers have had an undoubted effect on limiting the spread of birds elsewhere in the Peak.

Detailed field-work has been carried out on the local population, and some of the results are included in a recent paper by Marquiss and Newton (73) on the Goshawk in Britain. This shows that the population in the Sheffield area is far greater then anywhere else in Britain, and in 1979-80 constituted over a third of the reported breeding population nationally. The bulk of the local material is to be the subject of a detailed paper on the Goshawk in the Peak District (DH, in prep.).

Although Goshawks are relatively sedentary, there is some movement away from the natal area. In the winter months birds may be seen in many parts of the uplands. Ringing has simply underlined both the sedentary nature of the population and the subsequent fate of the young. The longest distance travelled was by a young female ringed on 11th June 1982 which was shot two years later near Beeley 34km to the south.

Interesting records away from the uplands include a male over Thrybergh Resr on 9th November and an immature female at Tinsley S.F. on 6th December, 1976. One was seen over Hillsborough Park on 6th May and a male was again at Tinsley on 30th December, 1980.

SPARROWHAWK *Accipiter nisus*

Resident breeder; woodland, moorland and farmland.

The Sparrowhawk has for centuries been a fairly common and widespread bird of prey found in most suitable habitat within the region. Whittaker (*13*) states that it was 'resident and by no means rare . . . . . nesting in favoured places in most woods in the area'. Dr I. Newton (*in litt.*) lists 16 nesting sites, largely to the south and east of the city, which were regularly used in the period 1950-58. By the end of that decade however, there was a drastic reduction in numbers. This was especially noticeable to the east but eventually occurred throughout the region. Thus, in the period 1960-70, Sparrowhawks were very thinly distributed in the Sheffield area, a situation directly attributable to pesticides and reflected throughout the country (*74*). Analyses of unhatched eggs removed from local nests in the early 1960s revealed high levels of DDT, DDE, Dieldrin and other pollutants (Dr I. Newton *in litt* to RAF). In 1964 only one bird fledged from a clutch of five eggs at a North Derbyshire site.

A few breeding pairs survived in the coniferous woodlands of the Peak, and this population began to recover after 1968. Herringhsaw and Gosney in their review of Sparrowhawk status (*74*) note that the period 1970-76 showed a steady increase. This was undoubtedly helped by maturation of extensive coniferous plantations in the Peak, as well as a reduction in pesticide usage nationally, although addled eggs analysed from this period still showed high levels of pollutants.

By 1974 an estimated total of 35 pairs bred in the area, and one pair reared six young. In 1975 there were records from over 40 localities, and more than 40 young were known to have been reared successfully. It was at this time that some coniferous plantations held high densities of nesting Sparrowhawks. In 100 ha of coniferous woodland around one reservoir five nests were located and a sixth suspected. These nests were spread only 0.5km apart. In 1976, of 37 nests located, 12 were outside the Peak.

Despite occasional years with poor nesting success (e.g. 1978) the population has continued to increase, and by 1985 most of the traditional sites in woodlands on the east of the city have been reoccupied. It is difficult to estimate the number of breeding pairs, but the total must be well over 100 (e.g. 12 nests were found on one estate in the south-west in 1983) and still expanding. However, densities are now lower and breeding pairs more widely scattered in Peak woodlands. This may be due, in part, to increased numbers of Goshawks within some of these woodlands, and to a resumption of persecution by keepers and egg-collectors.

Along with the quite rapid spread during the late 1970s came a multitude of reports away from normal breeding habitat. It is no longer unusual to see Sparrowhawks flying over any part of the city, and they are frequent, if at times unwelcome, visitors to suburban gardens in many areas. In the winter months they are often to be seen in urban areas where food is plentiful, e.g. Tinsley S.F.

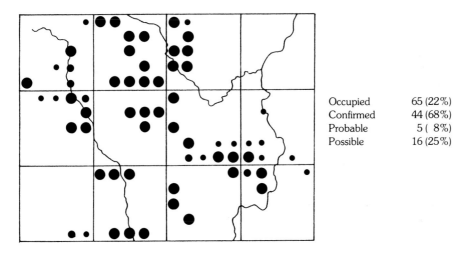

Occupied	65 (22%)
Confirmed	44 (68%)
Probable	5 (8%)
Possible	16 (25%)

The map indicates the distribution is mainly to the west and south of the city. The Sparrowhawk is found wherever coniferous woodlands occur, and, even in the 1975-80 'Atlas' period, it had colonised some of the larger deciduous woodlands to the south-west. There are notable areas where it does not occur, e.g. on the limestone plateau and in the built-up parts of the city. By 1980 it had yet to colonise the extreme south-east and north-east of the region, but this has subsequently occurred. There is a distinct lack of confirmed breeding evidence from the south-west, especially in the Wye valley. It seems likely that birds were overlooked in such areas.

As with their larger relative, Sparrowhawks are markedly sedentary. In 1976 there were three recoveries of first winter birds which had travelled 4km north, 4km north-east and 11km south-east before flying into windows or overhead wires. In 1979 one found dead at Harthill on 20th August had been ringed near Whitwell on 23rd July, having travelled 4km in 28 days.

BUZZARD *Buteo buteo*

Casual breeder, passage/winter visitor; woodlands and open areas.

Allis wrote in 1844 that the Buzzard was met with frequently near Sheffield, whilst Whitlock suggested that before the destruction of the Peak forest they bred there in large numbers. Sadly, Buzzards are no longer familiar inhabitants of the Peak District valleys; indeed, Arthur Whittaker's assessment in 1929 that they were 'an occasional visitor, specimens being shot most winters on the moors' still stands today, if 'seen' is substituted for 'shot'.

Although there is much suitable breeding habitat within the region, nesting was thought to have occurred only in the *myxomatosis* years of the mid to late 1950s, 1964-1965 and 1975. It may also have occurred in 1976 and 1979, but there is no definite evidence. In retrospect, Goshawk nests were probably mistaken for Buzzard prior to the 1970s, and thus the number of actual breeding attempts by Buzzard have been very limited. The most likely breeding sites are often those keenly keepered, and there is little doubt that some Peak District gamekeepers have been instrumental in preventing successful breeding.

In the period 1973-83 there have been over 100 acceptable records of Buzzards within the area, although confusion with Goshawk has been a problem in certain parts. They have been reported from almost every month of the year, but mostly on passage, with a small peak in March and April, and another much larger peak in August to October. Many have been seen on the uplands, but there are some lowland reports, and even one or two of individuals moving over built-up parts of the city. The Dales tend to provide more records in spring and summer, which suggests that nesting may not be out of the question in some of the hanging woodlands on the valley sides. Indeed, Buzzards have a better chance of becoming established in such localities, rather than in the northern Peak where birds sometimes winter.

The more interesting records include seven at Chatsworth on 10th and 11th October 1976; one over Malin Bridge on 2nd July 1980, and one found dead in suburban Rotherham on 18th March 1981.

ROUGH-LEGGED BUZZARD *Buteo lagopus*

Infrequent winter visitor; moorland.

The Rough-legged Buzzard was apparently much more regular in occurrence during the nineteenth century than it has been in the twentieth. Moorlands of the northern Peak were favoured, as indeed they are today. Thomas Allis (4) notes that 'many were seen and obtained near Sheffield in the winter of 1839/40'. Whitlock (7) quotes Henry Seebohm as stating that 'certain localities in the Peak, such as Strines, appear to be in the direct line of this species'. In the latter part of the nineteenth century one was shot near Kinder in the winter of 1884; two obtained at Derwent in October or November 1891 were sent to Reuben Webster, whilst Arnold Hutchinson mentions a female shot in Monsal Dale around 1889. However, in the period 1900-72 there were only five definite records of single birds: on Big Moor in 1903; Curbar in the early months of 1920; at Derwent in April 1923; 'near Sheffield' in November 1949; and at Treeton on 23rd January 1961.

Rough-legged Buzzards   F.J. Watson

Since 1973 at least 13 birds have been seen, which may merely indicate better coverage of moorland areas rather than a genuine increase in occurrence. All apart from two have been in upland areas, mainly on the Upper Derwent-Langsett/Midhope moorland. In 1973/74 one wintered on the Upper Ewden-Langsett moors from 28th October and was later joined by another, both remaining until 27th April (the latest ever date). A passage bird was on the Langsett-Howden Moors on 28th March 1975, but in the following winter one frequented the same area from 12th October until 7th March 1976. Later that year, birds were seen at Leash Fen on 10th October (the earliest arrival date) and Midhope on 13th November. In 1978/79 one was in the Upper Ewden-Midhope area from 26th December until 18th January.

There were no more records until 1982 when singles were reported from Big Moor on 15-16th October, Upper Derwent on 27th November and Strines on 22nd December. In the lowlands one was seen over Woolley Wood on 29th October, and this may have also been the bird reported as a *buteo* species from Darnall on the same day. Most recently, two birds wintered on the Upper Derwentdale-Langsett-Broomhead moors, the first sighting of a single bird occurring on 10th November 1984 with two on 8th December. Both remained in that area until at least February 1985.

OSPREY *Pandion haliaetus*

Infrequent visitor; upland reservoirs and parkland with rivers or lakes.

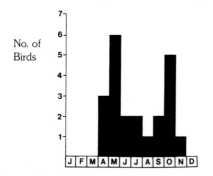

Fig. 32
Monthly distribution of Osprey
(1960-84)

Although the Osprey is mentioned by various authors as a scarce but regular passage visitor to the region, there are only two documented historical records prior to 1900. One was shot at Staveley in 1779 and three were shot on the Derbyshire moorlands near Sheffield in 1842. In the period 1900-1971 there were only three records - a young male shot in the Rivelin Valley on 8th September 1924, one at Derwent from 18-25th May 1955, and one at Treeton Dyke on 8th October 1961. However, since 1975 the Osprey has become almost an annual visitor mainly on either spring or autumn passage with a total of 15 records (to 1984), peaking at five in 1976. The numbers of reports in each month are summarised in Fig.32.

Several individuals have remained in the region for a period of time and have not moved straight through. In 1971 one and possibly two birds remained at Bradfield from 25th August to 15th September, and regularly fished Dam Flask Resr. One in Upper Derwentdale in 1977 stayed from 21st to 28th June, whilst in 1982 a bird in the Chatsworth area, from 11th May until 23rd July, was regularly seen fishing the River Derwent. The earliest date recorded was one at Langsett on 4th April 1976, whilst a bird on 21st November 1977 also at Langsett was the latest.

KESTREL *Falco tinnunculus*

Resident breeder, partial migrant; varied habitats in both urban and rural areas.

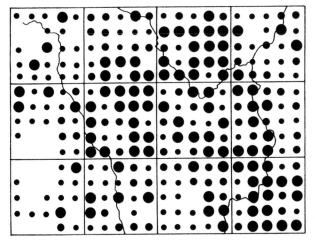

Occupied	267 (89%)
Confirmed	101 (38%)
Probable	56 (21%)
Possible	110 (41%)

All historical references agree that prior to 1960 the Kestrel was as widespread and common throughout the region, as indeed it is now. It is the most familiar bird of prey to the general public and birdwatchers alike. There are no published references to its past density, although W.E. Gibbs stated that at one gritstone locality near the city boundary there were seven pairs nesting annually in the period 1928-39 (21). The Kestrel may be seen throughout the region, both in open country (upland and lowland) and built-up areas, and is a familiar sight as it hovers over the motorway embankments. It is very catholic in its choice of nest sites and will utilise rock ledges, roofs of high-rise flats, church steeples, pylons, old buildings, railway bridges, viaducts, and old nests of Magpie and Carrion Crow.

As the map indicates, it is found throughout the region and is absent only from areas which offer little in the way of a viable nest site. Even so, there are really very few parts where the Kestrel is not to be found, and lack of definite breeding evidence is probably due to inadequate observation rather than an indication that the bird does not nest. This is especially the case in the south-west of the region where the bird regularly nests in the limestone dales.

Although undoubtedly affected by pesticides in the late 1950s, there is little information for the Sheffield area other than a survey of four common birds of prey organised by R.G. Hawley in 1964 on behalf of the BTO (75). Superficial though the survey undoubtedly was, a very small decline was detected but Kestrels were still considered to be numerous and widespread. It seems likely that this decline was only really noticeable away from the uplands where the species was especially numerous. Evidence obtained during the last few years strongly indicates that there may have been a decline in certain upland areas, although the reasons for this are unclear.

In a survey of the Kestrel organised by D. Gosney for the SBSG during the years 1972-76, a total of 97 nesting sites were found to be occupied out of 197 known sites. Of these, 27 were in bushes or trees, 20 on quarries or rocky outcrops, 23 in or on buildings and 5 on pylons (with 22 undescribed). During this period 79% of the occupied sites were known to be successful and only 7% unsuccessful, although this probably understates the failure rate as such sites are more likely to be missed. Gosney estimated that in 1972 a minimum of 97 pairs of Kestrels nested within the Sheffield recording area. It is difficult to be certain, but this is probably a considerable underestimate of the present population, which may well be 150-250 pairs, i.e. approaching Newton's (76) estimate of one per tetrad for the national density. Some indication of the numbers in the area is given by the total of six hunting birds counted along an 8km stretch of the M1 and M18 from Bramley to the Parkway, on 26th June 1981, and the ten seen on Broomhead Moor on 8th October 1979.

There is evidence to suggest that a small passage of Kestrels occurs through the region, a good example being at Concord Park on 2nd October 1983 when six flew south-west in a short space of time. Ringing recoveries have also helped to underline the regular movement of Kestrels through the region, together with the widespread post-breeding dispersal of young birds. One ringed at Maltby on 4th May 1977 was found dead in Miller's Dale on 15th February 1980, having travelled 43km, while one ringed at Padley on 12th June 1965 was recovered from the sea at Fleetwood, Lancs. a month later. Another ringed at Breck Farm on 26th July 1978 was recovered at Hillesden, Bucks. 150km south, whereas other juveniles have moved north, e.g. from Beighton to Kinross (345km) in 1973, and in 1983 from Staveley to Hartlepool (158km), where it was sucked into the fan of a chemical plant. Post-breeding dispersal may also take the bird a long distance very quickly, the best example being one ringed at Hathersage in July 1954 which was found dead three months later at Croix du Perche in France.

RED-FOOTED FALCON *Falco vespertinus*

Scarce visitor.

Prior to 1969 the Red-footed Falcon was recorded on only two occasions. One was killed in the neighbourhood of Sheffield and is recorded in the 1843 edition of *The Zoologist* by John Heppenstall. An adult male, shot on the moorlands of the Peak in May 1939, was obtained by Dr R.G. Abercrombie who removed it from a vermin pole. This specimen was also seen by Ralph Chislett (14) and Arthur Whittaker.

There have been four recent records. In 1969 a female was at Great Hucklow on 16th June (RAF), and a male was in Upper Derwentdale on 28th May 1977 (DG,DH,MET). A female was on East Moor on 7th June 1978 (KS), while in July 1979 there were two further records of females at Beeley Moor just outside our area, flying north on 1st and south on 24th.

The only other report was of an adult male flying over Lane Top, Sheffield on 8th July 1984 (CJ), which has yet to be accepted by the Yorkshire Reports Committee.

MERLIN *Falco columbarius*

Resident breeder, passage/winter visitor; moorland and lowland farmland.

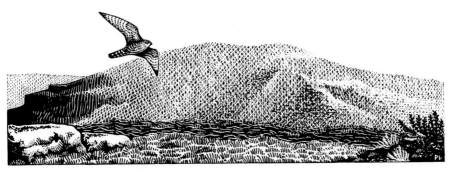

This agile little falcon has long been a familiar bird of the upland moorlands. Several of our past ornithologists visited its breeding haunts, and Henry Seebohm describes at length its nesting behaviour near Sheffield (*77*). He examined two places annually between 1869 and 1873, and both held pairs in every year except one (*10*). Whitlock stated that the Merlin was represented by a few pairs in the High Peak, but he is clearly understating the breeding density. All historical references, however, mention the persecution which was undoubtedly taking place as a result of game preserving interests. In 1873-91 a pair bred near Strines and was constantly persecuted until it eventually ceased to nest (*7*). Egg-collectors were also a problem: J.B. Wheat removed six clutches from a site in the Stanage area between 1898 and 1924, besides collecting regularly from six other sites.

Thus, despite Whittaker's statement that 'a few pairs frequent the moors' (*13*), even by the 1930s Merlins were still widespread in the Peak, if not quite so numerous as formerly. Newton *et al* (*78*) quote a total of 57 former nesting territories in the period 1870-1950, most of which were in the Sheffield region. In one area centred on Longshaw eight pairs nested regularly in 32km² (*78*). Prior to the 1960s nesting pairs could be found on most suitable moorlands (T.M., pers. comm.). In 1955 three or four pairs attempted breeding in the Derwent area alone (DOS), whilst T. Marshall recalls locating twelve nests in a single season during the mid-1950s. W.E. Gibbs located a site on Houndkirk Moor which was occupied by Merlins for thirteen consecutive years between 1930 and 1950, even though the gamekeeper destroyed both adult birds in each year and young were never reared. As Herringshaw and Gosney emphasise in their review of Merlin status (*72*), this indicates how healthy the population must have been in the years prior to the late 1950s. W. Rowan considered that an appreciable proportion of Yorkshire Merlins were reared outside the county (79). This would account for the way vacant territories were replaced annually without local young being reared.

By the late 1950s the population had crashed dramatically, presumably affected by pesticides as were many birds of prey nationally. In 1959 young were reared successfully at two nests - both in trees - but in 1960 a nest in a Rowan in Edale had two broken eggs (due to thin shell) at the base of the tree. In the period 1961-81 there was no confirmed breeding until 1970 when single pairs nested in both South Yorkshire and North Derbyshire. After this year, breeding probably or definitely occurred in seven years with the possibility of four pairs with either nests or holding territory in 1976. Even so, pesticides were most certainly still a problem. In 1974 an addled clutch was collected from Derwentdale and examined for shell thickness and organochlorine content. The eggs showed an average of 30% shell-thinning (compared with 17% in the country as a whole in 1971-79), the most fragile shells yet recorded from British Merlins. Analysis showed the eggs to have a high level of DDE (from DDT), twice the average for the country as whole.

Nevertheless, since 1970 reports of Merlin in the Peak have steadily increased, especially on the more southerly moorland, although latterly, nesting has occurred more frequently on the northern gritstone plateau. Since 1980 records of Merlin at any time of the year have become more numerous, and nesting suspected, though not proven, in 1981 and 1982. The following year, however, at least three pairs bred and a minimum of ten young were reared. In 1984 two pairs certainly nested and at least two others held territory. More intensive field work was undertaken in 1985 and further sites located; one nest was robbed and another predated, but ten young subsequently fledged successfully. Of the nests located this decade, 80% have been on the ground amidst Heather, and the others in disused Carrion Crow nests. It does, therefore, now seem likely that a slow recolonisation of former sites is under way. As this is seriously threatened by egg-collectors and others, the distribution map is not being published.

Away from the uplands, Merlins have been reported from numerous lowland localities, often in spring but more frequently in autumn, presumably attracted by large passerine flocks. In some areas, birds have remained for much of the winter; e.g. in 1982 four were in the Thrybergh area from September to the year end. Interesting reports were of a male flying over Fitzalan Square, Sheffield on 12th February 1981 and a young bird swooping at a dog in Concord Park on 6th August 1984.

Young tend to disperse from their natal area. One ringed as a *pullus* in North Derbyshire on 27th June 1959 was found dead at Brierley near Barnsley in December of that year. Another was killed by a car at Strines on 8th August 1978, having been ringed near Holmfirth (West Yorks) in the same season.

HOBBY *Falco subbuteo*
Summer visitor; woodland, moorland and lowland farmland.

In 1843 John Heppenstall stated that the Hobby was 'pretty generally distributed around Sheffield'. Unfortunately those days are long gone and this graceful falcon has, at least up to recent years, only rarely been recorded. F.B. Whitlock noted that a pair probably bred near Hathersage in 1891, and, more recently, a pair was reputed to have bred in Ecclesall Woods in 1945. Since that time there has been no evidence of nesting, although it was suspected on at least one occasion in the 1975-80 *Atlas* survey.

In the period 1968-84 there have been *c.*40 reports of Hobbies seen within the region. All have occurred between the months of April and September, the earliest date being one at Ladybower on 21st April 1983 (RPB), and the latest at Thorpe Hesley on 13th September 1981 and High Storrs on 16th September 1972. Over 75% of the records have occurred in July to September, many of which have probably been young birds, presumably on passage. There are only three early spring records other than the one above, namely singles in the Little Don Valley on 22nd April 1978, at Thrybergh on 7th May 1983, and on Big Moor on 5th May 1984. Most reports are of single birds, and thus three on Totley Moor on 2nd August 1979 (during a period when four one-year old birds frequented Beeley Moor (*80*) just to the south of our area), two at Agden on 3rd July 1981, and two at Treeton-Catcliffe from 14th July to 13th August 1982, are exceptional.

There have been eight reports within the breeding season (which is late for this species). It is one or two of these which have given rise to suspicions that breeding pairs may have been present. Almost all habitats are represented although there are slightly more records from upland areas, especially in August and September. Most birds are recorded on only one or two occasions, although one individual remained in the Strines-Broomhead-Langsett area from 8th June to 30th July 1975. An interesting, but unfortunate, record was of an immature found shot in the Loxley Valley on 16th August 1977, which was taken to the RSPB headquarters at Sandy but subsequently died.

Since the population is increasing nationally with a northward extension of range, the possibility of Hobbies breeding once again within the region should not be discounted.

PEREGRINE *Falco peregrinus*

Resident breeder, passage/winter visitor; moorland, cliffs and rocky outcrops.

Although it is highly probable that Peregrines did attempt to nest at suitable sites in the northern Peak throughout much of the last century, there are very few records of old eyries. Whitlock (7) could not cite definite evidence of breeding, and mentions only three instances where Peregrines were seen or shot between perhaps 1886 and 1892, all in the Stanage-Derwent-Kinder area. It thus seems highly likely that game-preserving interests had more or less successfully eliminated breeding pairs during the course of the nineteenth century. Ratcliffe (81) estimates that the higher moorlands and their 'edges' between Manchester and Sheffield have the potential for occupation by at least eleven pairs. Nesting attempts were probably made every year in the High Peak from 1919 until at least 1954-55, with three sites involved (20). Only rarely were they successful and in many cases one or both of the pair were shot.

The catastrophic post-1955 decline of the Peregrine within the British Isles has been fully documented (81), and was reflected more or less completely within the Sheffield region. In 1956-57 a pair was apparently present within the Peak and may have bred, since a juvenile was seen on 5th October 1957. However, in the period 1958-79 only 14 Peregrines were reported, so that records were not even of annual occurrence. In that time only three were in suitable habitat within the breeding season, although one of these was a male displaying in Upper Derwentdale on 31st March 1975. Four occurred in lowland areas: at Tinsley on 14th December 1961, Chesterfield (perched on the church weather-vane) in December 1972 to January 1973, and Middlewood, Sheffield on 4th May 1977.

In 1980, although the previous two years produced no reports, Peregrines were seen on three occasions - at Langsett on 9th March, an immature in North Derbyshire on 5th July and Langsett again on 23rd November. In retrospect it is possible that nesting occurred in that year but was overlooked. In 1981 a breeding pair was located by T. Marshall, eggs were undoubtedly laid, but snow in late April caused desertion. In that year there were several more reports from the High Peak, presumably relating to the breeding pair. The site was reoccupied in 1982 but the nest robbed; again there was an increase in the number of reports on the northern gritstone plateau. The pattern was repeated in 1983 with the nest robbed once more. However, in 1984 and 1985, a 24 hour-a-day wardening operation was maintained, with the assistance of the National Trust and (in 1985) the Peak Park Planning Board. This resulted in three and four young being reared successfully in the respective years.

It would thus seem that the Peregrine is once again established as a High Peak breeding bird, and if breeding success continues, one can expect additional ancient eyries to be reoccupied.

RED GROUSE *Lagopus lagopus*

Resident breeder; moorland.

Frederick J Watson

Both Whitlock (7) and Nelson (5) state that Red Grouse were widespread and common on all areas of moorland dominated by Heather. Its status remains much the same today, and the map shows how closely its distribution follows that of the gritstone plateau. However, it is not so numerous in many areas as it once was. Dr D.W. Yalden, in a survey of Red Grouse within the Peak District carried out in 1969-72 (*82a*), found a dramatic decline in bag numbers. For example eight moors which in 1935-36 yielded a total of 25,019 grouse shot, produced only 3,226 in 1957-58. He suggests that one reason for the decline is poorer moorland management due to the reduction in full-time gamekeepers to only 22 from 42 in the 1930s. Keeper numbers have fallen still further in subsequent years; e.g. the Longshaw Estate, where bags were around 4,500 birds per annum in 1900, is no longer keepered, and very few grouse remain. Yalden considers the main reason for the decline to be the sharp increase in numbers of hill sheep within the Peak; excessive grazing affects Heather growth with consequent reduction in numbers of Red Grouse (*82b*).

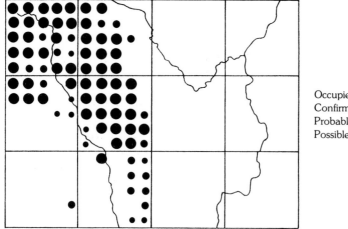

Occupied	83 (28%)
Confirmed	55 (66%)
Probable	19 (23%)
Possible	9 (11%)

Yalden shows that the main concentration of Red Grouse in our region is on the Kinder-Bleaklow plateau, and in the Derwent-Bamford area, with a very small southern extension onto the East Moors. There are one or two outlying populations on Longstone Moor, Eyam Moor and Abney Moor, as illustrated by the above map. Yalden estimated the total grouse population of the Peak District to be around 10,000 (*83a*) and from his data the population of our area would be 4,750 pairs, which may be compared with Nelson's account of 1,313 brace shot (by eleven guns) on Broomhead Moor on 6th September 1872.

More recent data indicate that numbers increased during the 1970s, possibly by as much as a third (*83b*). This is supported by reports of large flocks, including 400 on East Moors on 27th September and 120 in Upper Derwent on 4th October 1980, while the severe winter of 1978/79 produced some huge gatherings, such as 1,000 on Broomhead Moor on 3rd January, 4,500 at Langsett on 27th January and 300 on Howden Moor on 4th February 1979. A count of seven on Longstone Moor on 23rd January 1982 provides an interesting comparison. Indeed, in the 1980s, local keepers consider grouse stocks have fallen substantially, even on the best moors, perhaps affected by cold weather as well as increasing numbers of sheep. For example, bags of 800-1,000 brace were the norm on Langsett Moors in the previous decade, but only 200-300 brace are shot now. At these levels, the influence of predators and wandering hikers could be significant.

There have been no reports of Red Grouse from lowland areas in recent times, although Chislett (*14*) quotes that the remains of three were found in Ecclesall Woods in the spring of 1941 immediately following a severe winter.

BLACK GROUSE *Tetrao tetrix*

Resident breeder; moorland bordered by strands of deciduous and/or coniferous woodland.

When writing about Black Grouse in 1844 Allis (4) quotes Sheffield ornithologist John Heppenstall as saying that it is 'pretty abundant in some woods near Sheffield'. F.B. Whitlock (7) is sure it was once numerous in the pine woods throughout much of the Peak, but says it was local by 1893 although E.D. Doncaster had found it to be 'pretty numerous at Strines'.

Whittaker (13) summarised its status in the 1920s as 'Resident but not common'. The late W.E. Gibbs (pers. comm.) recorded flocks of 18 to 20 on Big Moor in winter during the 1930s, and estimated a breeding population of some 12 to 25 pairs between Owler Bar and Baslow in 1930 (21). It seems there was also an increase at Derwent in the late 1930s which Frost (20) suggests was related to the afforestation programme. However, the small population on Abney Moor, which had numbered at least nine birds in 1937, had disappeared by 1945 (84).

By the late 1940s leks, often centred on the margins of young conifer plantations, were present at Ewden, Strines, Howden, Ladybower, the Big Moor-Totley Moss area and perhaps Chatsworth (72). By the early 1960s most of these had disappeared and only low numbers remained, centred on Derwentdale, Strines and Big Moor-Longshaw. The small lek at Strines had certainly become extinct by 1970, as had the one in Upper Derwentdale. A remnant tiny population apparently persisted in the Ladybower area, where a female was seen with chicks in 1973. This may have survived until 1976, but there have been no subsequent substantiated reports, and it must now be considered to be extinct at this locality.

Thus, despite comments to the contrary, it would seem that by 1980 verifiable evidence was available for the existence of only one very small breeding population in North Derbyshire, which remains at no more than a handful of individuals at the time of writing. A lek containing three Blackcock was located in 1982, and a party of five males was seen 5km away on 22nd March 1985.

According to Lovenbury, Waterhouse and Yalden (85), and Yalden (86), the major reason for the massive decrease in the Peak District Black Grouse population is change in habitat. New afforestation in the 1940s and 1950s would have been temporarily beneficial, but large areas of mature plantations are of no food value to the species. The increasing grazing pressure by sheep has led to deterioration of Birch scrub, Pine scrub and Bilberry, so that no extensive area of prime habitat remains for the Black Grouse in the eastern Peak District.

RED-LEGGED PARTRIDGE *Alectoris rufa*

Resident breeder; farmland and wasteland.

Although the Red-legged Partridge was first introduced into England in about 1770, it probably did not appear in the Sheffield region until the latter years of the last century. Patten (12) refers to its periodical occurrence, and Whittaker (13) considered it to be more common to the north-east of the area.

The map emphasises its almost completely eastern distribution. It is especially numerous in the south-east but is also common in the north-east around Thrybergh and in the Catcliffe-Treeton-Ulley area. Near the city its major stronghold is the Moss Valley, where at least 25 pairs bred in 1976 and five adults were seen with 68 young in the same year. It is also to be found at Tinsley S.F. where three to four pairs regularly nested during the 1970s, although this has subsequently dropped to only one or two pairs. It nested at Neepsend in 1979 and one or two pairs have very recently spread onto demolition sites in the industrial parts of Sheffield. Away from the east, it also nests on Big Moor and, on the Carboniferous Limestone, at Coombs Dale and in the vicinity of Monsal Dale. There is some evidence of a recent spread on to both the gritstone and limestone plateaux, although whether this is a natural colonisation or deliberate introduction is not known.

Reports of large numbers include 28 at Thrybergh on 28th January and 21 at Barrow Hill on 15th October 1976, while two coveys at Troway on 19th September 1979 held a total of 61 birds. Interesting records include one found dead in a suburban garden at Endcliffe, Sheffield on 25th April 1979, and an individual at Concord Park on 31st March and in Woolley Wood on 14th April 1983.

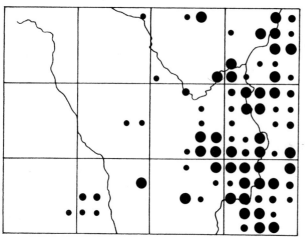

Occupied	80 (27%)
Confirmed	38 (48%)
Probable	12 (15%)
Possible	30 (38%)

GREY PARTRIDGE *Perdix perdix*

Resident breeder; farmland, wasteland and parkland.

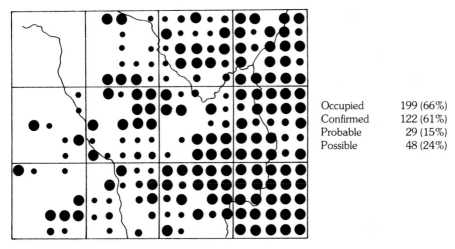

Occupied	199 (66%)
Confirmed	122 (61%)
Probable	29 (15%)
Possible	48 (24%)

All historical references to the Grey Partridge comment on its abundance within the region. Despite the national decline (70), it still remains widespread although by no means as common. The map indicates that, although it prefers the low ground to the east, it is found quite frequently on both the moorland fringe and the Carboniferous Limestone plateau. It does not occur on the highest moorlands of the Dark Peak, although Whitlock (7) found it near Kinder Scout in the last century. An indication of the population density on the Fitzwilliam Estate (where it is probably released) can be seen from the 84 brace that were shot in one day at Wentworth in 1975. One or two pairs nest regularly at Tinsley S.F. but it has not been found on industrial waste sites.

There are numerous reports of large coveys, but the most interesting were two coveys totalling 80 birds at Wentworth on 18th February 1979, and in 1977 there were 73 at Poolsbrook on 8th and 71 at Staveley on 9th January, and 80 at Thrybergh on 4th December. Interesting records include a pair with ten chicks at Manor Park, Sheffield, in 1977; five birds feeding in a suburban garden at Manor Park from 13th January to 7th February 1978; and one in Parkway Markets on 15th April 1983.

QUAIL *Coturnix coturnix*

Casual breeder, passage visitor; farmland.

The status of this small gamebird has not changed since 1844 when Allis (4) wrote that it was 'occasionally heard about Sheffield'. The first positive evidence of breeding on record this century was in 1951 when a nest with eggs was located at Mosborough. Since then, Quail have been found on at least 22 occasions, and in the last decade it has been an almost annual visitor to the area. Usually, calling males are heard, often on only one date in the period May to July, with over half in June. The earliest report was at Breck Farm, Barrow

Hill on 1st May 1977, and the latest at Abney on 5th September 1964. All but seven have been seen in lowland areas, normally on farmland but occasionally waste ground with long grasses has been frequented. Most upland records are of birds frequenting rough grazing on the moorland fringe, but the most recent records are from heather-dominated moorlands at Langsett and near Bradfield in the hot summer of 1976.

Some males have remained for a number of weeks, and on such occasions may have bred. Examples of longer stays include singles at Beighton throughout May 1959, Low Edges from 18th June to 10th July 1977, and Breck Farm from 1st May to 28th June 1977. Actual nesting has been confirmed on only three occasions since 1955. A male remained at Breck Farm from 10th June to 8th August 1975, and a female was seen with two chicks on 27th July. In 1980 a pair bred at an undisclosed locality and in 1982 young hatched successfully in a nest near Beighton.

PHEASANT *Phasianus colchicus*

Resident breeder; parkland, farmland, woodland, heathland and wasteland.

As with the Grey Partridge this sporting bird was considered by all historical authorities to be common in the region. Since it is reared in thousands by several sporting estates to the north and south-east of the city, it is perhaps not surprising that the map indicates the main breeding population to be in those areas. It is, however, found throughout most of the lowland farms and nests on areas of wasteland such as at Tinsley S.F. It also occurs on the moorland fringe where it has increased in recent years, doubtless as a result of deliberate introductions. It also occurs quite commonly in the Dales, and even on a few moorland areas where it now nests freely.

Reports of large numbers tend to come from the sporting estates and include 120 in a field at Wentworth on 25th October 1983 and 160 at Chatsworth on 4th October 1981. An interesting record is of a male in Shiregreen Cemetery on 23rd February 1982.

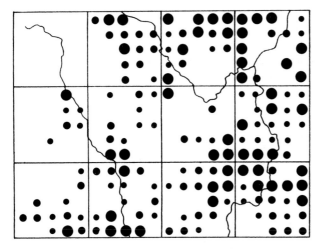

Occupied	157 (52%)
Confirmed	53 (34%)
Probable	50 (32%)
Possible	54 (34%)

GOLDEN PHEASANT *Chrysolophus pictus*

Scarce visitor/escaped species.

A male of unknown origin was occasionally seen in 1974 and 1975 until at least July, in a small coniferous plantation on the edge of Hallam Moors, near Wyming Brook.

WATER RAIL *Rallus aquaticus*

Resident/casual breeder, winter visitor; marshland and margins of lakes, reservoirs, ponds, streams and flashes.

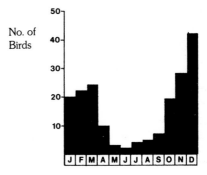

No. of Birds

Fig. 33
Monthly distribution of Water Rail
(1960-82)

115

Although most records of this elusive species are in the winter months, birds are seen in the spring and autumn of most years and occasionally throughout the summer. There have been at least eight confirmed breeding records, six of which occurred during the *Atlas* survey. It bred at "Killamarsh in several years between 1970-76" (20), and at three sites in 1978 and two in 1979. All but two of the Sheffield *Atlas* records were from the south and east, and comparison with the national *Atlas* shows an increase in breeding status in five 10km squares. However, this may not be a genuine increase, since *Atlas* fieldwork encouraged visits to little known localities and there is no firm evidence of a national increase.

The Water Rail is most prominent in the winter, as Fig 33 indicates. Sightings increase from late summer to a peak in December, then remain at a lower level until April when most birds depart. The influx is probably due to migrants from northern Europe as British Water Rails are considered to be resident.

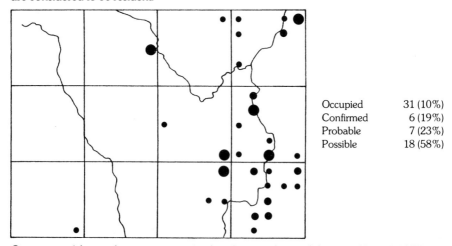

Occupied	31 (10%)
Confirmed	6 (19%)
Probable	7 (23%)
Possible	18 (58%)

On average 14 records a year are received, with no evidence of change, although 1975 and 1976 were peak years, probably related to low water levels. The maximum count was six at Killamarsh on 22nd September 1971. Birds have been seen at 36 localities, 23 of which lie to the east. The only upland records are of occasional single autumn migrants, from 23rd October (1982) to 4th December (1970), mainly occurring from 8-13th November. These have been seen alive at Moscar, Barbrook Resr and East Moor, and dead at Langsett and Midhope. A corpse was also found in a garden in the eastern suburbs of Sheffield on 8th April 1976.

SPOTTED CRAKE *Porzana porzana*

Scarce visitor.

There have been only three records this century. The first was of one which remained at Killamarsh from 18th-22nd September 1971 and was seen feeding with Water Rails in a small muddy pool. One was heard calling at Treeton Meadows on 1st September 1979 (RP) and another calling bird was heard at Staveley on 9th June 1984 (GPM).

CORNCRAKE *Crex Crex*

Infrequent visitor, former breeder; farmland.

The Corncrake has been uncommon in the area since at least the 1940s. Although it persisted as a breeding bird into the 1960s, last nesting at Dore in 1966 and 1967, and Burbage and Baslow in 1968 and 1969, these were only isolated pairs. There were only six other records in the 1960s. Birds apparently summered in 1972-74 on farmland, mainly in the east, and breeding was suspected at Killamarsh in 1974 but not confirmed. There were five records in the latter half of the 1970s but none since 29th May 1979 when one was calling in the Loxley Valley.

Birds have been heard mainly in upland agricultural valleys, with a few on farmland in the south-east, and one at Tinsley S.F. on 23rd April 1978 (CRM), which was the earliest record. The latest record was at Brampton on 5th October 1961.

Since the Corncrake has almost ceased to breed in England and Wales, and the populations in Scotland and Ireland have declined by possibly as much as 70% (87), it is likely that it will be an even scarcer visitor in the future.

MOORHEN *Gallinula chloropus*

Resident breeder; wetlands.

The Moorhen is found in most wetland habitats, including small ponds, rivers and some upland reservoirs, but not in fast flowing streams. The map indicates that it is widespread, breeding in approximately half the squares, but largely absent from the gritstone moorlands and limestone plateau. A nest at Redmires Resr in 1982, 350m a.s.l., was exceptional. Breeding was confirmed in a high proportion of squares, as nests are often easy to find, and it probably occurred in many of the other squares where birds were seen; some individuals are elusive and even small wetland areas may be occupied. Moorhens even breed near the city centre on the industrialised stretch of the River Don.

The total population is estimated to be in the range of 500-1,000 pairs, but is affected by weather as shown by the WBS data. The population of the eight rivers surveyed peaked at 142 occupied territories in 1978 (averaging 2.8 per km), fell by 44% in 1979 after the hard winter (compared to a national reduction of 16%), but recovered with a 27% increase the following year, remaining at a similar level in 1981-83. Moorhens were second only to Kingfishers amongst those waterway bird species affected by severe weather; weakened birds were caught by farm cats in early 1979 and doubtless by other predators.

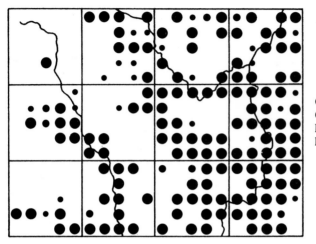

Occupied	164 (55%)
Confirmed	133 (81%)
Probable	8 (5%)
Possible	23 (14%)

The breeding biology of Moorhens on the River Noe has been studied since 1978 and the first three years' results reported (*88*). The breeding season usually spanned the five months from April to August, with 70% of first clutches started in the period mid-April to end of May. Over the years 1978-84, 67% of the 180 first clutches hatched at least one egg and 80% of the failures were replaced, so that 90% of the hens were eventually successful. A third then had second clutches, three-quarters of which were laid during June, and 88% were successful. Clutch size varied between two and ten eggs, with a mean of 6.2 for first and replacement clutches and 5.2 for second clutches, but a relatively high 8% contained only 2 or 3 eggs. Only 45% of eggs hatched, the main causes of failure being spate flooding, sterility and disappearance (possibly due to egg collecting).

Outside the breeding season some birds gather at favoured localities. The highest numbers recorded are at Wentworth - 115 on the lakes on 30th October in 1975 and 60 in a field on 25th November 1979 - and at both Catcliffe and Chatsworth where 56 have been seen in September and November, which is the period of maximum population on open water according to monthly wildfowl counts. Such gatherings probably include migrants, as many local birds seem to stay close to their breeding territory throughout the year. This is supported by the recovery of a Danish-ringed bird at Whitwell (just east of the area) in April 1976. Local movement is illustrated by occasional sightings in gardens and on roads away from wetland. The only direct evidence of longer movements is that of a bird ringed at Killamarsh in March 1962 which was found a year later near Leeds.

118

COOT *Fulica atra*

Resident breeder, winter visitor; reservoirs, lakes, flashes and ponds.

The Coot is a widespread and numerous breeding bird, particularly in the east. Scattered pairs breed at some of the lower western reservoirs and ponds such as Underbank, Broomhead, Rivelin Filters and Bradwell. This is a recent development, since previous authors have commented on its absence from these areas. Breeding was confirmed in SK 28in the local *Atlas* where none was recorded in the national *Atlas* (*19*). In addition to standing water, the Coot also breeds on the slower rivers to the west such as the Derwent andthe Wye where WBS results have shown that 12 territories are regularly present on a 6 km stretch. In the area as a whole, the number of territories recorded by the WBS has increased, paralleling a similar increase nationally (*61*). In an average year, breeding probably takes place at around 30 localities, involving many more pairs than that, as at least four sites hold more than five pairs and both the River Wye and Wentworth hold over ten pairs.

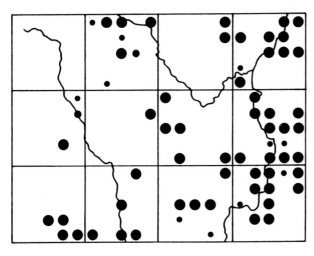

Occupied	68 (23%)
Confirmed	55 (81%)
Probable	2 (3%)
Possible	11 (16%)

Some of the continental birds which migrate to Britain during the winter probably visit Sheffield, as numbers build up from September to a peak in November. This is followed by a rapid fall off with no evidence of spring passage in March (*33*). The area maximum was

119

664 in November 1984. Since 1980 the wintering population has increased substantially so that the Coot is second only to Mallard numerically. Most birds winter at waters in the east, where the population has increased at the expense of Wentworth, which has suffered a marked decline from a regular presence of over 200 birds in the 1970s, its maximum being 339 on 21st January 1973.

Many birds moved out of the area in the hard weather of the 1978/79 and 1981/82 winters. For example, in January 1981 only 17 were counted compared with a long term monthly average of 352.

Coots have been seen at several unusual localities in recent years, including city parks, Barbrook Resr (four in September 1980), Redmires Resr where one in October 1982 was the first for ten years, and on the River Don at Tinsley, where seven were present on 21st December 1981.

OYSTERCATCHER *Haematopus ostralegus*

Passage visitor; reservoirs, sewage farms and flashes.

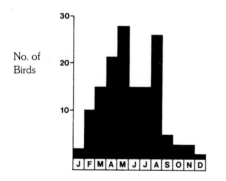

No. of Birds

Fig. 34
Monthly distribution of Oystercatcher (1960-82) - excluding 30 on 22nd Sept 1967

The status of the Oystercatcher has changed from that of a scarce visitor up to the mid-1950s, to an occasional autumn migrant until the early 1970s and a regular visitor in increasing numbers thereafter. In the latter half of the 1970s there was an average of eight records each year, involving eleven birds, but there were 24 records in both 1982 and 1983, involving 28 and 32 birds respectively. This increase can be related to the expansion of the inland breeding population, particularly in northern England - at least 27 pairs bred in North Yorkshire in 1982, compared to only a handful in the early 1970s. However, it is unlikely to become established as a breeding species in the Sheffield area because of the absence of gravel pits and slow-moving rivers with shingle banks, its favoured nesting habitats.

120

Although Oystercatchers are seen throughout the year, they are predominately passage birds with peaks in May and August/September (Fig. 34). Records are much more frequent in August than September, but September saw by far the biggest party ever recorded, namely 30 flying north-east at Burbage on 22nd in 1967 (PMa).

Records come from a wide variety of localities, and refer mainly to single birds, with twos not uncommon. Parties are unusual, the second largest being 14 at Middleton Moor on 28th July 1984 (PAA), which flew off to the west, followed by seven at Barbrook Resr on 4th September 1984.

121

BLACK-WINGED STILT *Himantopus himantopus*

Vagrant.

An individual of this species was reported at Treeton Dyke on 1st August 1963 (RGH). The record was accepted by the YNU Reports Committee but rejected by the *British Birds* Rarities Committee.

AVOCET *Recurvirostra avosetta*

Vagrant.

The first ever record was on 31st May 1983, a misty day, when four birds flew north-west over Thrybergh with a following wind (MAS). There were two at Barbrook Resr for at least four hours on 24th March 1984 during heavy rain and strong winds (RPB,MET). The wind was initially south-easterly but veered to north-westerly and the birds had departed by the time the rain had stopped. Elsewhere on the same day, a good wader passage at Thrybergh Resr included a party of five Bar-tailed Godwits and at least 23 other Avocets were seen in England (at seven localities) including one at Ingbirchworth, just to the north of our area.

STONE-CURLEW *Burhinus oedicnemus*

Vagrant.

There have been only two records this century, both of singles. On 2nd September 1961 one was flushed from a refuse tip at Woodhouse and flew to a field between Beighton and Hackenthorpe (FNB,RGH). The other was seen on 22nd May 1971 in an area of tussocky grassland on Big Moor near Barbrook Resr (RAF,MFS *et al*).

LITTLE RINGED PLOVER *Charadrius dubius*

Migrant breeder, passage visitor; reservoir margins, sewage farms, flashes and industrial wasteland.

The Little Ringed Plover was first recorded on 29th May 1957 when a single bird was seen at Barbrook Resr. In the ensuing years small numbers were reported on passage but breeding was confirmed only in 1960 at Treeton Dyke (FNB) and in 1968 at Staveley, when single pairs nested on industrial spoil. Three pairs nested in 1969 in similar habitat, and breeding numbers continued to increase in subsequent years, from five pairs in 1971-72 to 16 pairs by 1977. Since then, the lowland population appears to have stabilised at around 15-16 pairs, with a peak of 18 in 1978 but a few less in some years. Most of the birds nest on areas of industrial or colliery spoil, with as many as eight territorial pairs at a single locality (Killamarsh in 1977). Other habitats such as sewage farms and the margins of flashes are also used throughout the east of the area.

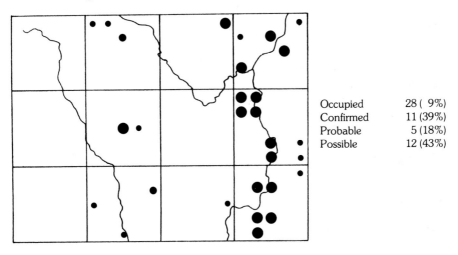

Occupied	28 (9%)
Confirmed	11 (39%)
Probable	5 (18%)
Possible	12 (43%)

Breeding was first recorded in the uplands in 1970, when three pairs were located. However, it was confirmed there in only seven of the following 15 years, with only one pair in five of those years. This is because breeding sites are mainly the rocky margins of reservoirs, which are sufficiently exposed only when the water levels are low in spring. One outstanding year in the uplands was 1974 when six pairs bred at four sites. Birds also summered and probably bred at clay pits in the Peak District in at least two years during the 1970s.

The first arrivals are normally in late March or early April. In 1982 two exceptionally early birds were seen at Beighton on 14th February (DJG) but they did not stay, and the following year two were present at nearby Treeton Dyke on 15th March, the earliest March record. As the species is not known to winter in Britain (40), the Beighton birds are likely to have been genuine early migrants, although one was present near Reading (Berkshire) in January 1974 (45).

Territories are occupied in April and early May. Small flocks of up to 16 birds, including juveniles, are recorded in late June and early July at localities such as Tinsley S.F. and Treeton Dyke. However, passage is most notable in August. A few birds may linger into late September and, occasionally, early October, the latest record being one at Treeton Dyke on 4th in 1982.

RINGED PLOVER *Charadrius hiaticula*

Passage visitor, casual breeder; reservoir margins, flashes and sewage farms.

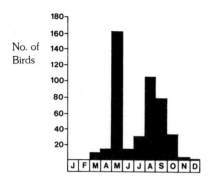

No. of Birds

Fig. 35
Monthly distribution of Ringed Plover
(1973-83)

The Ringed Plover is mainly a passage visitor to lowland localities, although it is also seen at upland flashes and reservoirs, particularly Redmires. The first breeding record occurred in 1978 at Killamarsh, in an area containing many well-developed pools. A pair hatched a second clutch after the first was apparently lost at a very early stage (89). The following year the site was much drier and more overgrown, but a pair successfully raised two young 2km further down the Rother Valley (DJG). However, no subsequent breeding attempts have been reported.

The species was poorly recorded in the 1960s but a marked increase occcurred in the early 1970s, coinciding with increased observer coverage. Fig. 35 shows that it is mainly seen in the period from March to October. The earliest date is 15th February 1984, when one was at Thrybergh Resr (SHH), the next earliest record being one at Treeton Dyke on 1st March 1982 (RP). Numbers increase slowly through March and April, and peak sharply in May, the main spring passage time. Few are seen in June. Return passage starts in mid July and peaks over two months, August and September, after which numbers decrease rapidly with only a very few stragglers in November, the latest being one at Broomhead Resr on 19th in 1978. The only December records have occurred at Thrybergh Resr where singles were present on 8th in 1973 and 4-5th in 1981. Scant information from 1960-72 does not change this general pattern, but serves only to accentuate the August/September peak. It is interesting to note that there were fewer records in the years 1976-81 than in the preceding three years, but in 1982 at least 121 birds were recorded, almost three times higher than the ten year average.

Most birds are seen alone or in small parties but there have been eight records of 20 or more. The biggest flocks were 30 at Rother Valley C.P. on 17th August 1983, 31 at Barbrook Resr on 28th May 1974 and 48 at Redmires Resr on 17th August 1970 (TJB,KK).

DOTTEREL *Charadrius morinellus*

Scarce visitor.

Dotterel were considered to be regular visitors to the area during the nineteenth century; small trips rested on migration in May or June, and birds were often shot. This century, records were very sparse, until the 1970s when there were annual reports from 1972 to 1976 during the period 10th to 25th May, although two had been seen on Houndkirk Moor on 4th June 1968 (RF).

The first of the '70s was one in May 1972 at Bleaklow Stones, at 625m a.s.l. The 1973 record of nine near Ramsley Moor was not substantiated, but a pair was on Houndkirk Moor in 1974, a single above Bradfield in 1975 and a pair at Derwentdale the following year. In 1977 none were seen in May but there were two reports in August -of three on East Moor on 21st and one at Stanage Edge on 22nd.

There have been no further records from the uplands until 1985. However, in 1981 eight were found on farmland near Harthill on 5th May; the party increased to 16 by 7th, after which 14 departed, leaving two until 12th (DHu). Although unique for this area, the record is comparable with several others in recent years which have occurred further to the east in north Notts.

The most recent records (subject to acceptance by the Records Committee) are of a pair at Concord Park, on a hill in the northern suburbs of Sheffield, on the very early date of 15th April 1984 (JPS), followed by one on the even earlier date of 12th April 1985 on Houndkirk Moor (RF). A trip of 27 was found at the latter locality on 11th May 1985 (JH) during a period of easterly winds.

LESSER GOLDEN PLOVER *Pluvialis dominica*

Vagrant.

A bird identified as this species by sight and call flew over Barbrook Resr on 6th August 1983 (RPB,KRG,MET). It was relocated at Middleton Moor and noted to be a juvenile of the American nominate race *dominica*, but soon departed. The record is under consideration by the *British Birds* Rarities Committee.

GOLDEN PLOVER *Pluvialis apricaria*

Migrant breeder, passage/winter visitor; moorland, farmland and reservoir margins.

In the Peak District the Golden Plover breeds exclusively on moorland at altitudes of 350 to 650m a.s.l., with a preference for 450 to 500m. This is the southern-most viable breeding population in the British Isles. Dr D. W. Yalden carried out a detailed survey of this population during 1970-1973 and estimated the average yearly total to be 390 pairs (90). Using his data, the number of breeding pairs in the Sheffield area would have been approximately 130 pairs, or one-third of the Peak District total. Seventy-five per cent of Sheffield's birds were in SK19, giving a breeding density in this 10 km square of one pair/km^2. Yalden showed that birds favoured areas rich in Cotton-grass mosses, although not so exclusively as does the Dunlin. He subsequently found that the population in 380 ha

125

immediately to the west of our area, along the line of the Pennine Way, had declined from an average of 22 pairs in 1972-75, to ten pairs in 1978-82 (*91*). Excluding 1980, when the moors were closed to the public and the population increased to 24 pairs, the decline was even more marked, with an average of only six pairs present, thus confirming Scottish findings that the species is very susceptible to disturbance.

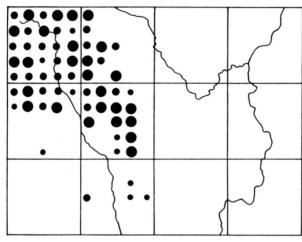

Occupied	63 (21%)
Confirmed	26 (41%)
Probable	26 (41%)
Possible	11 (17%)

Comparison of the above 1975-80 *Atlas* map with Yalden's distribution shows that breeding was confirmed or probable in 30 tetrads in both surveys, whilst Yalden found breeding birds in five tetrads where no evidence of breeding was found in 1975-80. In contrast, breeding did occur during the latter period in 22 squares where Yalden found none. As the *Atlas* survey spanned six years, compared to the four of Yalden's survey, occupation of more squares would be expected due to local movements, but the species' range certainly appears to have extended to the south-east, with birds firmly established on Barnside, Bradfield, Broomhead and East Moors. However, this probably reflects a reduction in numbers on Bleaklow and Kinder Moors, as found by Yalden in 1978-82, rather than an increase in the overall population. Certain moors to the south-east, namely Burbage, Moscar and perhaps Hallam, are likely to have been more attractive to Golden Plover after the severe fires in 1976 and 1981.

Evidence that there had not been a change in status is given by the results of (a) a partial survey of Peak Park moorland by the RSPB in 1981 (*92*) and (b) a re-survey of the Howden/Derwent Moors in 1984 (DWY-pers. comm.), both of which indicated no significant change in territorial numbers from those of 1970-73. The RSPB survey shows that numbers had declined on Kinder and southern Bleaklow in the south-west, but had increased further north. One of the highest breeding densities was found to be on Ronksley Moor, where there were 17 territories in 4 km². This level is comparable to those found by the RSPB in the best areas surveyed in Scotland in 1980 (92).

Away from the breeding sites, birds are recorded throughout the year but only in small numbers in mid-summer. By August the population starts to increase and usually peaks in November, by which time the moors are usually deserted, but birds gather at reservoir margins in some years, e.g. 250 were at Redmires Resr on 24th November 1975. Flocks of up to 500 are not uncommon during the winter, especially on farmland to the east and around Middleton Moor, where there were 1,127 on 19th November 1984. In some winters flocks in the Brampton and Todwick areas have built-up to 1,000-1,500 birds, and on 26th February 1978 there were over 1,700 at Woodhall.

Early birds are sometimes singing on the moors in late January, but breeding grounds are usually re-occupied in February and March. At this time passage birds augment the wintering population in the lowlands, and birds of the northern race *P.a. altifrons* can be seen, leaving by the end of April in the lowlands and by late May in the Peak District.

GREY PLOVER *Pluvialis squatarola*

Passage visitor; reservoir margins and flashes.

The Grey Plover was recorded only sporadically before 1975, since when it has been seen annually. The majority of sightings are in autumn, although it has been recorded in every month from May to October, with 60% of birds occurring in September. Outside this period there have been only six records, all in winter - one in February (1976), two in March (1969 and 1983) and three in December (1978, 1982 and 1984).

Although there have been 47 records since 1960, involving at least 87 birds, the species has been seen at only ten localities. These are mainly in the southern half of the area but widely scattered, including upland reservoirs and lowland flashes and sewage farms. The two favoured sites are Redmires and Barbrook Resrs, which have provided 57% of the records.

All but four reports involve less than four birds, the majority being singles. Three of the four exceptions relate to birds flying west in September: nine on 28th, 1972 at Ramsley; seven on 13th, 1981 at Redmires; and five on 4th, 1983 at Barbrook. The fourth - the only May record - was a party of five in full summer-plumage which stayed briefly at Treeton Dyke on 7th in 1981 (PW).

LAPWING *Vanellus vanellus*

Resident/migrant breeder; farmland, unimproved land, rough pasture, flashes and reservoir margins.

The map shows the Lapwing to be widely distributed and breeding in the majority of Sheffield's tetrads. The only extensive areas of absence are the high gritstone plateau in the north-west and the major conurbations of Sheffield, Rotherham and Chesterfield. Numbers breeding in the lowlands have decreased markedly since 1950, with changes in arable

land-use (they are especially attracted to ploughland but inevitably lose eggs or chicks through subsequent farming activities), so that densities have become generally very low. The Lapwing is now predominantly a bird of the upland unimproved pasture and moorland edge, nesting upto 500m a.s.l. It may have benefited from the increase in hill sheep farming, since it needs areas of short vegetation for feeding, although this has been partly offset by increased drainage (as boggy areas are favoured).

In late February and early March Lapwings arrive back on the breeding grounds and are often seen in small flocks, as they tend to nest in small colonies. They are often faithful to their natal area, as illustrated by two birds found dead at Bradfield in May 1981, which had been ringed as *pulli*, in one case in the same field in 1976 and the other 6km away at Bolsterstone in 1975.

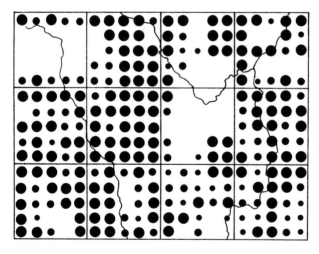

Occupied	240 (80%)
Confirmed	151 (63%)
Probable	62 (26%)
Possible	27 (11%)

J. Lintin Smith has studied the Lapwings breeding on farmland 320m a.s.l. at Lodge Moor on the western outskirts of the city. The population in 3km² of cereal and grass fields was 25-30 pairs in the mid-1970s but was halved after 1977, probably because the habitat changed, i.e. wet fields were drained and cover reduced by intensive sheep grazing (which also resulted in disturbance and nest destruction). Another reason for the decline may have been the deterioration in breeding success which became apparent after 1977. In the five years 1973-77, 58% of 112 nests were successful, with 1.83 eggs per nest hatching on average. In 1978 and 1979 only 20% of the nests succeeded and this poor performance

128

continued so that during 1978-84 an average of only 0.87 eggs hatched from 54 nests. The first eggs were usually laid by the end of the first week in April, with 24th March (1977) the earliest date. The mean clutch size was 3.6, with nearly a quarter of the nests containing three eggs. Lost clutches were usually replaced, even several times, and often in the same field (JLS *pers. comm.*). A survey of Lapwing within the Peak District organised in 1983-84 by K. Bayes gave densities of 3-4 pairs/km^2 in suitable habitat, with pockets of much higher density in favoured areas; the average breeding density on the limestone plateau was double that on gritstone (KBa *in litt.*).

There is insufficient census data from elsewhere to determine whether there has been a general decline in the last decade. At Breck Farm there were four pairs in 1970 but only two by 1980, but on Leash Fen the population has fluctuated between seven and eleven pairs in the 1980s where there were fewer than five pairs in 1978-9 (RAF). Seven nests were found on Abney Moor in 1975; three out of four pairs succeeded at Tinsley S.F. in 1978; six or seven pairs bred successfully at Staveley in 1980; and there were eight pairs in 2km^2 of the Hope Valley in 1984. It seems likely that the current breeding population is in the range 500-1,000 pairs.

Post-breeding flocks start to build up from June onwards in both upland and lowland localities, with upto 700 normal. A thousand or more have occurred in August at areas such as Wardlow, Elsecar and Redmires. Exceptionally, 2,000 were at Redmires on 31st August 1975 and 3,086 at Middleton Moor on 26th July 1983 (PAA). Away from these localities upland records are scarce after October, but winter flocks of 1,000-2,000 are not uncommon in the lowlands and 3,000 were at Breck Farm on 20th October 1974. Cold weather movements may occur when heavy frost or snow causes most of the population to leave our area and/or areas further to the north or east. These may involve thousands of birds, usually flying southerly to westerly; examples occurred on 1st January 1980 and 2nd December 1984 when 2,500 were counted at Midhope and Thrybergh respectively. Return movements are usually far more fragmented, e.g. a good number was 317 north in four hours at Tinsley S.F. on 26th February 1983.

KNOT *Calidris canutus*

Passage visitor; reservoir margins, flashes and sewage farms.

This is an occasional passage visitor, occurring almost entirely in autumn. Since 1960 it has been recorded only twice in March and once in April. There have been 36 records in the period 1960-84, involving 67 birds, from twelve widely scattered localities. Most have been singles in winter or juvenile plumage, although two at Redmires Resr on 2nd August 1976 were in full breeding dress.

The vast majority of birds (89%) are seen in August and September, with a few reports in late July and October and two in November. The March records concern one at Old Whittington S.F. on 16th, 1974, and the remains of another, thought to have been killed by a raptor, which were found at Barbrook Resr on 4th March 1979 (JH). The only spring record occurred in 1984 when one was seen at Redmires Resr on 12th April (AJM).

The species is not recorded annually, numbers fluctuating from year to year with no obvious trends. The three records involving the highest numbers all relate to birds seen in flight at upland reservoirs. The largest party was 17 moving west at Redmires on 26th August 1982 (PAA,PC), and the other two were at Barbrook - four south-west on 4th September 1965 and seven north on 24th August 1980.

SANDERLING *Calidris alba*

Passage/winter visitor; reservoir margins and flashes.

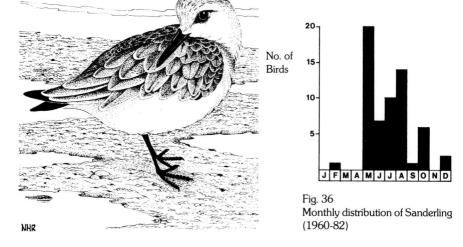

NHR

No. of Birds

Fig. 36
Monthly distribution of Sanderling (1960-82)

The Sanderling was only recorded in six years between 1960 and 1972, but has since become an annual visitor in small numbers. It is unusual among wader species in being seen as frequently in spring as in autumn, with a marked peak in May (Fig. 36). The only other waders with spring maxima are Oystercatcher and Dotterel, which are more common during their spring migrations, and Ringed Plover, which is more numerous in autumn, perhaps due to the longer periods of passage.

Sanderlings have been seen at only nine localities: Barrow Hill, Harthill Resr, Tinsley S.F. and Treeton Dyke in the eastern lowlands, and four upland reservoirs, of which Barbrook and Redmires, along with Middleton Moor, have produced more than 75% of the records. Most birds are seen alone, and the only records involving more than two birds have come from upland sites. At Redmires Resr in 1974 one was present from 22nd May to 12th June; two adults were seen from 17-27th July, with a juvenile from at least 22nd (KC). In the same year single birds occurred at Barbrook Resr in the period 20th May-8th June, with five there on 31st May. At Middleton Moor single birds were recorded on five dates between 20th May and 8th August 1982, with five there on 19th June, and in 1984 six were present on 18th May.

LITTLE STINT *Calidris minuta*

Passage visitor; reservoir margins, flashes and sewage farms.

The Little Stint was recorded in only four years during the 1960s but has been almost an annual autumn passage visitor since 1972; the exception being 1982 when none was recorded. Numbers have fluctuated, with an average of five to six birds per year between 1972 and 1982; 1978 being the peak year when 24 were recorded. Major influxes occurred in September of 1978 and 1983, in common with elsewhere in the British Isles. Birds were virtually restricted to upland sites then, with peak counts at Barbrook Resr of eleven and seven for the respective years. At Middleton Moor ten were present on 6th and 7th September 1978, and on 13th October 1979, a year when few were seen elsewhere in the area. Normally, most sightings relate to single birds, and only occasionally are more than two reported.

All records except three have been in the period August to October, with a pronounced peak in September, and the latest occurring at Redmires Resr on 24th October 1975. The exceptions were singles in May at Treeton Dyke on 17th in 1962 and Harthill Resr on 22nd in 1973, and on 5th July 1975 at Redmires Resr. Although birds have been seen at more lowland than upland localities, the majority of records, as with a number of wader species, have come from the two upland reservoirs, Redmires and Barbrook.

TEMMINCK'S STINT *Calidris temminckii*

Scarce visitor.

There have been only three records of this species, all of singles. The first was at Bolehill Flash on 17th August 1981 (RP); the second at Old Denaby from 27th August to 4th September 1984 (JL *et al*); and the most recent at Staveley on 15th May 1985 (RAF).

BAIRD'S SANDPIPER *Calidris bairdii*

Vagrant.

An adult in heavily worn plumage, found at Barbrook Resr on 9th September 1983 (RPB, JPH), was the first record of this Nearctic species for Sheffield and Derbyshire. The bird stayed until the evening of 12th September, at times feeding with up to seven Little Stint, and then left overnight. This correlates with an adult seen in Cornwall on 14th September and upto three juveniles in Devon and Cornwall throughout most of the month.

CURLEW SANDPIPER *Calidris ferruginea*

Passage visitor; reservoir margins and sewage farms.

The Curlew Sandpiper occurred only sporadically prior to 1975, since when it has been an annual visitor to the area, other than in the last two years. All records are between 2nd August and 12th October, with 67% in September. It has only been seen at Redmires, Barbrook and Elsecar Resrs, Middleton Moor and Tinsley S.F.

The annual total fluctuates, with up to three birds being usual (average of 2.2). The best year was 1975 when 16 were recorded. The summer had been hot and mainly dry, and water levels were low in autumn, thus providing ideal conditions for passing waders. Wallace reported flocks of up to 75 elsewhere inland, following an Atlantic depression with westerlies veering to strong north-easterlies in late August (*45*).

Altogether there have been 26 records, probably referring to 51 birds, most of which were seen singly or in twos. Four reports of higher numbers include eight at Redmires Resr on 13th September 1975 (KC,SJR), and six at Middleton Moor from 7-11th September 1981, with twelve on 9th (PAA). Only one bird in full summer plumage has been reported, at Barbrook Resr on 2nd August 1962, although one was in partial breeding dress at Redmires Resr on 13-14th August 1976.

PURPLE SANDPIPER *Calidris maritima*

Vagrant.

Single Purple Sandpipers have been seen on six occasions. The first for the area was a juvenile found at Weston Park on 6th November 1903. Over 50 years elapsed before one was seen at Ramsley Resr on 30th October 1955 (DRW). The next was feeding beside the icy River Don in industrial Sheffield in the hard winter of 1963 (DA). Then came two records from Barbrook Resr on 22nd August 1965 and 5th October 1974 (RAF). The most recent one was from Treeton Dyke, on 12th September 1984 (RP).

DUNLIN *Calidris alpina*

Migrant breeder, passage/winter visitor; moorland, reservoir margins, sewage farms and flashes.

The Dunlin breeds thinly on gritstone moors with a high predominance of Cotton-grass mosses mainly at altitudes of 400-550m a.s.l. From the results of D.W. Yalden's survey of 1970-73 (*90*) approximately 50 of the Peak District's 140 pairs breed in the Sheffield area, with 85% in SK19. Yalden found 19 Sheffield tetrads to be occupied with breeding birds, compared with 21 probable or confirmed breeding squares in the *Atlas* survey. The distribution was also similar, although slightly more to the east in 1975-80 with territorial birds at Burbage, Bradfield and western Broomhead Moors. This indicates that the population probably remained stable throughout the 1970s, a view reinforced by Yalden's further work in SK09 (90). Recent records of birds summering at Totley Moss and Barbrook Resr suggest a slight southward expansion. However, the density in even the most favoured area (Bleaklow) is much lower than the highest recorded by the RSPB in Sutherland (92).

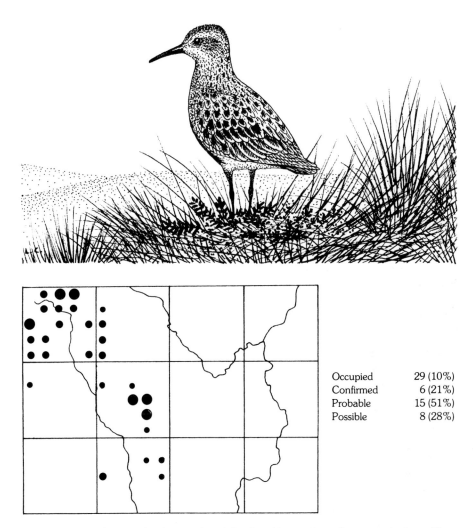

Occupied	29 (10%)
Confirmed	6 (21%)
Probable	15 (51%)
Possible	8 (28%)

Birds arrive on the moorland around mid-April and leave about three months later. They are most commonly seen on passage at reservoir margins in May and from mid-July to mid-October. Numbers recorded vary markedly from year to year. For example, after several lean years, spring passage in 1982 was heavy, with 11 at Middleton Moor at the end

133

of April, increasing to a passage of 59 there on 3rd May, a day when there were 21 at Thrybergh Resr. Autumn passage was exceptional at Redmires Resr in 1975 when in September there was a maximum of 33 on 29th and a second influx in October, with 63 birds on 11th, 61 on 26th, peaking at 70 on 1st November. In subsequent years autumn passage became increasingly light throughout the area but recovered after 1981; e.g. good numbers were seen in 1983 during the period late September to mid-November, peaking on 30th October when 17 flew west at Thrybergh Resr, 15 were at Middleton Moor and seven at Rother Valley C.P.

Winter numbers are normally low, and mainly involve transients. In 1976 cold weather caused a minor influx between 30th January and 2nd February when sightings at 11 localities involved a minimum of 26 birds. Two large parties have been recorded in December - 26 at Thrybergh Resr on Christmas day, 1973 and 29 over Fox House on 20th, 1974 - but by far the largest flock, 140, was seen near Castleton on 29th March 1977 (SA).

BUFF-BREASTED SANDPIPER *Tryngites subruficollis*
Vagrant.

On 10th September 1975 a juvenile Buff-breasted Sandpiper was found at Redmires Resr (DH,RTH,DG). The occurrence coincided with a massive autumn influx of Nearctic waders, between 20th August and 10th October, of which Buff-breasted Sandpiper was the most abundant with a total of 67 records, including at least two others in Yorkshire. The Redmires bird spent much of its time feeding on the rocky areas around the middle reservoir, tending to keep away from the water's edge. It was present until the 26th September, but was not seen again until the 11th October when it remained for three days (KC).

RUFF *Philomachus pugnax*
Passage visitor; reservoir margins, flashes, sewage farms and wet meadows.

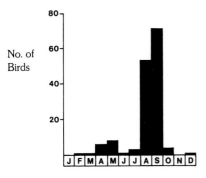

No. of Birds

Fig. 37
Monthly distribution of Ruff
(1960-83)

The Ruff has been recorded in all but three years since 1960 and has been annual since 1970. It has occurred at 15 localities, mainly in the eastern lowlands with only Redmires, Barbrook and Middleton Moor providing upland records. Although most have been single birds, parties of up to six have been seen, whilst at Middleton Moor ten were present on 23rd September 1983 (C & MP) and a roost was located in April 1985 which peaked at 36 on 18th (PAA).

Spring passage is usually light, as shown by Fig. 37. Males in breeding plumage are rare but include singles at Redmires Resr on 13th May 1974 and Thrybergh Resr on 21st June 1983, and four were present at Kilnhurst Flash on 6th April 1982 with three on 7th and two on 8-14th (NWA).

Return passage is noted from July to October, with a pronounced peak in August and September when 82% of all birds have been recorded. There have been three isolated winter records of singles: on flooded meadows by Ulley Brook on 15th February 1976 (KC et al), only six days before a Yellow Wagtail was seen at Staveley; and at Middleton Moor on 2nd December 1981 (PAA) and 11th March 1983 (RAF).

JACK SNIPE Lymnocryptes minimus

Passage/winter visitor; sewage farms and wetlands.

The Jack Snipe is usually seen from late September to mid-April. It favours marshy areas in the east; upland records are thus comparatively few, and, when occurring, are invariably of single birds. The earliest arrival date is 7th September 1973 and the latest 8th May 1985 (CRM), both at Tinsley S.F.. Numbers fluctuate from year to year, with most records in October, December, February and March, but very few have been seen in the three most recent winters (1982/83 to 84/85).

Although usually occurring singly or in twos, up to seven were not uncommon and double figures were recorded occasionally in the 1970s. The largest gatherings were 18 at Staveley in October 1973 (RAF) and c.20 at Killamarsh on 15th December 1974 (GPM).

A bird ringed at Killamarsh on 21st December 1968 was shot on 18th October 1969 at Kalingrad in the U.S.S.R.

SNIPE *Gallinago gallinago*

Resident/migrant breeder, passage/winter visitor; moorland, wetlands, reservoir margins and sewage farms.

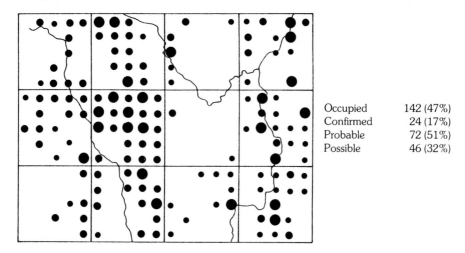

Occupied	142 (47%)
Confirmed	24 (17%)
Probable	72 (51%)
Possible	46 (32%)

The Snipe can be found breeding in almost any boggy area up to 550m a.s.l. but shows a preference for damp upland pastures and lower gritstone moors. Its distribution in the breeding season is similar to that of the Curlew, but unlike the latter it definitely does breed in wetlands to the east, albeit sparsely. Comparison of the breeding maps for the two species indicates that Snipe are not as widespread in the uplands as Curlew and that breeding was harder to prove. Snipe prefer a somewhat wetter habitat, but have a smaller territorial requirement, and there is a considerable overlap in the two species' breeding areas. It is likely that Snipe were under-recorded, as they are unobtrusive except when displaying ('drumming'), whereas Curlew are readily located.

In the early spring, starting in late February, it was not uncommon to see five or six birds displaying simultaneously in the uplands, and as many as twelve have been recorded. However, it is now rare to see more than three 'drumming' together, although the Snipe is still probably the most numerous wader of the gritstone, with a population of several hundred pairs. In the lowlands, drainage has destroyed much suitable breeding habitat during the last 20 years, so that the present population is unlikely to exceed 20-30 pairs.

There is usually little evidence of spring passage, but in autumn, from August to October, gatherings of up to 20 birds commonly occur at flashes and reservoir margins, and are sometimes much larger, with at least 100 at Barrow Hill on 14th September 1973 (SBRG) outstanding. Birds are also seen in flight at migration watch-points, the peak count being 30 (all north-west) on 28th October 1984 at Concord Park. High numbers are often recorded in November with the arrival of winter migrants, e.g. there were 94 at Redmires Resr in 1975 on 16th. After this, Snipe are only seen in small numbers in the uplands, 17 at Midhope on 7th December 1975 (DG,DH) being exceptional. In the east, however, winter wisps of around 60 birds are not unusual, and over 100 can be flushed from favoured marshy areas of the Rother Valley; 131 were counted at Barlborough Park on 1st January 1975 when the water level was low in the pond there (RAF).

Birds ringed locally in autumn and winter have been recovered during the breeding season in the U.S.S.R. near Leningrad and Vishera, over 3,000 km north-east. Some have been recovered locally in subsequent winters whilst others have moved to coastal areas on the continent, to Ireland or even to North Africa.

WOODCOCK *Scolopax rusticola*

Resident/migrant breeder, winter visitor; woodland and scrub.

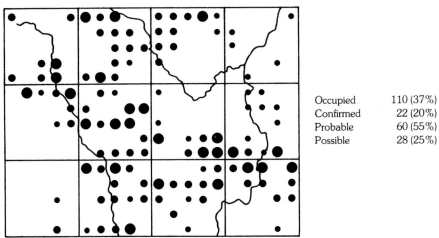

Occupied	110 (37%)
Confirmed	22 (20%)
Probable	60 (55%)
Possible	28 (25%)

The Woodcock breeds throughout the area in all types of woodland which is relatively undisturbed and not too small. Hence it is not normally found in suburban woodland. The breeding map indicates that it is largely absent from the north-east, where there is no extensive woodland, and the south-west, where it was probably overlooked in the wooded limestone dales. As it is crepuscular and ground-loving, the Woodcock's presence is difficult to detect except when performing its unique 'roding' display flight. This may be seen from early February to mid-summer at dawn and dusk, and two were roding at Rivelin Hagg on 25th December 1978 (KC).

Favoured habitat is a mosaic of woodland and ground cover such as Bracken, with damp patches or streams for feeding. An example of this is the Moss Valley where at least ten males were thought to be present in 1976 (DJG). Population densities are difficult to estimate because 'roding' is not a territorial flight, but as breeding was probable or confirmed in 82 squares, the total population of the area is likely to be of the order of several hundred birds.

The resident birds are joined by winter visitors from the continent. They appear to be much more numerous in certain years, such as the winter of 1979/80. As many as 30 birds have been seen at one locality, namely Chatsworth on 17th January 1976 (MP). Passage birds are sometimes recorded in unusual places, including flying round a Chesterfield car park in broad daylight (KS), and in suburban gardens in Sheffield and Rotherham, all in late October/early November, and dead on the railway near the city centre on 14th April 1975.

BLACK-TAILED GODWIT *Limosa limosa*

Scarce passage visitor.

The Black-tailed Godwit was first recorded at Thrybergh Resr on 7th October 1962, which remains the latest date. There have been only eight subsequent records in the area to 1984, all between April and September. The earliest being three birds in full summer plumage at Middleton Moor on 16th April 1983. The highest number reported was six: a juvenile and five adults in summer plumage at Middleton Moor on 10th August 1982 (PAA). The remaining records are of singles: at Staveley on 15-16th May 1967; at Middleton Moor on 12th and 13th July 1982 (thought to be different birds) and on 30th July 1981; at Redmires Resr on 1st August 1975; and at Harthill Resr on 12th September 1976.

Most recently a party of nine paused at Middleton Moor on 23rd June 1985 (PAA), subject to acceptance by the Records Committee.

BAR-TAILED GODWIT *Limosa lapponica*

Infrequent passage visitor; reservoir margins and flashes.

138

Apart from a record at Baslow in the last century, the first report was of one at Barbrook on 4-20th September 1953. There have been 24 records of Bar-tailed Godwit in the period 1960-1984 involving 107 birds, 62% of which have been seen in September mainly flying west to north-west, possibly to Morecambe Bay (40). They have come from eight localities, five of which were in the uplands. The only spring records are five south-east at Thrybergh on 24th March 1984, two north-west at East Moor on 27th April 1980, six at Middleton Moor on 1st May 1984, one at Staveley from 3rd-5th May 1966, and a bird which stayed at Middleton Moor from 3rd May to 11th June 1984.

Two birds in summer plumage at Middleton Moor on 15th July 1982 and three flying north at Concord Park on 15th August 1984 are, surprisingly, the only ones definitely reported in July and August, although a godwit at Middleton Moor on 2nd August 1982 was thought to be this species and a further unidentified godwit flew west at Redmires on 11th August 1981. The bulk of the records are in September, including the following five records of flocks. The largest party was 20 in a field near Lodge Moor on 8th in 1975 (PL); 17 flew west at Middleton Moor on 4th in 1979 and 13 paused briefly there on 14th in 1983; six were present at Redmires Resr with two Turnstones on 12th (1976), a day when there was a Black-tailed Godwit at Harthill Resr.

The only later reports are two in mid-October and on 30th October two flew west at Redmires, followed 20 minutes later by two more, thought to be different birds. Most recently a flock of twelve flew north-west at Thrybergh Resr on 3rd November 1984 (MAS).

WHIMBREL *Numenius phaeopus*

Passage visitor; reservoir margins and flashes.

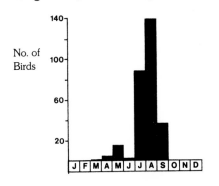

Fig. 38
Monthly distribution of Whimbrel (1960-82)

With an average of more than twelve birds per year, the Whimbrel is probably less scarce in the area than may be thought. Between 1960 and 1984 it has been recorded in all but two years, 1965 and 1968, in varying numbers and at widespread localities. The best year was 1978 with eight records involving 41 birds, including a flock of 31 flying south at Gleadless on 25th July (DJG). Most of the birds are either seen or heard in flight, few alighting either to feed or rest. Those that do land rarely stay for more than a day. The species has been recorded in every month from March to September, although the only March record was a single at Middleton Moor on 23rd in 1982 (PAA). June records are also scarce. The latest date is 16th September when there were two birds at Redmires Resr in 1976 and one over Barbrook Resr in 1978.

Spring passage peaks in May but is small compared to that of autumn, which is concentrated in the period late July to early September (Fig. 38). The spring birds are usually flying north or north-west, whereas the autumn passage is predominantly between south and west.

Parties of up to seven birds are regular and there have been seven records of flocks of 15 or more, the largest consisting of 38 flying south-west at Hackenthorpe on 31st July 1967 (FNB, RGH).

CURLEW *Numenius arquata*

Migrant breeder, passage visitor; moorland, rough pasture, reservoir margins and flashes.

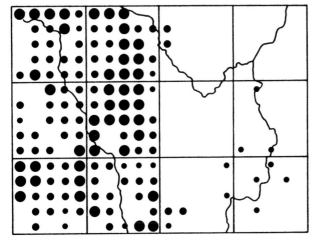

Occupied	139 (46%)
Confirmed	45 (31%)
Probable	74 (53%)
Possible	20 (14%)

The map shows that the Curlew is widespread as a breeding species in the western half of the region. It is primarily a bird of damp upland pasture, rushy hollows and moorland edge, at altitudes of 270-400m a.s.l. It nests as high as 600m, on damp moorland with grassy areas suitable for feeding, or as low as 160m, e.g. in a hay meadow in the Hope Valley. However, there has been no evidence of breeding in the eastern lowands, despite sightings of birds there in the breeding season.

The densities of territorial birds rarely exceed a few pairs per km^2 and are therefore much lower than those in favoured parts of the country, such as the North Yorkshire Pennines where 14-18 pairs per km^2 bred in the 1960s (93). Moorland birds are at particularly low densities, and the territorial flight of a single bird can enter several tetrads, whereas on unimproved pasture there are commonly three to five pairs in a few km^2. Numbers have certainly declined in some areas, e.g. there were 40 pairs on East Moor in 1953 where there are fewer than ten pairs now. The reason for this is not obvious, although drainage to improve grazing is doubtless a contributory factor.

During late February and March pre-breeding flocks occur, particularly at Midhope in the 1970s and Middleton Moor in the 1980s. The largest flocks usually peak in mid-March, at a mean maximum size of 90 in 1974-1983, and 167 roosted at Middleton Moor on 20th March 1985. From the numbers recorded in these flocks, the density estimates and the fact that 120 tetrads contained probable or confirmed breeding birds, the total annual breeding population is probably of the order of 150-300 pairs. The incomparable territorial display generally starts in the first half of March and continues into April and even May. During this time, passage carries on with small parties often recorded flying straight through, especially in the east.

In late summer, post-breeding flocks can be seen feeding on areas of exposed mud around lakes and on reservoir margins. These parties tend to be smaller than their spring counterparts, with a maximum of 15 to 20 birds, although 52 were at Middleton Moor on 18th August 1984 (PAA). By the end of August most birds have left the breeding grounds, although occasionally individuals have remained until October (e.g. six at Middleton Moor on 27th, 1984) and exceptionally until early November.

There is little evidence of autumn migration to west coast moulting grounds which is undertaken by many British Curlews. Flocks of 19 flying west at Ringinglow on 26th August 1981 and 22 north-west at Stanage on 27th August 1979 indicates that such movements do occur, and the species does move away from the Sheffield area for the winter. One ringed as a *pullus* at Bamford was found dead 18 months later at Pembrey (Dyfed). Although it has been recorded in every month of the year, it is rare in December and January.

SPOTTED REDSHANK *Tringa erythropus*

Passage visitor; reservoir margins and sewage farms.

The only spring records are of singles in the lowlands, twice in April and twice in June, the earliest being at Killamarsh on 23rd April 1978. There was also one at Middleton Moor on 6th June 1983. These were all in full breeding plumage, as were the five in the largest party recorded in the area, again at Middleton Moor but on the unusual date of 3rd July 1982 (PAA). Return passage is virtually restricted to August and September, with the only October record a single at Redmires Resr on 10th in 1970. There have been two reports of four birds: at Barbrook Resr on 10th August 1964 and Middleton Moor on 6th September 1972.

The Spotted Redshank is recorded in most years in very small numbers. Between 1960 and 1983 there were 42 records referring to at least 60 birds, 80% of which occurred in August and September. Although it has been reported from ten lowland and only four upland sites, 65% of the birds have been at the upland localities, with Barbrook, Redmires and Middleton Moor the most favoured.

142

REDSHANK *Tringa totanus*

Resident/migrant breeder, passage visitor; moorland, reservoir margins, flashes, wet meadows and sewage farms.

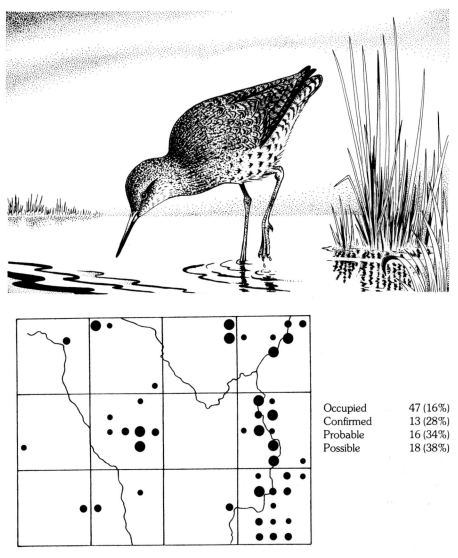

Occupied	47 (16%)
Confirmed	13 (28%)
Probable	16 (34%)
Possible	18 (38%)

The Redshank breeds sparingly in both the eastern lowlands and the western uplands. It has nested at various sites along the Rother and lower Don Valleys, in wet meadows, damp marshes and subsidence flashes. Numbers fluctuate from year to year, depending on water levels, but range from one or two to 10-15 territorial pairs. Two recent years were outstanding - 1979 and 1982, with birds at eight and ten sites, ranging from Staveley in the south to the Rother Valley C.P. area, to Tinsley S.F. and Old Denaby in the north.

In the uplands the breeding population is more stable, with birds reported from upto ten sites in certain years but on average from only five or six. It is doubtful whether breeding occurs at all these sites except in particularly 'wet' years. The sites, which rarely hold more than one or two pairs (although there were five on Ringinglow Bog in 1976), are on flat or gently sloping moorlands, usually not far from reservoirs. The favoured localities are Midhope and the Redmires - Hallam Moors - Ringinglow Bog area. Birds are seen on the moorland during the same period as the Curlew, i.e. from March to July and sometimes in February, with post-breeding and passage birds at the reservoirs and flashes from July to September. A bird at Langsett on 18th November 1984 was exceptionally late.

Frost states that the breeding population in Derbyshire collapsed after the 1962/63 winter and improved drainage has hampered recovery (20). In the last decade the Sheffield population appears to have been fairly stable at around 10-20 pairs. There is no evidence that it was ever appreciably higher in the uplands but loss of habitat has probably reduced numbers breeding in the lowlands.

In the east the species is usually recorded throughout the year. Analysis of reported maxima shows a peak in April, with the largest gathering 26 at Killamarsh on 2nd in 1978, In some winters few are seen, but movement can take place, as shown by the presence of 24 at Harthill Resr on 22nd December 1977. Furthermore, Redshank will quickly exploit areas of floodwater, as occur in the Rother Valley, e.g. at Staveley, Renishaw and at Barlborough where there were 20 birds on 12th January 1975.

An adult ringed at Bolsover on 14th June 1983 was recovered at Finistère in France on 12th March 1984.

GREENSHANK *Tringa nebularia*

Passage visitor; reservoir margins, flashes and sewage farms.

Frederick J Watson

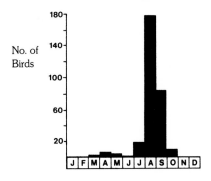

No. of Birds

Fig. 39
Monthly distribution of Greenshank
(1960-82)

The Greenshank has been recorded in all months from March to October, although there is only one June record. The earliest date recorded is 3rd March when, in 1974, there was a single bird at Redmires (IF, CRM). Spring passage however is very light and in many years is not observed at all, although there were three records in 1984. Return movement is usually noted in July in small numbers and is comparatively strong in August and September (Fig. 39) with a few stragglers in October, the latest being one flying south-east at Thrybergh Resr on 26th October 1983.

The species has been observed at most of the wetlands in the east of the area, including on the River Rother itself, and at almost all of the upland waters to the west, from Langsett Resr to Middleton Moor. Many records are of single birds but up to five are common, with higher numbers observed in some years. The largest parties have occurred on 21st August - eleven birds at Redmires in 1974 and 13 flying south-west at Thrybergh Resr in 1983 (AR, SHH).

GREEN SANDPIPER *Tringa ochropus*

Passage/winter visitor; flashes, sewage farms, streams and reservoir margins.

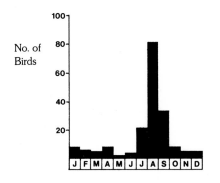

No. of Birds

Fig. 40
Monthly distribution of Green Sandpiper
(1960-83)

This species is recorded annually in varying numbers, the best year being 1978 when at least 44 birds were seen. It shows a marked preference for the lowlands with approximately 80% of all birds having been recorded to the east of the area, particularly at sewage farms, the Rother Valley and adjacent localities such as Hackenthorpe and Treeton Dyke. In the uplands it is rarely seen north of Redmires Resr but there are usually a few reports each autumn from sites such as Barbrook Resr and Middleton Moor. It has even been seen in the Hope Valley - on the River Noe in May and at Bradwell ponds in August.

Green Sandpipers have been observed in every month of the year, but are scarce in spring and early summer, there being little evidence of passage (Fig. 40). There is a pronounced peak in August, with 62% of birds seen on autumn passage between July and September. Although there are a few winter records in most years, mainly from the Rother Valley area, the only bird to spend the entire winter at one locality was at the higher Ewden Valley reservoirs, from 21st November 1975 until at least 20th March 1976.

Approximately 75% of records are of single birds and 22% refer to twos or threes. There were seven reports of higher numbers upto 1983, the largest being nine at Ramsley Resr on 15th August 1975 (MET) and eight at Killamarsh on 8th August 1978 (GPM).

WOOD SANDPIPER *Tringa glareola*

Passage visitor; flashes sewage farms and reservoir margins.

The Wood Sandpiper shows a preference for the east of the region where it has appeared at sewage farms and flashes such as Catcliffe and Bolehill. It has also occurred at four upland sites, namely Middleton Moor and Barbrook, Redmires and Ramsley Resrs. Although only recorded since the 1950s, there are 29 records for the period 1960-84, referring to 33 birds. There have been 23 singles and five 'pairs', although a party of five was reported at Beighton in 1959.

The species has been seen in every month from May to October. Before 1982 it had only been recorded twice on spring passage: singles in late May at Staveley in 1966 and nearby Old Whittington S.F. in 1977. However, in 1982 there was one at Middleton Moor on 11th May and three records in June including two at Bolehill Flash on 9th and one at Tinsley S.F. on the late date of 23rd (KB). There was also one on 29th May 1984 at Redmires Resr.

Most birds are seen on autumn passage, starting in late July but with a prominant peak in August when 54% of the records have occurred. The outstanding year for the species was 1980 when there were six records involving a total of nine birds, eight of which were seen in the short period 27th July to 7th August. There have been few reports in September and two of singles in October, which is late for this species: at Treeton Dyke on 8th in 1961 (RAF) and at Tinsley S.F. from 1st to 7th in 1975 (JH).

COMMON SANDPIPER *Actitis hypoleucos*

Migrant breeder, passage visitor; rivers, reservoir margins, flashes and sewage farms.

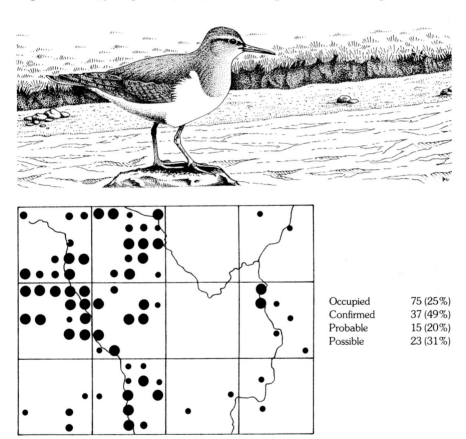

Occupied	75 (25%)
Confirmed	37 (49%)
Probable	15 (20%)
Possible	23 (31%)

The main breeding range of the Common Sandpiper is on the upland reservoirs and rivers including the lower reaches of the Derwent. There has been proof of breeding at two eastern sites, Treeton Dyke and Catcliffe, but this is an irregular occurrence in the lowlands. Dr. D. W. Yalden censused the breeding population in the Peak District in 1979-82 (*94*) and found

147

96 occupied territories in the Sheffield area, nearly half the total number in the whole Peak. The barren shores of Ladybower and Derwent Resrs and the many shingle banks along the River Ashop held 55% of the area's population, at densities as high as 2.5 pairs/km along 7.5km of the Ashop. However, elsewhere densities are generally much lower; e.g. from WBS results, 19km of the River Derwent from Bamford to Beeley averaged 6.6 pairs in the period 1973 to 1982 and the Wye is the only other river surveyed on which the species breeds in most years.

Annual surveys of the Derwent Valley reservoirs in the 1980s showed the population fluctuated between 27 pairs (in 1982) and 35-36 pairs (in 1980,81 and 84). These figures were considered to be underestimates for the number attempting to breed, because other pairs were thought to be present, e.g. eleven in 1984, either having failed or still incubating at the time of the survey (in late June). An additional twelve non-territorial single birds in 1984 indicated the population to be in a healthy state (DWY pers. comm.).

The breeding biology of the species has been studied in the Peak District (95). Egg laying most commonly occurred in the period 15-25th May and hatching from 4-14th June.

The Common Sandpiper has been recorded in every month, but only five times in winter (including the only January record - at Broomhead Dam on 2nd-6th, 1985), whereas it regularly overwinters in very small numbers further south in the Trent Valley. The first spring arrivals appear predominantly between 8th and 28th April, although early birds were reported from Derwent Resr on 26th March 1967 (RAF) and the River Rother on 31st March 1979 (DJG,PMG). Spring passage is fairly light with maxima of up to seven recorded at both lowland and upland localities.

Return passage is more marked, with maxima noted in July and August and occasionally September. There have been several gatherings of ten or more, the largest being in August: 20 at Redmires on 25th, 1974, 17 (including a flock of 13) at Thrybergh Resr on 7th, 1981 and 14 at Barbrook on 3rd, 1961. A few localities in the Don and Rother Valleys regularly hold several birds at this time of the year. The last records vary considerably from one year to the next, sometimes being in September, sometimes October with the latest date (excluding the 'wintering' birds) 23rd, 1973, when one was at Thrybergh Resr.

TURNSTONE *Arenaria interpres*

Passage/winter visitor; reservoir margins, sewage farms and flashes.

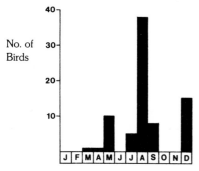

No. of Birds

Fig. 41
Monthly distribution of Turnstone
(1960-84)

148

The Turnstone was first recorded in August 1959, at Barbrook Resr and Beighton. It was an irregular visitor prior to 1973, but since then has been seen annually in small numbers, mainly on passage. It has been reported from nine localities, six of which are in the east of the area where it has been most frequently seen at Treeton Dyke and Tinsley S.F. However, the most favoured sites are in the west where, between 1960 and 1984, both Barbrook and Redmires Resrs have had nine records out of the area total of 39 (involving 67 birds).

Although not observed annually, spring passage occurs in May, the only exception being a single bird at Elsecar Resr on 28th April 1974. Records were unusually numerous in May 1984, with three birds at Thrybergh Resr on 3rd, and singles at Redmires Resr on 5th and Middleton Moor on 18th. Autumn passage starts in late July, the only record before 27th being a single on 15th (in 1974). It is seen predominantly in August, as shown by Fig. 41, with only a few September reports. There have been only three winter sightings: on 7th March 1976, during a cold spell, one was at Redmires Resr; on 30th December 1979 a party of twelve flew south at Middleton Moor (PAA), and on 31st December 1981 two birds at Tinsley S.F. departed north-east after a brief stay.

Most reports have been of one or two birds, with only two parties larger than four: the twelve at Middleton Moor, and seven at Redmires Resr on 19th August 1982.

RED-NECKED PHALAROPE *Phalaropus lobatus*

Scarce visitor.

The only fully substantiated record of Red-necked Phalarope is of an adult observed feeding at Middleton Moor on 3rd July 1981 (PAA).

A phalarope at Catcliffe on 5th September 1967 was not specifically identified but was thought to be of this species (TJB, GEJ).

GREY PHALAROPE *Phalaropus fulicarius*

Scarce Visitor

There are two historical records of this species: one shot at Staveley in 1720 and two shot at Little London Dam, Sheffield, in 1867. Since then there have been four records of single Grey Phalaropes, one in August and the remainder in October. In 1969 there was one at Barbrook Resr, first seen on 30th October and staying until 2nd November (RAF). In 1972 one again stayed at Barbrook, from 26th to 28th October (RAF), whilst another, or the same bird, was on Midhope Resr on 28th October (DH *et al*). More recently an adult in transitional plumage was at Beighton on 18th August 1982 (DHu).

149

ARCTIC SKUA *Stercorarius parasiticus*

Scarce passage visitor.

Frederick J Watson

The Arctic Skua was first recorded in the area in 1953, when three were seen at Derwent, "one of which was unfortunately shot" (EHP). Since then there have been seven definite records of this species, two in spring and five in autumn. Six of these occurred in the period 1974-1983, the only other earlier record being a single at Ramsley on 22nd August 1957. The spring occurrences were of single birds, at Thrybergh Resr on 25th April 1981 following gale force easterlies, and flying north-east over Wharncliffe Chase on 2nd May 1978 at a time when much of England was under total cloud cover with prevailing south-westerly winds. The latter record coincided with a period of heavy inland passage of terns across the country, including a flock of 90 'commic' terns over Wharncliffe Chase immediately beforehand.

All the autumn records, except the most recent, occurred in the period 18th August to 19th September. Three birds moved west over Big Moor on 18th August 1974, following a period of easterly winds over much of the country. Coincidentally, the next report was also of three birds at nearby Leash Fen, on 11th September 1976. A dark phase adult flew west after a brief stay at Redmires Resr on 19th September 1982, the same day that an immature Long-tailed Skua flew north from Ogston Resr, 28 km south of Redmires. The latest bird was seen at Chesterfield on 4th November 1983 in very dull, foggy weather - it flew around calling and then settled on a factory roof.

Also in 1982 three skuas at Thrybergh Resr, which departed to the south-west on 29th October, were reported as Arctic although accepted as 'Skua species'.

LONG-TAILED SKUA *Stercorarius longicaudus*

Vagrant.

The Long-tailed Skua is a recent addition to the Sheffield list. A first-year bird was found dead at Middleton Moor on 5th October 1978 (TBC). This followed a period of strong north-westerly winds which caused a major movement of Leach's Petrel in north-west England. The specimen is now in the collection of the Sheffield City Museum. An adult flying north-east over Thrybergh Resr on 6th May 1984 (MAS *et al*) will, if accepted by the County Reports Committee, be the second record for the area. This bird was also recorded a little later at Sprotborough flash, a few km north-east of the area.

MEDITERRANEAN GULL *Larus melanocephalus*

Scarce visitor.

This gull was seen for the first time in 1981, since when it has been recorded annually. This change in status reflects the general increase in inland records nationally.

In 1981 an adult was at Greasbrough Tip during the period 19th to 25th February and an adult roosted at Langsett Resr on 22nd November. A first-winter bird circled Broomhead Resr on 7th January 1982, and flew off east without stopping. A first-winter bird was at Staveley S.F. on 18th December 1983 and another, possibly the same bird, was at Blackburn Tip on 31st January 1984. The only record outside the winter season occurred in 1984 when a first summer bird was at Middleton Moor on 27th and 28th May. (PAA,RAF).

LITTLE GULL *Larus minutus*

Infrequent visitor; lakes, reservoirs and flashes.

The Little Gull was first recorded in 1959, on the River Don at Swinton on 21st November. It was only seen in five subsequent years until 1978, since when it has been recorded annually. The total number of records up to 1984 is 24, referring to 45 birds. Hutchinson and Neath (*96*) documented an increase in records from inland counties which began in the mid 1960s and was especially notable in the early 1970s. This increase is paralleled in Derbyshire (*20*) but appears later in Sheffield, possibly because observer coverage is an overriding factor.

The great majority of birds are passage migrants, with records equally split between spring (6th May to 18th June) and autumn (22nd July to 16th September, with exceptions at Redmires Resr on 9-10th July 1984 and 19th October 1975). The only winter records apart from the Swinton bird of 1959, occurred on 31st December 1983 when one was at Ulley Resr (YNU), and in February 1974 following southerly gales (which caused an influx of Little Gulls to Ireland (*45*)): an adult was seen at Wentworth on 10th, and was followed by an immature there on 17th. Reports have come equally from the upland localities of Redmires and Barbrook Resrs and Middleton Moor, and the eastern waters of Thrybergh Resr, Treeton Dyke, Catcliffe and Tinsley S.F.

Most reports are of single immature birds. Only three adults have been seen, except for a flock of 18, with two immatures, which arrived at Treeton Dyke during southerly winds on 7th May 1980 (PW).

BLACK-HEADED GULL *Larus ridibundus*

Casual breeder, winter/passage visitor; reservoirs, refuse tips, sewage farms, fields and flashes.

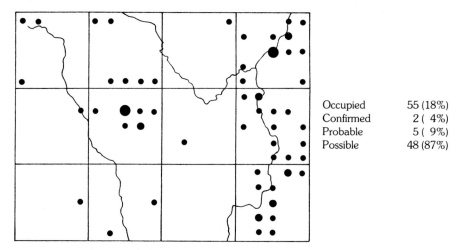

Occupied	55 (18%)
Confirmed	2 (4%)
Probable	5 (9%)
Possible	48 (87%)

The Black-headed Gull is the commonest gull and the only one which has bred. It is the most catholic in its choice of habitat and is found feeding throughout the area, although rarely on the gritstone moorlands. Numbers appear to have changed little since 1960, flocks of several thousand in winter roosts being reported throughout the period.

During the nineteenth century there was a marked decline in numbers. It was not mentioned by Allis (4) in 1844, and although it undoubtedly occurred in subsequent years it was certainly not common. A recolonisation took place towards the end of the century and Patten (12) referred to it as a periodical visitor. By 1929 Whittaker (13) noted that it was common at all times of the year, and there were at least six upland breeding colonies. These colonies continued to grow and by 1938 there were 250 pairs on Broomhead Moors, 200 pairs on Howden Moors, up to 200 pairs near Hathersage and 50 pairs at Redmires, whilst Leash Fen held over 100 pairs in some years up to 1944. In the lowlands, Aldwarke S.F. held 700 birds and numerous young in 1949 and other sites were active.

However by the early 1960s only three colonies (at Aldwarke, Tinsley and Ringinglow) were still occupied, although ten pairs bred at Beighton in 1963, with perhaps a total of 100 pairs nesting in some years. By 1970, breeding had ceased at Ringinglow and was rare at Tinsley (e.g. one pair nested in 1973). At Aldwarke 200 pairs were present in 1966 and slightly lower numbers in the mid-1970s, but only twelve pairs were nesting by 1978 when the site was destroyed. Breeding success was often poor, although *c.* 75 young were reared in 1975. Breeding was suspected, but not proven, at Catcliffe Tip in 1979 and since 1977 one or two pairs have shown signs of nesting at Thrybergh Banks. Birds are reported displaying at certain moorland localities in most years and a single pair nested on a pond on Hallam Moors in 1978, with two pairs at the same locality in 1982 and 1984 and a single pair successful in 1985.

Autumn passage begins in early July and reaches a peak in August. Movement is usually in a westerly direction and initially involves mostly immatures. Up to 115 birds per hour passing over Redmires is the maximum recorded at this time of the year. Large feeding/roosting flocks build-up to the east at wetland localities such as Treeton Dyke, where 2,000 roosted on 23rd August 1980.

Autumn passage declines during September but by October there is a resurgence in numbers present as the winter roosts begin to form. Tinsley S.F. was formerly the major roost site, with 6,000 in December 1963 and 4,000 in January 1976. However, in 1976 most of the sewage lagoons on which the birds roosted were filled-in and the roost moved to a nearby steelworks roof at Tinsley Park (97). In the 1980s Thrybergh Resr and Rother Valley C.P. have also held 1,500 or more birds. There are two major upland roosts at Broomhead and Langsett Resrs where several thousand birds may be present in winter. A count of 6,000 at Broomhead on 1st January 1983 was exceptional. Numbers at these sites fluctuate in response to weather conditions due to their exposed position, and in bad weather more birds roost at the lower Thrybergh Resr, Rother Valley C.P. or Tinsley Park sites, even roosting inside the works at the height of a cold spell in January 1980. Maximum numbers are present in December and January: the largest figure recorded was 7,600 in the major roosts on 18th December 1977. In most recent winters, a population of 4,000-5,000 has been present in the area from late November until the end of January.

A wide range of habitat is exploited by the Black-headed Gull for winter feeding. Sewage farms and refuse tips, mostly to the east of the city, attract the largest numbers, but birds are also frequently recorded on rivers, canals, ponds, farmland and, in severe weather, in urban gardens and streets. Ringing recoveries have shown that Black-headed Gulls wintering in Britain originate from northern Europe, mainly around the Baltic Sea (98), and this is supported by the foreign recoveries of birds ringed in Sheffield (from Sweden, Finland, West Germany, Denmark and the Netherlands). An adult ringed at Beighton on 2nd February 1963 was controlled in Denmark on 26th August 1984 and was therefore at least 22 years old.

By February, numbers in the roosts have begun to fall, often quite rapidly, and return passage begins. Although poorly recorded, movement is often in a north-westerly direction and continues until June (97); after March the majority of birds involved are immatures. Several areas to the east of the city are important at this time of year, e.g. Thrybergh Resr (2,000 in March 1974) and Aldwarke (1,500 in March 1978).

COMMON GULL *Larus canus*

Passage/winter visitor; reservoirs, refuse tips, fields and flashes.

The Common Gull is present in small numbers throughout most of the year, usually in association with other gulls, although it tends to be absent or rare in May and June. The past status of this species has been summarised by Clarkson (97), who also documented an increase in roosting numbers during the mid-1970s.

After a period during the breeding season when few are recorded, autumn movement in a westerly or southerly direction begins in July. Passage in this season occurs in two phases in most years, the first in July and August and the second in October and/or November. Autumn numbers can be relatively large, e.g. 70 at Arkwright on 13th August 1975 and 70 moving west over the Little Don Valley in two hours in November 1978.

Frederick J Watson

Common Gulls are present in the winter moorland roosts from November to the end of January, but total numbers in the area rarely exceed 100 birds. Throughout the 1960s and early 1970s numbers were much smaller than this, usually only in single figures at any one locality. In the winter of 1974/5 larger numbers were recorded for the first time, with 64 on Broomhead Resr on 29th December and 45 still present two weeks later. During January 1977 the total population reached 110, with flocks of 20-30 regularly present on farmland to the east of the city. The largest concentrations occurred in the recent severe winters: in 1979 there were 200 at Catcliffe on 26th January and a late flock of 50 at Agden Resr on 4th March; in 1982 there were 267 at Langsett Resr on 24th January and c.155 at Middleton Moor on 23rd February.

Spring passage occurs mainly in the months of March and April but is not well-defined. Northerly or easterly passage involving up to 50 birds was noted at Barrow Hill in April 1974 and 1976; these movements were in agreement with the national trend demonstrated by Vernon (99), but were exceptional numbers as spring records are normally very few.

LESSER BLACK-BACKED GULL *Larus fuscus*

Passage/winter and summer visitor; reservoirs, refuse tips, fields and flashes.

Of the three common species of large gull occurring in winter, the Lesser Black-backed Gull is the only one also present in large numbers during the summer months. Both winter and summer occurrences are relatively recent events in Sheffield, as prior to the 1950s this species was considered to be purely a passage migrant. Since then, a summer population of

154

immatures and sub-adults has developed and, in line with a significant increase in the wintering population in Britain as a whole (*100*), birds have begun wintering in the area. Although present throughout the year, numbers can vary greatly over a few weeks, and occasionally the majority of the local population may move out of the area as happened in January 1980 (*101*).

The summer population, first recorded in 1959, was at a high level in the early 1960s, peaking at 450 at Beighton Tip in 1962. Numbers then declined more or less steadily, so that from 1973 to 1978 almost all summer records involved less than 100 birds. However, since 1979 Middleton Moor has become a favoured site: 300 were counted in June 1979, making it the fourth largest roost in the country at that time (*102*), and in June 1980, 872 were present on 22nd, increasing to at least 3,000 by 13th July. In subsequent years the roost formed in May, again peaking in July, e.g. 444 were counted on 17th May 1981 and c.1,015 on 18th July 1981. Elsewhere most reports of birds at this season are from lowland waters and refuse tips to the south and east, with the exception of Redmires Resr in the west.

In July, adults begin to move through the area, mainly in a south-westerly direction, and numbers increase throughout the autumn, usually reaching a peak in October or early November. During the autumn, flocks of over 100 are frequently reported from a variety of sites including playing fields and arable farmland, and the total number present in the area exceeded 1,000 in several years during the 1970s; the maximum being 1,500 at Redmires Resr on 28th September 1977. During August and September, the main roost sites are Barbrook and Redmires Resrs, and Middleton Moor where roosts exceeding 1,000 birds have been recorded in the 1980s. By mid-November these sites have usually been deserted in favour of more sheltered roosts at Broomhead, Langsett and Thrybergh Resrs and Treeton Dyke, although in 1983 there were still 586 present at Middleton Moor on 6th December.

Numbers in January and February tend to be smaller than in the first half of winter and a significant reduction in the population often occurs in December. Total numbers of wintering birds also dropped during the 1970s; e.g. the maximum winter count in 1979/80 was only 250 compared to 500 for 1973/4, but increased in the 1980s. By February, numbers have generally fallen to a winter minimum but the local population increases at the end of the month. This continues through March as spring passage begins and roosts are augmented by migrants. The majority of movement is in a north-westerly direction and can be quite pronounced, sometimes involving more than 100 birds per hour. Passage of adults is heaviest in early April with immatures peaking about a month later. By early June, passage has virtually ceased.

Individuals showing the characteristics of the Scandinavian sub-species *L. f. fuscus* have been recorded, for example: at Arkwright, Broomhead, Rawmarsh and Barbrook in autumn; in late winter at Greasbrough Tip and Beighton where there were 24 on 19th February 1983 (DJG); and on spring passage over Rivelin Edge and Barbrook where eight flew north-west on 6th April 1983.

A bird found dead at Barbrook Resr on 26th Septmber 1978 had been ringed as a *pullus* in July 1966 at Flanders Moss, Stirling.

155

HERRING GULL *Larus argentatus*

Passage/winter visitor; reservoirs, refuse tips, fields and flashes.

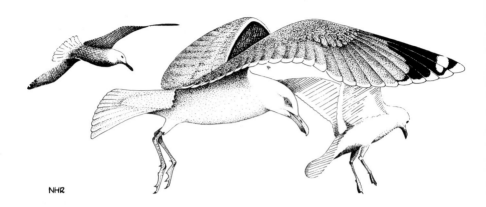

NHR

Twenty-five years ago the Herring Gull was a much less common winter visitor to the area but it is now numerous and small numbers are present in the summer and on passage. Large feeding flocks developed in the late 1950s, frequenting areas to the south and east of the city, but it was not until the early 1970s that birds began to roost locally on the upland reservoirs. This increase in winter records reflects the national trend during this period described by Hickling (*103*), who estimated that the number of gulls wintering inland in January 1973 was almost three times the number doing so in January 1953.

Although numbers vary from winter to winter, a basic trend is apparent. A major influx occurs, usually in November, and numbers remain high until January when a slow decline starts, continuing until March, by which time most birds have left the area. Winter maxima were highest in the early and mid-1970s, e.g. in January 1974 when 2,000 were counted on Broomhead Resr. The size of winter roosts declined during 1976-8, the largest count in 1978 being 600, but subsequently increased to a maximum of 1,597 in 1982. A national gull count organised in January 1983 showed that the Herring Gull population roosting at inland sites had decreased by 54% since 1973 (*104*). At Broomhead Resr there were 463 on the national census date, but numbers subsequently increased to at least 1,200 on 6th February. The other major roost site is Langsett Resr, although numbers are generally smaller than at Broomhead. There have been very few reports of birds roosting anywhere else in winter, but the most interesting additional site is a steelworks roof at Tinsley Park where up to 20 have been recorded amongst Black-headed Gulls.

Spring and autumn movements are poorly defined with only occasional records of single birds and small parties moving through the area. A flock of 76 at Middleton Moor on 7th May 1982 (PAA) represents the largest concentration outside the winter months. The small number of migrant birds recorded in autumn are adults and first year birds, mostly moving in a south-westerly direction. They are often recorded in the autumnal Lesser Black-backed Gull roosts in the uplands to the west of the city.

Small numbers of birds, mostly immatures, have been recorded during the summer months, although not in the last few years. Records are mainly of single birds or very small groups at refuse tips and sewage farms. The total number present in this season has probably never exceeded ten birds at any one time. In September 1975 and on five dates from mid-August to mid-October 1983, single birds with yellow legs and dark mantles were present at Redmires Resr, and may have been of either North European or Mediterranean origin. Pure white, albino birds have also been seen on several occasions, e.g. at Greasbrough Tip on 8th and 18th January 1981.

ICELAND GULL *Larus glaucoides*

Infrequent winter visitor; reservoirs, refuse tips and fields.

The first Iceland Gull to be recorded in the area was a second-winter bird at Beighton Tip on 25th November 1966, although a 'white-winged' gull, thought to be an Iceland, had been seen at Beighton on 13th January 1962 (RGH,DBC). Since then records of a further 18 birds have been accepted. Broomhead Resr has provided six of these, but the remaining sightings have come from a variety of localities in the eastern half of the area, mainly refuse tips with Shirecliffe the most favoured.

The Iceland Gull has occurred in 13 of the last 20 years and so is now approaching the status of an annual winter visitor. In only three years (1976, 1977 and 1984) has more than one bird been seen. All reports occurred in the period 12th November to 18th February, until 1984 when there was an unprecedented influx nationally and two were seen on 27th February, with one on 4th and 22nd March.

The proportion of second-winter and adult birds, at 27% and 33%, is higher than for Glaucous Gull (13% and 27% including sub-adults). This accords with observations in the West Midlands (105) and Derbyshire (106), although in these areas over 50% were adults.

GLAUCOUS GULL *Larus hyperboreus*

Winter visitor; reservoirs, refuse tips and fields.

157

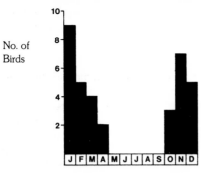

No. of Birds

Fig. 42
Monthly distribution of Glaucous Gull
(1963-83)

The Glaucous Gull was first recorded on 16th January 1963 when an adult was seen at Woodhouse Tip. There were no further reports until 1969 after which it has been seen annually. By mid-1979 a total of 17 birds had been recorded and in the subsequent four winters sightings were more numerous involving at least 13 birds. Hence the Glaucous Gull has undergone a significant change in status during the last twenty years, from that of a very scarce winter visitor to one of a regular, if uncommon, winter visitor. Part of this increase may be due to greater observer coverage of local gull roosts and refuse tips in latter years and to the formation, in the early 1970s, of regular moorland reservoir roosts where large numbers of gulls could be readily checked. However, a pronounced influx occurred in November and December 1974 when four or five birds were recorded in six weeks. Since then numbers have fluctuated from one to three birds a winter, except for 1978/79 when none was seen and 1980 when there was an influx in late January/early February involving at least four birds. A similar increase in occurrences was noted in the West Midlands (105) and Derbyshire (106) although in both these areas the increase was noticed around 1967, earlier than in Sheffield.

The earliest record is of one at Middleton Moor on 21st October 1982, although one flying north at Concord Park on 16th September 1984 (JPS) is under consideration, and the latest on 3rd April 1980 (when one was at Greasbrough Tip). The majority of birds are sighted from November to February with a peak in January (Fig 42). Most (60%) are first winter birds, but all other identifiable ages have been seen. The 1970s records mainly involve birds at the two major roosts - Broomhead and Langsett Resrs -but more recently, sightings from refuse tips and eastern localities such as Thrybergh Resr, Rother Valley C.P. and Staveley S.F. have predominated.

There have also been seven records of 'white-winged' gulls since 1974, which were considered to be either Glaucous or Iceland Gulls.

GREAT BLACK-BACKED GULL *Larus marinus*

Winter/passage visitor; refuse-tips, fields and flashes.

The numbers of Great Black-backed Gulls have increased greatly in the area since the 1950s. This has also been noted in Doncaster where the species was described as a regular visitor after 1954 (107). This change may well be directly related to the threefold increase in the national breeding population between 1930 and 1956 (19). With the establishment of

158

the moorland roosts in Sheffield in the early 1970s, a fairly stable winter population developed and has remained until the present time, although numbers fluctuate considerably from year to year.

This gull is primarily a winter visitor and in most years the majority arrive in November. The influx is usually pronounced, with winter maxima often occurring only three to four weeks after birds are first recorded in the roosts. In most years during the last decade, the maximum count at Broomhead Resr (the major roost site in the area) has been between 150 and 200. Numbers usually fall considerably in the early months of the year, although in the severe winter of 1978/79 the Broomhead roost still held 200 birds well into January. The only other significant roost site is Langsett Resr which usually holds smaller numbers than Broomhead. The birds feed mainly at refuse tips (especially Shirecliffe, Rotherham and Beighton), except in the Moss Valley where over 100 have been recorded on farmland in January.

By the end of February the winter population has declined to a handful of birds. Very few are noted on spring passage; singles and small groups move in a west-north-west direction through the area from March to early June, after which there is usually a dearth of records until a more pronounced but small autumn passage begins in late July. Passage birds are recorded until October, usually moving south-west, with 50-60 at Peak Forest on 27th September 1984 (DAm) a notable record. After this sightings become confused with movements between feeding sites and roosts, but passage probably rarely continues beyond early November.

KITTIWAKE *Rissa tridactyla*

Passage/winter visitor; reservoirs, lakes and flashes.

Although the Kittiwake is almost exclusively marine in its distribution at all times of the year, inland records do occur when birds are on spring passage or are blown across the country by strong winds and adverse weather conditions.

There were three Sheffield records in the 1960s, three in the early 1970s, but since 1974 this species has achieved annual status. The recent increase in the number of reports is related to an increase in observers and the formation of regular winter gull roosts in the early 1970s. The increase in the population of Kittiwakes breeding on the east coast of England during this time may also have been contributory (108). Seven records have come from Broomhead Resr, the main gull roost site, including the remarkable number of 105 (predominantly adult birds) present on 16th January 1981 (KC), a time when large numbers were seen inland elsewhere in the British Isles.

Most records are in winter and spring with all but ten (out of a total of 72 from 1960 - 1983) being in the months December to May inclusive. An adult flying north in Upper Derwentdale on 6th June 1983 (DR) in fine weather was unusual. Records in the early months of the year probably involve birds moving from their wintering areas in the North Sea and North Atlantic back to the breeding cliffs and, on some occasions, being driven across the country in the process by strong winds; over a third of all records are in March and April. That adverse weather conditions are often associated with inland Kittiwakes is underlined by the fact that six of the Sheffield records are of birds found dead, presumably from exhaustion. Most sightings are of single adults; immatures and large groups are rare. The flock of 105 is by far the largest concentration ever recorded; the only other reports of large parties are c.20 on Derwent Resr on 29th March 1962 (DBC), 33 (6 adults and 27 second-winter) at Redmires on 1st March 1984 (AJM,KC), 27 (including one party of 23) flying south-west at Concord Park on 4th November 1984 (JPS) and 12 (including 10 adults) which spent two hours at Thrybergh Resr on 12th June 1985 (SHH *et al*).

Kittiwakes have been observed at a wide variety of localities, with Broomhead, Redmires, Thrybergh and Derwent/Howden Resrs the most favoured.

SANDWICH TERN *Sterna sandvicensis*

Scarce visitor.

The first record of live Sandwich Terns in the area occurred on 24th September 1967 when two were seen flying south-west over open countryside at Staveley (RAF), although a fresh corpse had been found at Ulley Resr on 1st November 1942 (a very late date). From then until 1984, only two birds were seen on spring passage and six on return passage, all at different times.

The spring records were both on 29th April, the peak month for Sandwich Tern migration - at Langsett Resr in 1977 and Tinsley S.F. in 1981. The earliest autumn record was on 30th July, at Catcliffe in 1980, and was followed by two August reports, both at Redmires Resr, on 15th in 1974 and 20th in 1982. The outstanding year for the species was 1978 (when Derbyshire had an exceptional five records): birds were seen in September at Treeton Dyke, Elsecar Resr, and Broomhead Resr where one bird lingered a second day, leaving on 1st October.

However, in May 1985 during a long period of mainly easterly winds, there were three records (all subject to acceptance) at Thrybergh Resr. Firstly, a party of four birds flew north-east on 4th, followed by a party of eight on 14th and a single bird on 24th. Finally, one was seen at Treeton Dyke on 11th June 1985.

COMMON TERN *Sterna hirundo*

Passage visitor; reservoirs, flashes and lakes.

The Common Tern is a passage visitor to the area, with an average of about six records per annum in the 1970s and an increasing number in the 1980s. There are only five records for the years 1960-1972 when the species was undoubtedly under-recorded. The increase in sightings in recent years is related to the frequency of observations at lowland sites such as Thrybergh Resr, although there may be considerable fluctuation from year to year; e.g. four in 1977 and 17 in 1980. The situation is also complicated by reports of 'commic terns', i.e. birds which could have been Common or Arctic Terns.

The earliest date on which a Common Tern has been recorded is 13th April (1968 and 1980), about ten days before the main arrivals on the south coast (98). There are no peaks in numbers corresponding to spring and autumn passage and birds have been seen throughout the summer months until the end of October. The latest report was of two on 25th October 1976, although a 'commic' was at Ramsley on 6th November 1982. Most records fall in the month of June. The occurrence of birds in the summer and the very high proportion of adults suggest that many of these may be non-breeders.

Most sightings are at reservoirs or lakes where birds stop to feed, but some records are of single birds or small parties flying over moorland or farmland. Most records involve less than five birds together, but larger groups are occasionally noted; e.g. 31 at Ulley and 18 at Poolsbrook, both on 19th June 1977, and 18 at Treeton Dyke on 18th May 1981. There was a notable passage on 12th September 1976 when 16 terns, three of which were identified as Common and one as Arctic, were recorded at seven localities throughout the area. Over 75% of all sightings are from localities to the east of the city, such as Thrybergh, Ulley, Treeton and Wentworth, perhaps indicating the use of the lowland river valleys as migration routes. There was an interesting record of a single bird which spent all afternoon of 19th June 1975 fishing the River Don in the centre of Sheffield.

ARCTIC TERN *Sterna paradisaea*

Passage visitor; reservoirs, flashes and lakes.

The Arctic Tern is recorded approximately half as frequently as the Common Tern, which is to be expected considering its more northerly and coastal breeding distrubtion. There were only about three records per year in the 1970s and even fewer in the 1960s when, like the Common Tern, the species was probably under-recorded, but in the first few years of the 1980s there have been some 7.5 records per year. Dates of sightings run from April (earliest - 5th April 1984) until early October, although an immature stayed an unusually long time at Pebley Pond from 23rd October to 12th November 1967 (RAF). Records have occurred in all months in between with slight peaks in May and September, the major months for spring and autumn passage for this species (98). The paucity of summer records compared with Common Tern may result from the distances from the breeding colonies: the nearest Arctic Tern colony is 150 km away on the Norfolk coast whilst there were sixteen 10 km squares containing breeding Common Terns within 100 km of Sheffield in the period 1968-72 (19).

The majority of reports come from areas of water to the east of the city, especially Treeton Dyke, and Thrybergh Resr (in recent years) and Elsecar Resr, although a third of all sightings are on moorland reservoirs in the west of the area. Although most records are of singles or small parties, this species is occasionally displaced from the North Sea in large numbers on spring passage, especially in early May. This was particularly evident at Thrybergh Resr in 1985 when birds were seen almost daily from 26th April to 24th May with a peak of 59 on 3rd May. The largest single flock specifically identified was 33 on 2nd May 1983, at Thrybergh Resr, along with a further c.40 'commic' terns almost certainly of this species (WD). These were preceded by twelve on 1st May at Barlborough. An even bigger flock, c.90, which was probably largely (or entirely) of this species, was seen flying north over Wharncliffe Chase on 2nd May 1978, shortly followed by an Arctic Skua (FJW).

LITTLE TERN *Sterna albifrons*

Scarce visitor.

Allis (4) reports two Little Terns were shot at Ecclesfield Dam but apart from two possible records from Redmires Resr in 1955 and 1958, the species was not identified again until 15th June 1961 when one was at Barbrook Resr. All subsequent records have been from lowland waters in the east, the first occurring on 13th July 1961 at Treeton Dyke. The only other report that decade was of one at Pebley Pond on 17th September 1967, the latest record. The next record was not until 21st July 1973, when a single was at Ulley Resr, but Little Terns have been seen in six of the subsequent twelve years.

All the recent reports have been during the period 1st May to 12th June, except for one on 7th August 1981 and three on 2nd September 1975. They probably involved birds on spring passage which were disoriented by bad weather or prolonged easterlies. The latter conditions certainly applied in 1985, the only year with more than one spring record. Little Terns were then seen on the following four occasions at Thrybergh Resr: one on 15th May, two on 23rd May and 3rd June, and three on 4th June. Apart from the above, the only time more than one bird has been seen was on 16th May 1975 when three were at Treeton Dyke.

BLACK TERN *Chlidonias niger*

Passage visitor; reservoirs, flashes and lakes.

No. of Birds

Fig. 43   Monthly distribution of Black Tern (1973-83)

162

The Black Tern has been recorded on passage on more than 70 occasions since 1960, with the vast majority of sightings since the early 1970s. Spring passage occurs throughout May and June, the earliest date being 6th May at Treeton Dyke in 1970 and Harthill in 1976. It is usually very light, but there were two exceptional days at the end of May: in 1966 there were twelve birds at Wentworth on 30th (c.f. a total of 53 recorded on the same day at two reservoirs further south in Derbyshire), and in 1973 fifteen flew over Barbrook Resr on 28th. Birds rarely linger in spring, but a pair spent some time at Tinsley S.F. on 24th May 1976, frequently calling - possibly attracted by suitable breeding habitat.

Return passage is virtually restricted to August and September (Fig. 43), although there have been three records in the last week of July including another 'big day' at Barbrook - 22nd July 1969 when 22 birds were seen.

Most records are of single birds, but small parties occur occasionally and in 1982 there were 24 immature birds at Harthill Resr, on 10th September (DHu). A flock of c. 40 flew south-west at Middleton Moor on 14th August 1985 (PAA). Birds sometimes stay for several days, as was the case with two of the three October records, the latest leaving Barbrook Resr on 5th in 1977.

Perhaps surprisingly, as most Black Terns appear to migrate via river valleys (98), half the records come from upland reservoirs, with 16 from Barbrook and 14 from Redmires. The remaining reports are from a wide selection of waters to the east and north, with Treeton Dyke, and Harthill, Elsecar and Thrybergh Resrs, particularly favoured.

WHITE-WINGED BLACK TERN *Chlidonias leucopterus*
Vagrant.

On 18th September 1966 an immature bird was present at Elsecar Resr (HC,JIM,DJS), the first and only record for the area. Within four weeks of this, there were seven other sightings elsewhere in England, mostly of immature birds.

LITTLE AUK *Alle alle*
Vagrant.

Prior to 1960 there were four reports of Little Auk in the area: singles at Tinsley Park Wood on 5th December 1917, Attercliffe in 1930, Millers Dale on 18th November 1957, and two at Redmires on 27th November 1947. The first subsequent record was of a bird found injured near Curbar on 31st October 1967, a time of year when coastal sightings are most frequent. There were two reports in February 1983: one on Underbank Resr on 8th, which had gone by the following morning, and a corpse found in a woodland in the same area on 27th, which showed the characteristic evidence of a Goshawk victim (MW). The latter records are the only evidence in Sheffield of the largest British auk wreck ever recorded. Large numbers of Little Auks on the east coast and many inland sightings were reported from 5th February and were caused by prolonged stormy weather (*109*).

In 1984 a lightly oiled bird was found swimming in a garden pond at Gleadless on 24th October, a relatively early date, during strong westerly winds. It was taken into care but subsequently died. Then on 7th November a corpse was found at Stocksbridge and a bird was seen on Redmires Resr but died overnight; bad weather with easterlies on 6th had pushed many Little Auks onshore - 2000 were counted passing Flamborough. The most recent record was also in February (1985) - a bird was seen swimming on Broomhead Resr on 5th, during easterlies, but was later found dead.

PUFFIN *Fratercula arctica*

Vagrant.

The first Puffin to be seen in the area was recorded by Willughby (*1*) in 1676. The next was found in Springvale Road, Sheffield in 1906, since when single Puffins have been found either dead or exhausted on four occasions. Three records were in the period 14th to 29th October at the time of strong westerlies. In 1969 an immature was discovered at Old Whittington and subsequently died (*per* 'The Derbyshire Times'). The following year another immature was found dead at Monsal Head (TBC), but one found in Norwood, Sheffield in 1974 survived and was released on the Yorkshire coast (RS). The most recent record was of a bird picked up at Hope Cement Works on 16th March 1980 (BAM); the winds had been west to north-westerly in March until 15th when cold easterly conditions prevailed. This bird was also successfully released on the coast.

FERAL PIGEON *Columba livia*

Resident breeder; urban and suburban areas and farmland.

Until the *Atlas* project was initiated in 1975, there was very little information on the distribution of the Feral Pigeon (or Feral Rock Dove) in the area. Because of its feral status and the possibility of confusion with domestic racing pigeons, observers rarely report the species and consequently its past status is almost unrecorded. The distribution map indicates the bird to be widespread in and to the east of the city and in Chesterfield and Rotherham, where it breeds freely on tall buildings such as office-blocks, flats and shops and abundantly on factories and derelict buildings in the industrial areas. There are only scattered instances of breeding to the west. It occurs at much lower densities on housing estates, which generally lack suitable buildings for nesting, and this can be seen in the few records (other than of possible breeding) in south-east Rotherham and the south-east and south-west corners of the city.

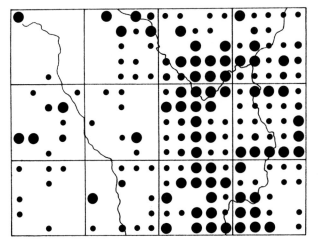

Occupied	180 (60%)
Confirmed	69 (52%)
Probable	18 (10%)
Possible	93 (38%)

Outside built-up areas, Feral Pigeons are still largely reliant on man-made structures to provide nesting sites and frequent use is made of road and railway bridges, particularly steel girder structures which offer numerous suitable ledges. Otherwise buildings such as barns and out-houses, often derelict, are used. At least two of the breeding records in the west are associated with railways: the tetrad near Edale (SK1688), and the most isolated breeding record in the area, involving birds nesting in the mouth of the Woodhead tunnel in SK1098. These records indicate that it is able to move out of urban areas, provided suitable breeding sites are available.

Winter feeding flocks are occasionally reported; e.g. 100 at Ringinglow on 8th February 1981, 350 at Bolehill Flash on 5th January 1983 and 350 on farmland in the Moss Valley in December 1982 which increased to 550 by February 1983 (JPH). However there is insufficient information to comment further on the species' status outside the breeding season.

STOCK DOVE *Columba oenas*

Resident breeder; farmland and parkland.

The *Atlas* has revealed that the Stock Dove is widespread over much of the area, although nowhere is it abundant. It is difficult to census because it occurs at low densities and is a cavity nester, often sitting tight, which accounts for the rather patchy distribution map. The Stock Dove occurs primarily in farmland and parkland, but also in large suburban gardens and deciduous woodland. It is absent from the high moorlands to the west (although it bred in a disused farm in the upper Little Don Valley in 1983), and housing estates in the city where there is no suitable habitat. It is also scarce on the Carboniferous Limestone plateau, as evidenced by the paucity of probable or confirmed breeding records (although it will nest on limestone cliffs or in quarries), but it is a quite common and typical bird of the Magnesian Limestone.

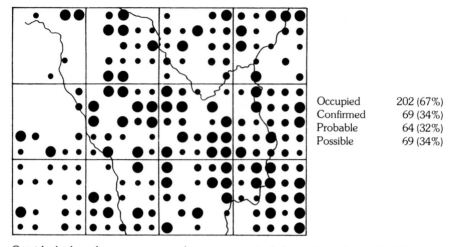

Occupied	202 (67%)
Confirmed	69 (34%)
Probable	64 (32%)
Possible	69 (34%)

Outside the breeding season, records are comparatively few and mostly confined to counts of large flocks and roosts. Sightings of winter flocks, often feeding or roosting in association with Woodpigeons, begin in November and continue until March. In the early 1970s a roost at Renishaw regularly held c.500 birds but has been depleted in recent years, with only 115 there in February 1980. However numbers have increased elsewhere; e.g. up to 130 wintered in the Moss Valley in the late 1970s; 153 were at Thrybergh Resr on 13th October 1982; and in 1983, a roost at Catcliffe held 100 birds on 3rd November and 110 were on farmland at Pebley Pond on 10th December. This upward trend is in line with the national CBC data which indicate a six-fold increase since 1966 (110).

WOODPIGEON *Columba palumbus*

Resident breeder, passage/winter visitor; farmland and woodland.

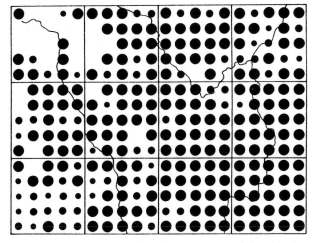

Occupied	277 (92%)
Confirmed	214 (76%)
Probable	45 (18%)
Possible	18 (6%)

The Woodpigeon is an abundant species which breeds throughout the area, except for parts of the gritstone moorlands and limestone plateau. Its status appears to have remained unchanged in recent years. Nesting occurs in deciduous, coniferous and mixed woodlands, and in farmland and built-up areas where there are trees or bushes to provide nest-sites. In the city itself, the species utilises large suburban gardens, roadside trees, parks and allotments. The map shows how successfully it has adapted to the urban environment: it was recorded in all but two of the city tetrads, and in one of these (SK3690) it was probably overlooked. The species is less common in the north-east, around Rotherham and especially along the Don Valley, reflecting the greater industrialisation here and consequent reduction in suitable breeding habitat. To the south-west, particularly in SK17, the bird is under-recorded although numbers are much lower here than to the east. The only area where the Woodpigeon does not breed is the gritstone moorland in the north-west, although use is made of the mainly coniferous woodlands in the nearby valleys.

Passage has only been recorded in the autumn. The main period is October and November, with much smaller movements in August and September and some migrants reported in December. The general direction of movement is between south and west. At Redmires, peak migration normally occurs during the last few days of October or early November, and over 1,000 birds per hour have been recorded on some days in each year since 1980. Over 25,000 birds were counted in 1984, peaking at 4,823 on 27th October. Movements of flocks of several hundreds are reported in late autumn from other areas (e.g. Broomhead, Gleadless, Pilsley), but by December true migrants may be confused with movement of local flocks searching for food.

In the winter months, most Woodpigeons are found on arable farmland, feeding in parties by day and roosting in flocks in nearby woodland. The flock sizes vary from a few hundred up to ten thousand. The largest have been recorded in January: 10,000 in the Cordwell Valley (1985), 7,000 at Wentworth (1983) and 4,500 in the Moss Valley (1975), a locality which has a regular wintering population exceeding 1,000 birds. Other four-figure flocks have been reported from a wide variety of places, including Stannington, Holmesfield,

Broomhead, Ecclesall Woods, Wentworth and Elsecar, and are probably attracted by local abundance of food such as Beech mast or Clover crops. They persist until February, and then break-up with the onset of the breeding season. Large movements during the winter may also be observed: in January 1983 at least 5,000 flew south of Chesterfield in five minutes on 19th and 4,000 flew over Catcliffe in 15 minutes on 30th, whilst on 31st December 1984 at Redmires 4,280 flew north-east in our hour including one flock of 3,000.

COLLARED DOVE *Streptopelia decaocto*

Resident breeder; parks, suburban gardens and farmland.

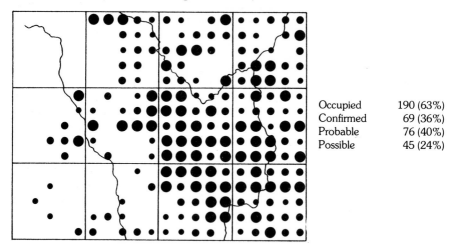

Occupied	190 (63%)
Confirmed	69 (36%)
Probable	76 (40%)
Possible	45 (24%)

The display flight of the Collared Dove can be seen throughout the year in Sheffield and the surrounding towns and villages, although it is still uncommon in much of the west including the limestone dales. It favours suburban conditions with scattered tall trees, and is absent from areas with few trees, little vegetation or which are more thickly wooded.

The first record of a Collared Dove in the Sheffield area was not until the end of 1959 when a single bird was seen at Fulwood (*111,21*). Sixteen were present there the following autumn and by the mid-1960s, breeding or attempted breeding had occurred at several sites. It continued to spread, initially to the east and south of the city, and first bred at Dore in 1967. By 1973 its status was described in the Sheffield Bird Report as "abundant in many localities, particularly in suburban areas and many rural villages" to the east. In December of the same year a flock of 64 was reported from Midhopestones. The map indicates that a further spread to the west occurred in 1975-80 but the species was still totally absent from SK19 and there were few records from SK17 in the south-west. However, colonisation to the north and especially the west is taking place fairly rapidly in the 1980s, along with consolidation to the south and east, but some valleys such as Edale had still not been occupied by early 1985.

In 1978 a breeding survey of the Collared Dove was carried out in SK38, which contains most of the city. The population was estimated to be 250-300 pairs, with densities ranging

168

from nil in 40% of the 1km squares to 20 in the square containing the Botanical Gardens. In the latter square 17 territories were found in half the area, which is a very similar density to the 35 pairs per km² recorded by Hudson (112) for large suburban gardens in Sussex. However, such high concentrations were only found in a few other areas such as Endcliffe Park, Ecclesall and Millhouses. Four pairs were the most commonly found number in occupied 1km squares.

The survey revealed the presence of birds in the industrial Don Valley between Tinsley and Rotherham, where use is made of overgrown, derelict land and allotments. They were absent from some heavily built-up industrialised areas, and from farmland and woodland of the upper Moss Valley. They were found around farms and gardens in the lower Moss Valley where conifers or Holly were present. Nineteen nests were located, all but one in trees of which half were conifers and most of the others Holly or Hawthorn. The exceptional nest was on a ledge in the eaves of a house (in Millhouses). Nest heights ranged from two to twelve metres, with a mean of six metres.

The breeding season begins early: a pair was recorded feeding young on 17th February 1975 at Ecclesall, and on 9th February 1976 a pair was nest-building at Redmires when snow was still on the ground. From mid-October until the end of February or early March, the birds congregate into flocks, often located near food sources such as grain stores. Typical winter flocks hold between 20 and 50 birds, although over 200 were present in the Moss Valley in October 1976 and 100 have been reported from Wentworth and Killamarsh. The most favoured locality in recent years has been the Hovis factory in Rotherham where large numbers are regularly seen on the roof or in the yard in winter. Peak numbers occur there in mid-October - 520 on 18th in 1983 (SJH) and 250 on 13th in 1984 - perhaps indicative of post-breeding dispersal.

TURTLE DOVE *Streptopelia turtur*

Migrant breeder, passage/winter visitor; farmland and woodland.

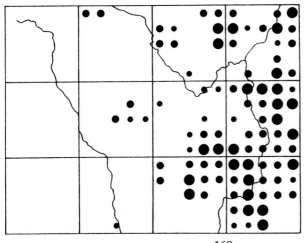

Occupied	92 (31%)
Confirmed	26 (28%)
Probable	49 (53%)
Possible	17 (18%)

The Turtle Dove is primarily a species of low-lying arable farmland and this is reflected by its distribution in the area. It is widespread on the Coal Measures to the east and rare or absent on the gritstone uplands to the west. Although only recorded in 31% of the total tetrads, Turtle Doves were found in 70% of those to the east of the city centre. All the records of definite breeding are in the eastern half of the area, with the few singing birds in the west restricted to Midhope, Langsett, Wharncliffe, Redmires, Rivelin and Totley. It is conspicuously absent from built-up areas.

The first spring migrants arrive in Sheffield at about the beginning of May. There are occasional records in April, the earliest being on 15th when an exhausted bird was found in a Gleadless garden in 1978 (PMG). Sightings of migrants in non-breeding areas are reported in most years but these have usually moved on by the end of May. There are never more than a few pairs breeding in any one area. The only flocks reported were in 1982, when 15 were seen at Bolsover on 18th August, and on 19th June a heavy thunderstorm grounded 42 birds at Poolsbrook - late migrants, presumably, as all were adults (MAB). Otherwise passage is invariably light - eight at Thrybergh Resr on 23rd August 1982 being a typical peak.

The majority of breeding birds have moved south by early September but occasional sightings occur until late September or even early October. The latest record was of two in the Moss Valley on 8th in 1976.

CUCKOO *Cuculus canorus*

Migrant breeder; moorland, heathland and woodland.

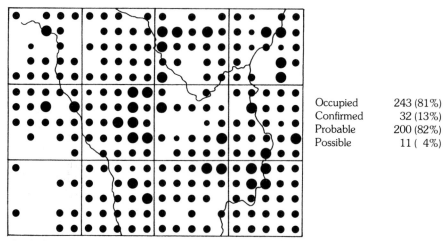

Occupied	243 (81%)
Confirmed	32 (13%)
Probable	200 (82%)
Possible	11 (4%)

The map shows the Cuckoo to be widespread throughout the area, although breeding was difficult to prove because adults do not visit nests after egg-laying. The only significant gap is over much of the Carboniferous Limestone plateau, which may be related to the relative scarcity there of the Meadow Pipit, the Cuckoo's favourite host. Numbers of Cuckoos are not related to distribution as density is generally much greater on heather/Ling moorland

170

where Meadow Pipits are abundant. They are fairly scarce in the lowlands but can be relatively numerous, e.g. in areas with large amounts of woodland edge such as the Moss Valley where there were at least nine singing males in 1976.

The first birds normally arrive in the last week of April, although occasional birds may be seen earlier, e.g. there were five records in the 1970s in the period 14th to 17th April. However, in 1985 a remarkably early bird was seen at Hackenthorpe on 4th and 6th March (GPM). Small numbers may occur together in spring indulging in communal courtship display, with six at Redmires on 11th May 1975 the largest party recorded. Birds may also occasionally sing briefly in unusual places, such as a Chapeltown garden and from a TV aerial in a Sheffield housing estate. They will gather in force when there is an exceptional supply of caterpillars, particularly of the Northern Eggar moth; e.g. on Beeley Moor there were c.30 on 28th May 1978 and 14 in July and August 1980. The adults leave in July and most of the juveniles in August. Occasionally juveniles are seen until mid-September, and there have been two later records - at Derwentdale on 26th September 1976 (TP) and Barrow Hill on 7th October 1977 (SBRG), both after long hot summers.

BARN OWL *Tyto alba*
Resident breeder; farmland, rough pasture and wasteland.

Although the map (from which one active site has been omitted) suggests that the Barn Owl is fairly widespread, it is now rarely reported and is undoubtedly our scarcest owl. Up to the mid-1970s the number of pairs breeding annually was probably well into double figures. Farmland to the north-east, east and south-east of Sheffield was the most favoured habitat, although there were a few pairs to the west and south-west of the city. Two broods were raised by one pair near Dore in 1976,and young were still in a nest near Sheffield on 15th November 1978, perhaps indicating that this was a second brood. Numbers in the north and west of the area appeared to decline in the late 1970s and by 1981 all areas were affected, with very few pairs known to be breeding. Birds were reported from a mere handful of sites throughout the area, although it seems likely that breeding pairs have been overlooked to the north, east and south of the city. Release of captive birds, e.g. after recovery from injury, has supplemented the population and resulted in the successful re-occupation of at least one breeding site in the 1980s.

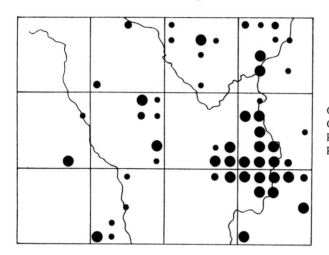

Occupied	55 (18%)
Confirmed	27 (49%)
Probable	8 (15%)
Possible	20 (36%)

The reason for the decline is not obvious. There appears to have been no major change in habitat and there is no apparent shortage of suitable nest-sites; old buildings and large tree holes have been equally favoured in the past, and even cliffs used on occasions. It is possible that pesticides were responsible for a decline in the 1960s. A Barn Owl picked up near Aston on 12th August 1964 was in a field recently sprayed with 'Groxin K', and subsequent analysis revealed a high level (4.5 p.p.m.) of chlorinated residues in the liver. Even so the local results of a Nature Conservancy Council survey of certain birds of prey carried out in 1964 caused R.G. Hawley (75) to conclude that the decline was not so marked around Sheffield. However, coverage in this survey was poor and evidence was provided of only five localities where Barn Owls were present. Hard weather in several recent winters may have increased mortality, but another factor may be shortage of prey due to changes in farming practice, e.g. more cereal growing at the expense of pasture. Its particular susceptibility to collision with road vehicles is also likely to have contributed to its decline.

Analysis of pellets has shown the Short-tailed Vole to be the principal prey, as in other parts of the country: 57% of prey units extracted from 277 pellets located in three different areas of Sheffield was found to be this species. Common Shrew (18%) and Wood Mouse (13%) accounted for much of the remaining items. Water Shrew and Bank Vole were of significance to Barn Owls in the south-west and north, respectively, whilst House Sparrow and Brown Rat were taken by a pair which formerly nested at Catcliffe (JH & GPM). This latter pair bred successfully for at least two years under a concrete bridge below a major road.

From ringing results, the young appear to disperse randomly, most not moving far. An exceptionally long distance record was of one ringed at Hassop on 16th July 1970 and found dead at Llanfarian (Dyfed) 190 km away.

EAGLE OWL *Bubo bubo*

Vagrant/escaped species.

A bird was resident in upper Coombs Dale for over two months in the spring of 1977. It was seen hunting in daylight and survived largely on Rabbits until 13th June when it was found dead in a field (*per* RBa). The mounted skin is in the possession of a local farmer. Although presumed to be an escape, there was no evidence of captive origin, (or cause of death).

LITTLE OWL *Athene noctua*

Resident breeder; farmland and rough pasture.

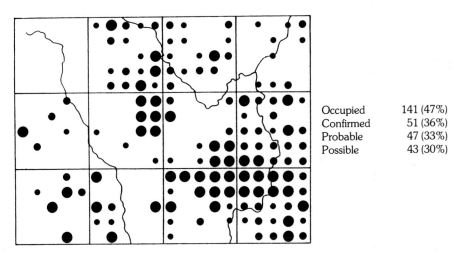

Occupied	141 (47%)
Confirmed	51 (36%)
Probable	47 (33%)
Possible	43 (30%)

This species was introduced into Britain in the late 19th century and was breeding in the Peak District by 1918, when it was also first recorded in Sheffield - in Cordwell Valley in November. By 1929 Whitaker considered the Little Owl to be a not uncommon resident, which broadly remains its status today. It is common in certain areas but rarely seen in others. As the map shows its stronghold is in the south-east, for example in the Clowne area where in 1974 and 1980 three pairs fledged ten and nine young, and in the Moss Valley where up to eight pairs have been found annually. In 1983 there were estimated to be 12-14 pairs (DJG). It is also fairly common on the western fringe of the city, with four or five pairs resident in the Rivelin Valley in recent years. The total population, therefore, is likely to be in the region of 100-300 pairs.

One surprise of the *Atlas* survey was the paucity of records in the Derwent Valley, for which there is no ready explanation. Dry stone walls, where available, are favoured nesting sites and their use has been recorded in the last decade at Bradfield, Leash Fen, Rivelin and Troway. Open heather moorland is generally avoided although there are occasional sightings, such as one at Carl Walk on Hathersage Moor on 22nd October 1977.

Birds are seen in breeding areas throughout the year but there is some movement outside the breeding season, as illustrated by the sight of one flying over Weston Park Museum on 7th December 1978 and a corpse at the nearby University Arts Tower on 18th September 1980. Other unusual sites include Shirecliffe Tip in November 1978; a bird table in a garden at Gleadless on 28th February 1978; the roof of a house on the edge of Ecclesall Woods on 31st August 1980; Spruce woodland by Howden Resr on 1st February 1981; and Brightside on 20th August 1984.

TAWNY OWL *Strix aluco*

Resident breeder; woodland, parkland, farmland and gardens.

The Tawny Owl is by far the commonest owl, breeding throughout the area wherever there are mature trees. Whereas the maps for the other owls are considered to be reasonably comprehensive illustrations of distribution, the Tawny Owl map is likely to be an under-statement, because the bird is easily overlooked, and, unlike the rarer owls, has not been specially sought out. As it is found in the inner city and suburbs, e.g. in Weston Park (1km from the Town Hall) and Ecclesall churchyard, it is likely to breed in almost all tetrads, excluding the virtually bare moorland in SK18 and 19.

Some idea of its concentration is given by the following records of singing/calling birds: ten in the Cordwell Valley (August 1964), five at Linacre Resr (March 1974), nine on a 5km walk down Ewden Valley (October 1976), five at Ladybower Resr north arm (February 1978) and nine within hearing distance of Lane Top, Sheffield (February 1979).

The status of the Tawny Owl does not appear to have changed since 1945 when Whitaker reported it had become commoner than the Barn Owl in Dore and Totley. The total population is probably in the range 250 - 1,000 pairs. Breeding records include a nest with eggs in late February 1978 at Ecclesfield, and an adult brooding two chicks on the ground in a slight depression at the base of a Beech tree at Chatsworth on 15th May 1981. Tawny Owls normally roost in trees, but one roosted on a cliff at Longstone Edge on 1st February 1981, and another in the roof of a busy foundry at Chesterfield on 27th April 1979.

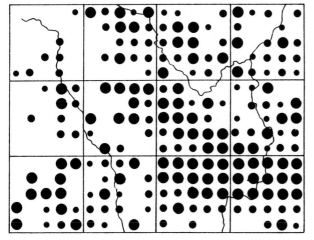

Occupied	201 (67%)
Confirmed	93 (46%)
Probable	75 (37%)
Possible	33 (16%)

Interesting feeding records include one on a garden lawn at Lowedges after heavy rain apparently catching earthworms, on 19th March 1982, and one feeding on Common Frogs in the Limb Valley on 9th May 1980. There have been occasional sightings of birds hunting on moorland, e.g. Big Moor in August 1979 and 1981.

Ringing returns show that most Tawny Owls are highly sedentary; e.g. two were recorded 4 km from where they had been ringed 10 years and 13 years previously.

LONG-EARED OWL *Asio otus*

Resident/migrant breeder; coniferous woodland, Hawthorn scrub and Willow carr.

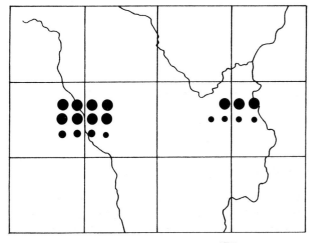

Occupied	19 (6%)
Confirmed	11 (58%)
Probable	3 (16%)
Possible	5 (26%)

Dots centralised in western and eastern halves.

L. CORNTHWAITE

The Long-eared is certainly the most elusive of our breeding owls. Small numbers regularly nest in coniferous plantations on the margins of the gritstone moorland. Its presence within the woodland is more often revealed by pellets or prey remains than a sighting of the bird itself. Wing clapping and song are sometimes noted, particularly in February and March, and if breeding is successful the characteristic 'squeaky-gate' calls of the young may be heard at dusk in June. A few pairs also breed away from moorland, and in such areas old Magpie nests are sometimes utilised in Hawthorn bushes. As this species is still threatened by egg-collectors, the map is not plotted accurately and only shows the predominantly westerly distribution.

It is difficult to know whether the status of Long-eared Owl has changed markedly since 1960. Frost (*20*) believes there has been a marked long-term decline in Derbyshire and this may well be true for the Sheffield area. Even so, breeding pairs are undoubtedly under-recorded and the steady maturation of coniferous plantations may have initiated a slight increase in numbers in certain areas to the north-west. In 1978 twelve pairs bred at four sites and several more localities held breeding birds during the late 1970s. Only a few nests are found annually because of the difficulty in locating them. There is some evidence to suggest that Goshawks may be the biggest threat. In one area two deserted nests, each containing five eggs, were located in 1979 along with a corpse which appeared to have been a Goshawk victim. However, Owls were still present in this area up to the time of writing. In at least one other locality, a Goshawk breeding pair apparently exterminated Long-eared Owls which traditionally nested within that particular woodland.

Interestingly, on 6th April 1981, a cache of four Short-tailed Voles and a Fieldfare was found under upturned tree roots 20m from a nest containing five eggs, in a plantation to the north-west of the city.

Winter roosts are found in most years in the south-east of the area and often hold up to three birds. Larger numbers have been found in three years:-

1975   12 birds present in Scots Pine.
1976   8 in Willow carr and 4/5 in Hawthorn.
1979   7 in Larch and 4 in Hawthorn.

The 1976 Willow carr roost was regularly monitored; most birds left by mid-March and the last sighting was on 14th April, perhaps indicating that these birds were of continental origin.

SHORT-EARED OWL *Asio flammeus*

Migrant breeder, passage/winter visitor; moorland, rough pasture and wasteland.

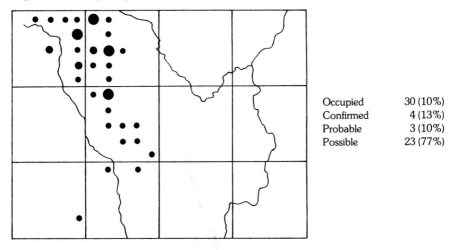

Occupied	30 (10%)
Confirmed	4 (13%)
Probable	3 (10%)
Possible	23 (77%)

In the summer the Short-eared Owl is normally seen only in the north-west uplands where it breeds, in small numbers, on open moorland between 300 and 500m a.s.l. Numbers of breeding pairs fluctuate from year to year and are thought to be related to the density of its principal prey item, the Short-tailed Vole. Unfortunately, little is known about the population cycle of this vole species as it is very difficult to trap (DW). There were few breeding records in the 1960s but 1972 was an exceptional year for voles with the result that at least eight pairs of Short-eared Owls bred in the area (113), including one or two pairs in the southern part of the gritstone moors. Many birds overwintered that year. In contrast, only three or four pairs were known to have nested in 1973. Since then annual breeding numbers appear to have varied between three and six pairs, except in 1981 when only one pair was found.

The breeding performance of one pair over four years on Bleaklow is known from a detailed study by R.A.Ford (pers. comm.), and is summarised in Table 3.

Table 3 : Breeding data for a Short-eared Owl nest on gritstone moorland

Year	79	80	81	82
No. of eggs			7	
No. of young found	6	7	5	4
No. of young fledged	3	3	3	3

Three young fledged every year, but mortality was high after hatching, due to cannibalism by siblings. In 1982, a very wet year, one juvenile died shortly before fledging time and one shortly after, both due to starvation. Meadow Pipits were a common item of prey, as well as voles, supplemented by shrews and young Grouse. The adults also ate young Mountain Hares. No nest or fledglings could be found in 1983 or 84, but a pair (of which at least the female was thought to be a different bird) raised three young from four eggs in 1985.

Spring and autumn passage birds are regularly recorded hunting in the daytime in suitable habitat throughout the area. In the winter most birds desert the uplands but some are seen in the lowlands to the south-east and one or two stayed at Tinsley S.F. in 1981/82. A bird ringed as a *pullus* on 15th May 1965 at Redmires was recovered in France five months later. Wintering birds are usually few in number but in certain years are augmented by migrants, presumably from the continent. A notable year was 1979 when records were numerous from the Rother Valley and up to eleven were at Staveley in February hunting on grassy mounds among coal waste, with five still present on 3rd April. This was the time of the hard weather influx of divers and grebes (*32*).

There was an interesting report of a bird at Little Longstone on 2nd December 1978 apparently caching prey in snow-covered farmland. It was seen carrying four items of prey, at least two of which (Short-tailed Voles) were deposited and left in grass close to thistles (*114*).

NIGHTJAR *Caprimulgus europaeus*

Migrant breeder; heathland and moorland edges.

Whitlock considered the Nightjar to be common on moors on the Sheffield side of Derbyshire (7). Whitaker recorded it at Dore Moor and Ecclesall Woods in 1928 but thought it uncommon (13). Since then it has declined further and has not been seen at either of these localities for many years. It was a regular breeder until at least the early 1970s at several sites, especially below gritstone edges. Birds arrived in the latter part of May and departed by mid-August, the latest recent date being 18th (in 1975), although there is a record from a garden on the outskirts of the city on 13th September 1948 (YNU). The strong-hold was Wharncliffe where nine birds were heard 'churring' in 1973. A feature of these sites was extensive areas of Bracken and scattered Birch trees, both apparently favoured by Nightjars nationally (115).

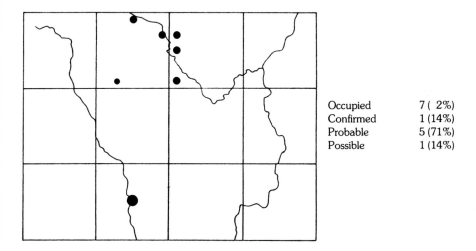

Occupied	7 (2%)
Confirmed	1 (14%)
Probable	5 (71%)
Possible	1 (14%)

A few pairs were present each year at the southern end of the main gritstone edges until 1978 when they failed to return. Numbers declined in the north-west in the 1970s and none was seen in 1980 or 1982, but upto three birds were recorded in 1983 and 1984.

An omen of this demise was the fate of one of the last birds to be ringed - a juvenile at Curbar on the 12th August 1975 which was killed by a car seven days later at Widnes, 70km west-north-west. However, the real cause of the decline is probably a change in climate (wetter and cooler springs), because most of the breeding habitat has not changed significantly and a comparable decline has occurred elsewhere in Derbyshire, and to a lesser extent in South Yorkshire and nationally.

SWIFT *Apus apus*

Migrant breeder, passage visitor.

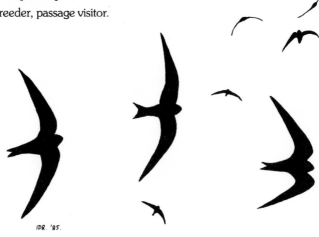

IDR. '85.

From mid-May to early August the Swift is a familiar sight throughout the area, for although it nests only in buildings, it covers much ground in its search for airbourne insects. For this reason the category of 'possible breeder' has little meaning, e.g. birds are regularly seen over moorland, and so has been omitted from the map.

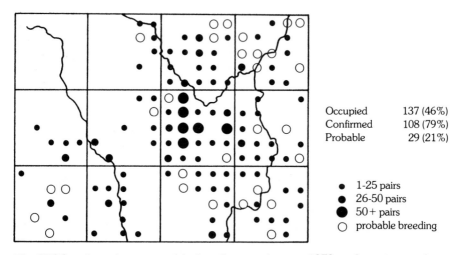

Occupied   137 (46%)
Confirmed   108 (79%)
Probable   29 (21%)

- 1-25 pairs
- 26-50 pairs
- 50+ pairs
○ probable breeding

The SBSG undertook a survey of the breeding population in 1979, to determine numbers, distribution and details of breeding sites, the results of which were supplemented by a further study in 1980 (*116*). The map summarises the results and includes breeding records for 1975-78. It can be seen that Swifts are particularly numerous on the west side of the city and in the larger old villages of Derbyshire, but relatively few are found to the north and east

180

of Sheffield. This is because they favour nesting in holes at the junction of roof and wall, 5-10m high, in pre-war pitch-roofed buildings which are often either the larger stone-built type with exposed rafters or old, poorly maintained properties.

The total population was estimated to be in the range 1,165-2,470 pairs, the greatest concentration being in the city, with 560-1,040 pairs in the 10 km square SK38. The mean densities of 7.2 breeding pairs per km^2 and 0.8 pairs per km^2 for SK38 and the remainder of the area, respectively, are very similar to those found in 1978 for Northampton town and county (117).

The first birds are usually seen at the end of April or beginning of May, with the earliest reported on 24th April 1969 (GPM) and 1973 (MGR). Birds are usually noted around breeding sites during the second week in May. In the three years 1980-82 the first bird was seen flying around Millhouses on the same date, i.e. 7th May. Major breeding sites are occupied almost immediately and numbers rapidly build-up. The largest gatherings are often seen in late May, e.g. 800 were at Dronfield S.F. on 25th May 1981 and 600 at Redmires Resr on 30th May 1976.

Screaming parties may be seen near any breeding area from May to July. They increase in size towards the end of July when on fine evenings as many as 200 birds may congregate high in the sky on the western side of the city. Large feeding parties are also evident at this time, a notable example being in 1979 when 550 were feeding on mayflies emerging from the River Sheaf at Woodseats (GPM).

Departure of most of the population for Africa is sudden, e.g. several thousand flew south-west over Redmires Resr on 1st August 1976, and few remain by mid-August. A few late breeders linger into September; numbers and dates vary from year to year: after the hot summer of 1976, September sightings were minimal but in 1977 young were still in the nest on 6th September and there were many sightings that month including 30 at Hackenthorpe on the 24th. Normally, the last birds are seen at the end of September or in early October, but 1978 was exceptional with 17 reports in October, the latest on the 18th, and young still being fed at Bradwell on the 7th (JSW). The only November record was in 1982, on the 9th at Hackenthorpe (A & PW).

Birds ringed locally have been found in Morocco, Tanzania and Zimbabwe, and many have been controlled at the same site up to nine years later.

KINGFISHER *Alcedo atthis*

Resident breeder; rivers, lakes, reservoirs and flashes.

The Kingfisher is a widely, but sparsely, distributed resident breeder throughout the area. It occurs principally along the main rivers and streams and at lakes and ponds. Since the early 1970s it has been regularly seen along the industrial stretches of the River Don which was formerly too polluted for fish to survive, and even bred there in 1985.

Despite its brilliant plumage, it is very elusive. Breeding was confirmed in only 17 tetrads and birds seen in a further 29, which was probably an underestimate of the distribution, at least during 1976-78. Seven or eight territories were located by the WBS throughout 1975-78 but in 1979 only two were occupied as the hard winter had severely reduced the population, particularly in the western half of the area. Subsequent years have seen a partial recovery, to four occupied WBS territories by 1983. In Derbyshire the population was greatly reduced by the severe 1962/63 winter but had fully recovered by 1969 (20). The total breeding population probably lies in the range 10 to 100 pairs.

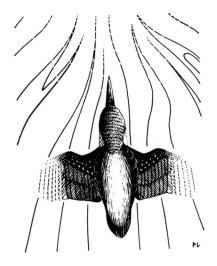

Although breeding performance is affected by human disturbance, and nests within the city boundary are often robbed or vandalised, Sheffield Kingfishers appear to be reasonably successful. Of five pairs studied in 1975, three succeeded in raising one brood each, one pair two broods and only one pair was unsuccessful (118). In the five years that two pairs were present on the Noe (1975-78,1981), both bred successfully except for one pair in 1977. In 1977 a pair nested in Millhouses Park, Sheffield in a bank of the River Sheaf subsequently used by children as a slide. Five young were fledged, one leaving two days after the others, even though the nest-hole was blocked one day. The adults then started to excavate new holes nearby for a second nesting and tried again the following year, but abandoned both these attempts due to disturbance. In 1979, when breeding records were very scarce, young were seen on the River Sheaf, having fledged from a site on a feeder stream.

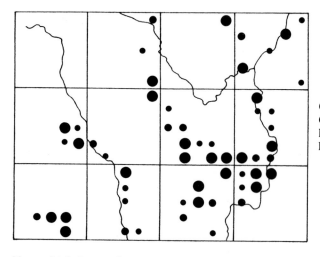

Occupied	49 (16%)
Confirmed	19 (39%)
Probable	4 (8%)
Possible	26 (53%)

Young birds frequently move away from their natal area, striking examples being singles ringed at Kilnhurst (in 1962), the Rother Valley (1979) and Hackenthorpe (1981) which

182

were recovered in the autumn at Hexham (Northumberland), Wisbech and Coventry, respectively. Although adults usually stay on breeding territory, in winter birds are seen in non-breeding areas such as upland reservoirs and lowland ponds, e.g. in Graves Park and at Aston.

BEE-EATER *Merops apiaster*

Vagrant.

Apart from a report from Sheffield in 1849 (6), the only record is of a bird near Midhope on 6th September 1971. It was watched for 15 minutes on a dead tree and then flew off in the characteristic gliding flight (MW).

HOOPOE *Upupa epops*

Scarce visitor.

There were only two records this century (Chesterfield in 1911 and Elsecar in 1912) before 1961 when one was seen in a garden at Bolsover on 3rd August (JCW). Since then five birds have been seen in spring: one in old lime kilns between Barlow and Old Brampton on 26th April 1967 (*per* Brit.B); one in a quarry near Padley Gorge on 8th May 1977 (DV); and most extraordinary of all, on 25th May 1978 at Tinsley in industrial Sheffield, a bird partly submerged in the River Don was seen to clamber up onto the bank and into a tree (*per* DH). The only report of two birds was on 21st April 1979 on open farmland between Thurcroft and Whiston (DWil). Most recently, in 1984, a bird was found dead on the road at Underbank -again on 25th May - and is now in the Sheffield City Museum - and one was seen at Chatsworth on 28th July (PT).

WRYNECK *Jynx torquilla*

Scarce visitor.

Although the species was undoubtedly found in this area during the last century, albeit uncommonly, it was not recorded in this century until 1972 when one on Abney Moor heralded a run of six records in ten years. Five of the birds were seen during the period 29th August to 29th September. The exception was a female caught and ringed at Old Whittington S.F. on 27th May 1978.

In 1976, when there was an unprecedented number of autumn Wryneck in Derbyshire (four) and inland Yorkshire (thirteen), one was killed flying into a farm window near Bolsover on 25th September, and another was seen on a footpath at Langsett four days later. The other records came from Dronfield in 1980 and Clowne in 1981.

GREEN WOODPECKER *Picus viridis*

Resident breeder; open deciduous woodland, wooded heathland.

The Green Woodpecker is present in most areas where there is open deciduous woodland. The map shows that it is fairly widespread, being found in many of the lowland areas to the south and east and penetrating areas of higher ground to the west. There is a marked dependence on river systems and the bird is found along the Derwent, Little Don, Don, Ewden, Loxley, Rivelin, Moss and Porter Valleys, except within urban areas. An unusual breeding record concerns a nest with young found in 1973 at Birley Carr, near the Don Valley, in an isolated dead tree at the edge of a council housing estate (JH).

The population is generally low except in a few favoured areas such as Wharncliffe Woods, Padley Gorge, and the Moss Valley where 13 pairs were located in 1976. There is some evidence to suggest that numbers increased in the 1970s in the lowlands and there were reports of birds appearing in areas where they had not been recorded for many years, e.g. at Clowne and Dronfield. In upland areas, probable breeding was recorded in two tetrads in the Upper Derwent Valley in SK19, a 10km square from which the species was absent in the national *Atlas*, and breeding was confirmed in a tetrad in SK18 where only possible breeding was recorded in the national *Atlas*.

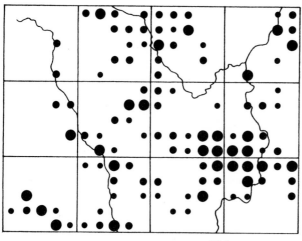

Occupied	111 (37%)
Confirmed	29 (26%)
Probable	48 (43%)
Possible	34 (31%)

Birds appear to remain in the breeding woods throughout the winter, although there have been some records of individuals moving into unusual habitats at this time of year, such as suburban Banner Cross (March 1978) and Staveley Chemical Works (November 1979). Smith (21) states that the population suffered a large reduction locally in the severe winter of 1962/63 and that numbers recovered only slowly afterwards, many sites still being unoccupied in 1966. The hard winter of 1979 appears to have had a similar effect, particularly on the higher ground where numbers were still low in 1983 at prime sites like Wharncliffe.

GREAT SPOTTED WOODPECKER *Dendrocopos major*

Resident breeder; deciduous and coniferous woodland.

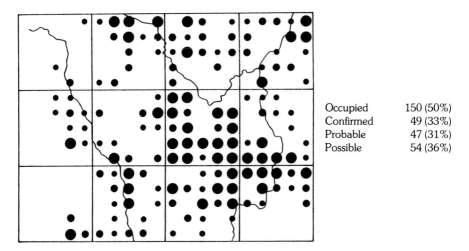

Occupied	150 (50%)
Confirmed	49 (33%)
Probable	47 (31%)
Possible	54 (36%)

The Great Spotted Woodpecker is more widespread and numerous than the other woodpeckers since it occurs in all types of woodland, from pure coniferous stands, through mixed woods to wholly deciduous areas. However, it does exhibit a preference for soft-wood trees, especially for Birch, diseased Elm and conifers.

With the exception of a few reports from the Derwent, Noe and Wye Valleys, breeding records are scarce in the west, which is particularly surprising in the wooded dales. The bird is commoner in SK29, where it utilises the many tracts of commercial plantations in association with the upland reservoirs. Breeding records are numerous from SK38, the city square, proving that it is able to penetrate suburban areas successfully. In support of this, there are frequent sightings in gardens and city parks, especially in winter, and even occasionally in the city centre. In the east, breeding is widespread and birds can be found in most woodlands. It is not found in the industrial area between Sheffield and Rotherham, nor in the extreme south-east due to lack of woodland.

An indication of the numbers present in favoured areas is given by the fact that 26 pairs were located in 1976 in the Moss Valley (from Norton to Eckington) and six pairs bred in Padley

185

Gorge in 1978. There were eight on a single dead tree, with one Green Woodpecker, at Longshaw on 2nd August 1980. The total population is estimated to be in the range 250 - 750 pairs.

There is inconclusive evidence that the winter population may be augmented by immigrants. For example, a bird was seen moving west onto the moors at Strines on 8th November 1976, and singles were at Tinsley S.F. in January and November 1976, while singles flew through housing estates at Woodhouse on 27th December 1975 and Handsworth on 31st January 1982.

Interesting records of feeding habits include a pair feeding young with flies picked from leaves in Bowden Houstead Wood, and one methodically stripping all the bark from a Sycamore at Ewden on 10th January 1979 during severe weather.

LESSER SPOTTED WOODPECKER *Dendrocopos minor.*

Resident breeder; deciduous woodland and parkland.

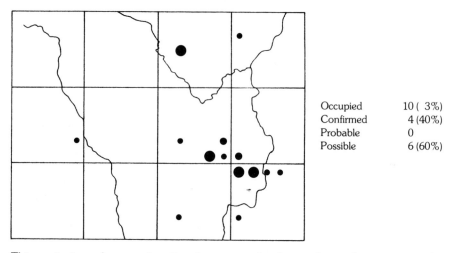

Occupied	10 (3%)
Confirmed	4 (40%)
Probable	0
Possible	6 (60%)

This species is much scarcer than the other two woodpeckers and so unobtrusive, except for the brief period of drumming and calling in early spring, that it is rarely recorded. The map is therefore likely to be an under-statement of its distribution, particularly the absence of records from the Peak District and the scarcity of even probable breeding in the east. In no single locality have more than two pairs been found, and the total population is unlikely to exceed ten pairs.

The Lesser Spotted Woodpecker favours open woodland with old deciduous trees. It avoids conifers but will feed, and even nest, in hedgerow trees, and so there appears to be much suitable habitat in the area which is not regularly occupied. In the period 1973-83 breeding was only confirmed at Hathersage, Moss Valley, Renishaw and Greno Woods. Outside the breeding season it is seen occasionally in additional localities, from Derwentdale and Edale to Chatsworth and Linacre, and even in suburban gardens. This could be because the birds range more widely during this time and are easier to see when trees are not in leaf.

The number of records fluctuates from year to year, but there does appear to have been a general increase in sightings in the north-east since 1977, whilst in the Peak District numbers have continued to be very low. As there are so few breeding pairs, the population may possibly be sustained by immigrants from the healthier population in the Dukeries, as evidenced by the easterly bias in the distribution.

WOODLARK Lullula arborea

Scarce visitor.

There are only two records this century. The first was of a male in full song at Longshaw on 26th April 1958 which did not stay (RGH et al). The second was in 1975 when one was seen at Midhope Resr on 18th, 26th, and 29th October (JED et al).

SKYLARK Alauda arvensis

Resident breeder; farmland, heathland and wasteland.

The Skylark is the most widespread of all the breeding species in the area. It is absent only from most of the built-up parts of Sheffield, Rotherham and Chesterfield. Its distribution suggests that it is most abundant on the limestone plateau, the moorland fringes (rather than the Ling moors themselves) and the low-lying farmland to the south-east, including Breck Farm at Barrow Hill where it is the commonest breeding bird. Here, however, it has declined from 28 pairs in 1970 to only 14 pairs in 1980, whilst on the higher ground at Tor Farm, Hathersage, there were five pairs in 1975 but only one pair subsequently. There is no evidence that this is part of a national decline, and it is still numerous on the moorland fringe, e.g. 70 singing birds were counted on a walk across Big Moor on 2nd April 1983.

Skylarks do not remain so widespread throughout the year. In winter they are absent from most moorland areas, usually from the end of October until the end of January. Their autumn movements, mainly to the south or west, occur regularly from mid-September to late October but are usually most obvious in the middle fortnight of October. The maximum counted was 650 over Redmires on 22nd October 1977, and 'many hundreds' passed there on 10th October 1980. However, numbers were progressively lower in subsequent years, the peak in 1982 being 77 in one hour.

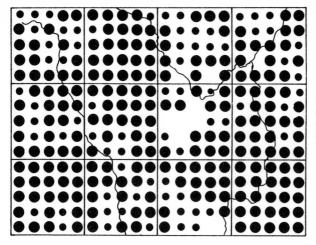

Occupied	290 (97%)
Confirmed	220 (76%)
Probable	69 (24%)
Possible	1 (0%)

Unless there is a prolonged spell of severe weather, flocks of up to 200 birds may be found in December and January in lowland areas such as Wentworth, Thrybergh, Staveley and Mosborough where the largest flock of 275 was counted on 11th December 1976. However, if their feeding areas become snow-covered, they depart, in a southerly direction. These 'cold weather movements', and especially the return migrations, have not been well documented locally but the largest such passage was in January 1984 at Thrybergh when 314 moved south on 22nd followed by 180 the next day. A return passage after cold weather was noted on 31st December 1981 when 60 flew north at Staveley and 45 north-east in one hour at Tinsley. Another consequence of cold weather is that birds may then feed in gardens (e.g. up to six at Swallownest in January 1982).

Large flocks may occur as birds return to upland breeding areas; e.g. 270 were at Alport on 14th February 1981 and 169 at Lodge Moor on 23rd March 1982 during a short cold spell.

SHORE LARK *Eremophila alpestris*

Scarce visitor.

The only accepted record is of three flying west-north-west at Abney on 18th October 1971 (RAF).

SAND MARTIN *Riparia riparia*

Migrant breeder, passage visitor; rivers, lakes, reservoirs, sewage farms and flashes.

The Sand Martin is a localised breeder in the Sheffield area, with its stronghold in the south-east where small colonies occur, such as in the banks of oxbow lakes beside the rivers Rother and Doe Lea. Numbers fluctuate from year to year; e.g. at Breck Farm there were c.60 active nests in a pile of sand in 1968, 9 in 1972, at least 20 in 1977, but none in the

1980s due to the destruction of the site. It may also breed in the Don Valley - e.g. at Tinsley S.F., Thrybergh Banks, Old Denaby - and at other localities in the Rother Valley such as Treeton and Killamarsh where there were up to 20 nests in the colliery spoil in the early/mid 1970s, and Catcliffe where there were eight nest holes in industrial waste in 1982. In the Peak District it breeds most years in small numbers in the banks of the River Derwent at Chatsworth and Noe at Edale. A few pairs may breed sporadically on the rivers Ashop, Alport and elsewhere on the Derwent, Noe or even in the banks of Ladybower Resr. Numbers also fluctuate here: e.g. at Chatsworth only five nests were counted in 1977, whereas there were 14 in 1982. However, in 1984 and 85 the population appeared to be very low throughout the area, reflecting the national situation (126).

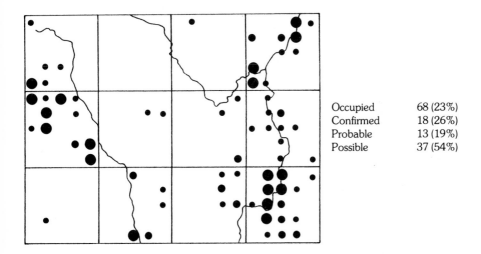

Occupied	68 (23%)
Confirmed	18 (26%)
Probable	13 (19%)
Possible	37 (54%)

The first migrant is usually recorded in late March, the earliest date being 20th in 1983 (at Thrybergh Resr). The main arrival occurs during the middle ten days of April, but numbers may peak in late April or early May. Passage is predominantly to the north or west along the Rother and Don Valleys, although small numbers may be seen almost anywhere. In 1983 there were 57 at Thrybergh Resr on 17th April and several parties of c.20 passed through Rother Valley C.P.; on 30th April at least 60 were at Thrybergh Resr compared to a peak of 75 there the previous year on 3rd May.

Return passage occurs mainly from early August to mid September, and is again most marked at lowland localities such as Thrybergh Resr, where 2,650 were counted moving south during this time in 1982, with a maximum of 330 on 1st September. In contrast, only occasional birds are sighted at upland localities. A few stragglers are seen most years in late September but October records are scarce. A young bird caught at Old Whittington S.F. on 12th October 1981 had been ringed at a Highland colony 526km north on 29th August 1981, and a report of one at Baslow on 12th November 1978 (MGO) was exceptionally late.

SWALLOW *Hirundo rustica*

Migrant breeder, passage visitor; farmland, wasteland and wetlands.

This very widespread species was located in all parts of the area except for the high gritstone moorland, the industrial regions of the Don Valley and many urban areas. Indeed, the only urban sites where nesting Swallows have been located are at Tinsley S.F. and the Canal Basin of the Sheaf. Nest sites are to be found in a variety of buildings including, for two years, the doorway of a public house in suburban Millhouses (which was superceded by the porch of a nearby church), to a natural cave at Castleton. In 1973/74 a total of ten nests were reported in gardens (*119*) and in 1975/76 Swallows were recorded in 19 of the 36 city parks (*120*).

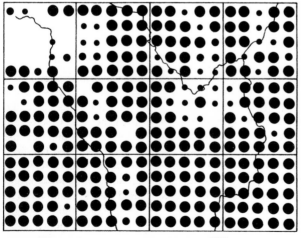

Occupied	281 (94%)
Confirmed	231 (82%)
Probable	14 (5%)
Possible	36 (13%)

Most Swallows arrive from mid-April onwards but there are usually a few reports in early April. The only March records occurred in 1983 near Fox House on 28th, in 1985 at Hassop on 24th, and in 1977 at Ladybower on 13th although on this same date in 1983 a hirundine species, thought to be a Swallow, was seen in Edale. Spring passage is usually inconspicuous, although 'streams' of birds passed over Monsal Dale on 27th April 1977 (AS). At a few places spring flocks may be found, the largest being 450 at Dronfield S.F. on 6th May 1978. Large numbers are more frequently reported after the breeding season. The largest diurnal gathering was of 800 at Redmires on 31st August 1975, but even larger numbers occur in August and September at the favoured roosting places such as Aston Ponds; Staveley; Old Denaby; Treeton; Catcliffe and Poolsbrook which both held 4,000 in 1979; Clowne (4,400 max. in 1984) and Old Whittington S.F. where there were 6,000 on 6th September 1977. Birds ringed at some of these roosts have been found to make erratic movements before leaving the country such as north to Barnsley, north-east to Doncaster and west to Chorlton. An individual controlled at Poolsbrook had moved 57km east since being ringed near Congleton almost two months earlier. The control in Omsala, Sweden, on 3rd June 1981, of a juvenile ringed at Poolsbrook in September 1980, indicates that Swallows reared in this area do not necessarily return to nest.

From visible migration studies it is clear that most passage is to the south and west, beginning in July. At Redmires in 1981, 100-200 were counted on most suitable mornings during the peak period between mid-August and the end of September. At this time of year similar numbers have been counted at Thrybergh, Tinsley and Barbrook, with even larger movements at Hackenthorpe, Broomhead, Oughtibridge (max. of 350 west in 15 minutes on 20th August 1980), Concord Park (max. of 577 south-west on 25th September 1983), and Wadsley Common where 1,600 flew south in one hour on 27th September 1982.

Numbers diminish rapidly in early October and most birds have left the area by mid-month. However, two pairs were still feeding young at Rotherham on 15th October 1977, and there are usually several sightings in late October and even November, the latest being 25th November 1980 at Tinsley S.F. One at Barlborough on 17th December 1967 (RAF) was exceptional.

HOUSE MARTIN *Delichon urbica*

Migrant breeder, passage visitor; nesting on buildings, bridges and limestone cliffs.

The distribution of the House Martin to the west and south of Sheffield appears to be limited by the availability of nesting sites and mud for nest construction. The map shows that it is largely absent from the higher gritstone areas where there are few villages, and the Carboniferous Limestone plateau where there is little or no permanent water. Colonies are therefore restricted to the network of villages in the valleys of the Derwent and Noe, the chain of suitable cliff faces in the limestone dales and the broad suburban belt from Stocksbridge, through western Sheffield and Dronfield to Chesterfield. Further evidence of this is provided by the results of the 1977 House Martin survey, analysed by Mawson and Crabtree (*121*) who found that nearly half the 640 nests reported were in suburban areas and a quarter were on the limestone cliffs. As only 2% of the nests were on farm buildings, bridges are important sites for birds in rural areas away from limestone, e.g. there were 36 nests under the road bridge at Chatsworth in 1982. The need for permanent water (to provide mud) was well demonstrated in 1978 when part of the river Wye was drained for repair of banks and the House Martins in Miller's Dale abandoned their attempts to nest.

IDR. '85.

The majority of the colonies, largely those in suburban areas, hold only one or two nests (79% of those located in the 1977 survey). The largest colonies are on Carboniferous Limestone cliffs, i.e. at Stoney Middleton (80 nests in 1977) and Chee Dale (62 nests), and these have increased in size since 1965 when they contained only 40 and 10 nests, respectively. The total of 640 nests for the region gives an average density of 53 pairs per 10km², although this is an underestimate due to incomplete coverage in 1977. The highest density was in the Edale/Hope 10km² (160 nests), whilst in the Upper Derwentdale square only one nest was found, at Howden Dam.

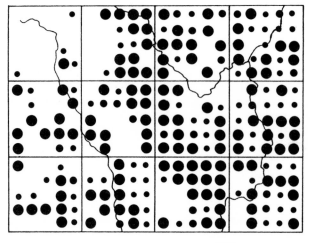

Occupied	220 (73%)
Confirmed	126 (57%)
Probable	20 (9%)
Possible	74 (34%)

G.P.Mawson has shown that the population of House Martins breeding in suburban Dronfield gradually grew from 24 pairs in 1968 to 100 in 1978, even though most nests are moved to a different location the next year, due to their destruction by householders (*122*). The growth is attributed to an abundance of nesting sites and mud, thanks to extensive private housing development, and the attraction of the nearby sewage farm as a feeding locality.

To the north and east of Sheffield recently improved observer coverage has shown that House Martins are less scarce than the 1977 survey implied, but they are still absent from many areas where habitat appears to be suitable. Atmospheric pollution may be a factor, as the prevailing south-westerly winds carry Sheffield's industrial by-products in that direction; if so, recolonisation might be expected in the coming years as the air is now much cleaner.

The main arrival of House Martins is not usually until May but small numbers can be expected in the last ten days of April. Occasionally one or two may appear as early as March, e.g. in 1978 when two were seen on the 20th and one on the 29th, but in 1983 one flew east over Gleadless on the remarkably early date of 2nd February (AW).

Spring flocks are rarely reported, except from Dronfield S.F. where up to 1,000 may gather in May. Flocks of over 100 birds have been seen at many localities in August and September, the largest being 750 at Redmires on 23rd August 1975.

Migrating House Martins are usually seen drifting south or west in loose but localised flocks at various times of day. Therefore much of their movement is not observed during dawn migration watches. Passage probably peaks in late September, e.g. in 1982 at this time there were 125 at Herringthorpe Park and 100 at Wisewood. As with Swallows, most of the population has departed by mid-October, but there are usually one or two more sightings, sometimes into November, the latest being on 16th in 1974.

RICHARD'S PIPIT *Anthus novaeseelandiae*

Vagrant.

The only record of Richard's Pipit is of one observed at Concord Park during the afternoon of 5th October 1984 (JPS) after north-easterly winds. It was first seen with a flock of Linnet but later fed on its own, apparently taking Craneflies from the short grassland. It had gone by the following morning, when exceptional numbers of Redwing passed over the park along with a variety of other species. The record is subject to acceptance by the YNU Reports Committee.

Richard's Pipits can be relatively numerous vagrants on the east coast in October although not inland, but in 1984 were apparently scarce, whereas 20 Red-breasted Flycatchers (another species of easterly origin) were found along the East coast from 4th-7th (Brit. B.).

TREE PIPIT *Anthus trivialis*

Migrant breeder, passage visitor; heathland, woodland margins and scrub with scattered trees.

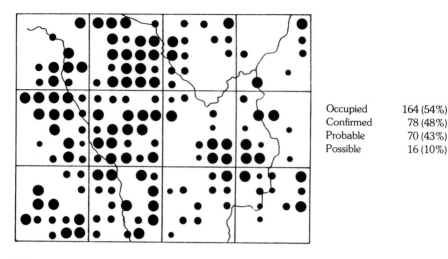

Occupied	164 (54%)
Confirmed	78 (48%)
Probable	70 (43%)
Possible	16 (10%)

This species is clearly more abundant on the higher ground to the west of Sheffield where it is present in most tetrads except those with few or no trees. The uplands provide more areas of open scattered trees including heathy valleys and cloughs, Hawthorn banks, woodland margins and clearings, and young conifer plantations. In the eastern half of the area it is absent from the many tetrads where the terrain is either built-up or extensively cultivated. It does, however, occur between Gleadless and Whittington (including the Moss Valley where twelve pairs were located in 1976); between Wadsley and Tankersley (including Wharncliffe Woods where it is numerous, and Greno Woods where it is surprisingly scarce); around Wentworth, Treeton, Canklow and Linacre; and in the Magnesian Limestone areas around Clowne and Hooton Roberts. Singing birds in or near the city have been reported from Rivelin, Loxley, Norton, Tinsley Park and by Sheffield Parkway, but not from any other areas covered by the Sheffield Parks Survey.

In the scattered trees of Swinden Plantation it was the fifth commonest bird, averaging seven pairs, and there were at least 15 males in the nearby Upper Little Don Valley in 1982. At other CBC sites there was evidence of a slight decline during the 1970s, e.g. at Tor Farm from seven pairs in 1975 to an average of only three in 1978-80, and a further gradual decline was noted in 1983 at the Moss Valley.

With the exception of singles at Hope on 6th April 1969 (JTH) and Unstone on 9th, 1965, the first sightings of the year have always been in the middle ten days of April, most sites being occupied by the end of that month. Until recently there were very few records of this species on passage, but now that many local observers are familiar with its call it has been found at Tinsley S.F. (regular in both spring and autumn), by Sheffield Parkway and at all the migration watch-points. For example, at Mickleover a maximum of 32 flew south on

25th August 1982, while at Redmires in 1981, movement to the south-west was noted almost daily throughout August and early September with a maximum of ten on 13th August. Tree Pipits become very scarce during late September and there have been only three October records, the latest being one by the Parkway on 7th October 1980.

MEADOW PIPIT *Anthus pratensis*

Resident/migrant breeder, winter/passage visitor; moorlands, heathland, wasteland and farmland.

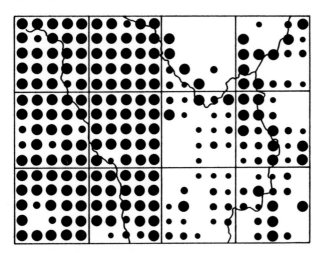

Occupied	242 (81%)
Confirmed	166 (68%)
Probable	45 (19%)
Possible	31 (13%)

The map shows a striking east-west contrast in the breeding distribution of the Meadow Pipit. In the western half, where nearly every tetrad contains land above 300m, it is almost ubiquitous and is not only the commonest species in most moorland areas (whatever their vegetation type), but also frequents many of the grassy or Bracken-covered slopes, moorland margins, and limestone plateaux. Hence the Meadow Pipit is found in every square to the west of Sheffield except around Chee Dale and between Ashford and Hassop. In the eastern half of the area the preference is for waste-ground (such as at Tinsley S.F.), areas of vegetation on colliery spoil, and the land beside the Rivers Don and Rother which is too wet to be properly cultivated. It was also recorded at eight of the 36 areas covered by the Sheffield Parks Survey, with breeding established at Shirecliffe and Bowden Housteads Wood (*120*).

Average numbers in the CBC study areas were one pair at Breck Farm, three pairs at Swinden (Langsett), and four pairs at Tor Farm where numbers have declined since 1975-77 when the average was eight pairs.

In winter the Meadow Pipit is usually absent from all upland areas, although in the exceptionally mild winters of the mid-1970s a few lingered on the hills, including 50 on Bradfield Moors on 3rd January 1975. On lower ground there are usually several winter flocks of 50-150 birds although these may depart during cold periods. In such circumstances individuals are often reported from suburban gardens and hard weather movements may occur (e.g. west over Dronfield on 5th December 1976).

Spring passage is most evident in late March and early April when flock sizes increase in lowland areas (e.g. 170 in Moss Valley on 7th April 1977) and flocks of about 100 birds appear at several localities on the moorland fringe (e.g. Chatsworth, Limb Valley and Langsett). Although these upland flocks may continue to grow during April (e.g. 300 at Alport in 1978, and over 1,100 at Broomhead Moor on 12th April 1983), many males have already established moorland territories by late March (e.g. 20 displaying birds at Burbage on 25th March 1977). A late cold spell may cause an influx into suburban gardens, as happened at Hillsborough and Stannington in late April 1980.

Post-breeding flocks begin to gather from July in both upland pastures and the hills, the largest being 400 on Big Moor on 25th August 1983. They disperse in September and there is then a corresponding increase in numbers on lower ground (e.g. 300 at Breck Farm by 8th October 1973).

This is one of the most numerous birds recorded during dawn migration watches. In 1981 at Redmires up to 250 passed SW daily from late July to mid October. The peak period was between 21st September and 11th October when over 500 were counted at Redmires on seven dates and Mickleden on two dates. Largest counts were 2,900 over Redmires on 29th September 1981, 2,600 over Mickleden on 24th September 1980 and 885 at Concord Park on 6th October 1983. Up to 100 birds also occur daily at other areas including the Loxley Valley. A bird ringed at Hathersage in April 1974 was recovered in Somerset, 230km to the south, in March 1975.

A few migrants continue to pass over up to mid-November, after which movement more or less ceases and any birds remaining in the west are usually to be found on low ground.

ROCK PIPIT *Anthus spinoletta*

Passage/winter visitor; sewage farms and reservoir margins.

Greater observer coverage has resulted in an increased number of records of this species in the Sheffield area. All three races occur, but, since their identification is often in doubt and a detailed examination of plumage can only be made occasionally, it is not possible to make more than guarded statements about the status of each. However, by analysing the monthly occurrences of each race, some distinctive patterns emerge.

The British Rock Pipit - *A.s. petrosus* - occurs most commonly as an autumn passage migrant from late September (earliest date 21st, 1972) to November, with most records occurring in October. There are occasional winter records and a less obvious return migration in spring with records from 30th March to 22nd April. The species was first identified in the area in 1959 when one was trapped at Swinton on 8th November. It was not recorded again until 1965, since when at least 64 birds of this race have been seen, 53% of which occurred in October. A further 21 were not sub-specifically identified but most were probably *petrosus*.

The Water Pipit - *A.s. spinoletta* - is, or was, more of a winter than a passage visitor, often not arriving until November when most British Rock Pipits have passed through, and remaining until March or early April. It was first recorded at Old Whittington S.F. in November 1966 (RAF), the bird remaining until 14th April 1967, the latest spring date. From 1970-75 a small number regularly over-wintered at Old Whittington S.F., the earliest arrival being on 14th October 1973. A maximum of ten were recorded there in March 1972 when they roosted in a bed of Reedmace. Elsewhere, the sub-species, has only been recorded sparingly at Barbrook, Ramsley, Redmires, Harthill, Staveley and Rother Valley C.P. All have occurred singly, most commonly in late October or November but occasionally in other months up to April.

There have been six records accepted of birds showing the characteristics of the Scandinavian Rock Pipit - *A.s. littoralis*. This sub-species from the Scandinavian coast has been found to be a regular passage migrant on the Yorkshire coast from mid-March to mid-April, but only two of the Sheffield reports occurred at this time. Records are of singles at Staveley on 25th March 1969, Barbrook Resr from 28th October 1975 to 4th April 1976, Tinsley S.F. on 1st to 3rd April 1981, Kilnhurst Flash on 22nd to 26th February and Harthill Resr on 23rd March 1982. One caught and ringed at Hackenthorpe on 30th October 1976 provided positive proof of identification, whilst another defended a feeding territory from 30th November to 7th December 1983 at Redmires Resr against an individual showing the characteristics of the British race.

YELLOW WAGTAIL *Motacilla flava*

Migrant breeder, passage visitor; farmland, wet meadows, sewage farms and reservoir margins.

Before the *Atlas* project, the Yellow Wagtail, *M.f. flavissima*, was regarded as being rather locally distributed, although in good numbers, in the wet meadows of the Don and, especially, the Rother Valleys and on some of the pastures of the Carboniferous Limestone plateau. However, the map shows it to be more widespread than anticipated, occupying quite diverse sites to the east of Sheffield (including sewage farms, waste ground and lowland meadows). It also occurs in many of the gritstone valleys, including Derwentdale and the Woodlands Valley. There is some evidence of a spread to such upland areas, with birds breeding for the first time at Loxley in 1977 and Lodge Moor in 1980. Conversely, the map shows a conspicuous absence of this species in the city 10km², although breeding was confirmed during the 1968-72 *Atlas* survey. Indeed, Whiteley Woods was the only city park from which it was reported in the 1975-76 survey and it has been noted in very few gardens.

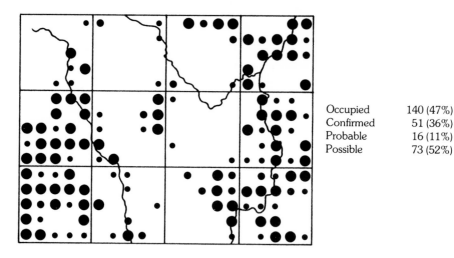

Occupied	140 (47%)
Confirmed	51 (36%)
Probable	16 (11%)
Possible	73 (52%)

The WBS has shown that up to seven males have held territory by the River Derwent and up to nine males by the River Noe, but the breeding population since 1977 has fallen to no more than three pairs in each valley. Unfortunately, there are no details of numbers on lowland rivers, except for the small stretch of the Rother included in the Breck Farm study area where only one or two pairs breed regularly now compared with five pairs in 1970, nor on the limestone plateau where high densities have occurred on unimproved pasture. Since 1980 there appears to have been a contraction in the breeding range of the Yellow Wagtail and many sites where it formerly bred quite commonly are now either unoccupied or hold very few pairs. This seems to be the case in upland areas, although reduced numbers are undoubtedly present in lowland areas where very few have been ringed since the mid-1970s before which more than ten per year were processed.

The first birds of the year are usually seen in the middle ten days of April although singles have occurred at Tinsley and in the Moss Valley in late March. The largest spring flocks reported have been in late April and early May at Chatsworth (18 birds), Redmires (max. 23 birds) and Thrybergh (max. 29 birds), but autumn flocks are more common, especially from late August to mid-September. Largest numbers have been at Redmires Resr (up to 20), Tinsley S.F. (up to 40, roosting), Thrybergh Resr (up to 50) and Killamarsh (max. 100 on 23rd August 1962).

After mid-September numbers decline quickly, and usually there are only isolated sightings in the last ten days of September. Two lingered until 2nd October in 1977 and singles occurred on 3rd and 4th October 1981, but one at Hathersage S.F. on 13th October 1980 was exceptionally late. One which occurred daily at Swinton from 27th January to 3rd February when it was trapped and identified beyond doubt, was the first wintering record for Yorkshire and only the fourth for Britain. Since then, wintering Yellow Wagtails have been found to be less scarce nationally and an adult male which was at Staveley S.F. from 27th November to 3rd December 1970 (RAF) presumably stayed in this country. One at the same locality on 21st February 1976 (TG) may have wintered but as the date almost coincides with exceptionally early sightings of Wheatear and Whinchat in the area, it could have been an early migrant.

A bird showing characteristics of the continental Blue-headed Wagtail, *M.f. flava* was seen at Tinsley S.F. on 13th October 1976 (JH), and remains the only autumn record of this race. The first spring report of this race was also from Tinsley S.F. - on 22nd April 1977. In early May 1980 there was an influx of singles at Hope on 3rd, Treeton on 5th and 8th (different birds) and Pebley on 10th. At Thrybergh Resr in 1982, three Blue-headed males arrived with 13 Yellow Wagtails on 23rd April, and up to three females showing characteristics of this race were recorded on a further 27 days. In 1983 a male was at Barbrook Resr on 29th April with two females almost certainly of this sub-species, and a male was at Thrybergh Resr on 18th May. Non-British female *flava* wagtails were also seen at Thrybergh Resr from 17th-21st April along with a male showing characteristics of the Ashy-headed race, *M.f. cinereocapilla,* on 17th (AR,PL).

GREY WAGTAIL *Motacilla cinerea*

Resident/migrant breeder, passage/winter visitor; rivers, sewage farms, reservoir margins and wetlands.

The distribution of the Grey Wagtail follows the courses of the main Peak District rivers where densities ranging from 0.4 pairs per km on the Derwent to 1.3 pairs per km on the Noe have been found (WBS). Small numbers also breed on the Don, Little Don, Rivelin,

Loxley, Porter, Sheaf, Barlow Brook and several tributary streams in the hills. Hence the distribution in the western half of the area is very similar to that of the Dipper, but a little more extensive, and the species is found in urban Sheffield on the Don and Sheaf virtually in the city centre. Seven pairs were counted along 8km of the Sheaf in 1974. Breeding was also proven in many tetrads in the Dronfield area and at Wentworth, Harthill and Shirebrook where Dippers are totally absent. Such records represent a recent expansion of range since the species was not proved to breed in the Staveley, Chapeltown or Rotherham 10km squares during the national *Atlas* project. In addition it bred for the first time in the Moss Valley in 1977 and at Elsecar in 1978. It is significant that this increase occurred during the mid-1970s when winters were noticeably mild. The total population at this time was probably around 100 pairs.

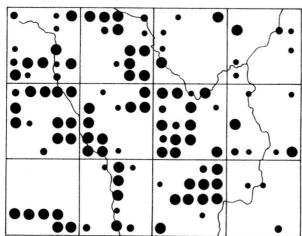

Occupied	116 (39%)
Confirmed	69 (59%)
Probable	16 (14%)
Possible	31 (27%)

On the seven rivers most consistently studied in the WBS (covering 47 km) the population of 34 pairs in 1975 gradually declined to 21 pairs in 1980, crashed to only 11 pairs but recovered to 23 in 1983. This trend is in accord with the national WBS results (*123*) but the start of the decline is not entirely attributable to the hard winter of 1978/79 because it began in 1976. The 1982 crash did follow a severe winter. However, Grey Wagtails seem to have the potential for rapid recovery. On the Noe, young fledged from an average of at least 3.5 of the 4.5 territories present throughout the years 1975-84 and many pairs succeeded in rearing second broods.

Up to seven birds are noted almost daily during dawn migration watches from August to early November. Such movements can be related to the arrival of this species on the east coast during autumn, or with movements from Scotland to England as shown by national ringing records.

In winter the Grey Wagtail is absent from many of its upland breeding areas but is frequently seen at lowland sites which are near to water, in both urban and suburban Sheffield. Unlike the Pied Wagtail, it is not noted for communal roosting, but there were 15 at Redmires on 19th August 1975 and 13 roosting with Pied Wagtails on a factory roof in Chesterfield on 29th November 1976 (LO).

PIED WAGTAIL *Motacilla alba*

Resident/migrant breeder, passage/winter visitor; farmland, rivers, sewage farms, reservoir margins and suburban areas.

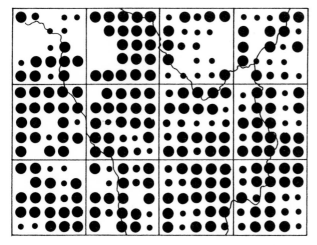

Occupied	270 (90%)
Confirmed	185 (69%)
Probable	32 (12%)
Possible	53 (20%)

The Pied Wagtail (*M.a.yarrellii*) is a widespread breeding species, especially to the west of the city where it can nest in the many nooks and crannies provided by the dry stone walls, rock-faces and assorted stone buildings of the gritstone and limestone. Its absence from the high gritstone plateau is not as surprising as the fact that to the north-east of the area it is absent from many tetrads and remarkably scarce in others, even where breeding was confirmed. This scarcity, especially in the rural areas around Rotherham and due north of Sheffield, has yet to be explained. It is quite familiar as a town bird, nesting in many of the most urban areas and occurring in winter in the city centre, the nearby parks (including Weston Park and Norfolk Park) and regularly in a minority of gardens. It was found in 20 of Sheffield's parks in 1975-76.

The WBS results show that the population on 47km of seven rivers in 1975-78 was 30-35 pairs, at a density of one pair per km on the Derwent and Noe. Numbers were badly affected by the hard winters, to a greater degree than nationally, falling to 19 pairs in 1979 and 18 in 1982. The species appears able to recover more quickly than the Grey Wagtail (Table 4), even though breeding success rate may be lower, judging by results on the Noe where young fledged from a minimum of 3.4 of the 5.4 territories present on average during 1975-84. However, this may not be a true reflection of the total population as birds may leave drier sites to occupy vacant riverside territories, a strategy not open to the wholly riparian Grey Wagtail. One other recent estimate of a local population is by D. W. Yalden at Ladybower and Derwent Resrs where 17 territories were counted in June 1983, giving a minimum density of 0.66 per km of margin, which is similar to the 0.77 per km on the rivers Noe and Derwent in the same year.

Table 4.
Annual variation of numbers of Grey Wagtail (GL) and Pied Wagtail (PW) territories on seven WBS rivers.

Year		75	76	77	78	79	80	81	82	83
No. of	GL	34	31	28	25	23	21	25	11	23
territories	PW	35	33	30	32	19	29	28	18	27

An annual spring influx of the Pied Wagtail gives rise to flocks of 10-50 birds at flashes and sewage farms where large numbers are not otherwise recorded. This usually occurs from late March to the end of April although it is sometimes noted as early as late February (e.g. 60 were at Kilnhurst Flash on 25th February 1982). There may be even higher concentrations, such as 95 at Hathersage S.F. on 28th March 1985 and 243 at Tinsley Park on 8th March 1983 (CRM).

The autumn passage is more obvious with flocks of equivalent size occurring from mid-July onwards, especially at localities close to the moors, i.e. Broomhead, Oughtibridge, Redmires, Bamford Golf Course, Middleton Moor and Chatsworth. The species is regularly recorded during dawn migration watches when up to ten fly south or west almost daily until mid-October, with greatest numbers in late September/early October (maximum 50 per hour west over Redmires on 24th September 1979 and 72 south at Concord Park on 2nd October 1983). In addition, up to 100 may be present by day on the margins of Redmires Resr, and even larger numbers may come to rest in the Bracken dominated areas (maximum 250 on 7th September 1976). At least 60 roosted in a Larch plantation at Baslow on 5th October 1972. All other roosts have been at lowland sites, which may remain unoccupied throughout the winter. These include office and factory rooftops in Stocksbridge, Chesterfield and Sheffield (130 near Midland Station on 7th October 1984); *Phragmites* beds at Bolsover (maximum 250, October 1973) and *Typha* beds at Old Whittington (maximum 410, November 1978). Roosting birds ringed at this time have been recovered in winter in Southampton, Portugal and southern Spain. Further flocks of up to 50 birds may occur in winter at places such as Wentworth, Thrybergh Banks and Chatsworth, with a maximum of 100 at Dronfield S.F. on 14th February 1981.

The continental race *M.a. alba* (or White Wagtail) occurs regularly as a spring migrant from late March to early May with 72% seen in April. The earliest record was one at Staveley on 1st March 1970 (JP). Five of the seven individuals recorded in late May were in 1975 during a period of marked westerly drift of Scandinavian species. There have been ten or more records a year in the 1980s, usually of singles, occasionally twos, on the margins of reservoirs, subsidence flashes or, most commonly, at sewage farms. Up to four have been seen regularly at Tinsley S.F. and Thrybergh Resr, the only larger numbers being six at Hathersage S.F. on 21st March 1971 and 9th April 1972, and an estimated 25 roosting at Staveley S.F. on 12th April 1966 (RAF).

Although probably occurring annually in autumn, very few records are acceptable as the White Wagtail is difficult to identify conclusively.

WAXWING *Bombycilla garrulus*

Winter/passage visitor; gardens, parks and hedgerows.

The Waxwing is an almost annual winter visitor, feeding on berries, especially Cotoneaster species in suburban gardens and parks, or in Hawthorn bushes and hedgerows. However, since the 1950s it has only been recorded on more than a few occasions in four winters. The average interval between these winters is five years, but there has not been an 'invasion' in the ten years since 1974/5. Indeed, in the five winters following 1978/79, there have been only three records on single dates, apart from a bird which visited gardens at Whiston, Rotherham for several weeks during three of the years 1979 to 1982.

The winter of 1970/71 was sufficiently outstanding to be remembered, even by many non-birdwatchers in Sheffield and Chesterfield, as the time when Waxwings occurred in gardens or nearby bushes and parks. Strangely, there were no records from the Rotherham area. According to Wallace (45), nearly 2,000 birds were scattered throughout Britain. The major concentration in Sheffield was in the Hope Valley where at least 50 were present at Hope from the end of October to 23rd November, 200 were near Bamford on 29th November, and 80, probably from Bamford, were at Hathersage on 4th December. In the new year the Bamford flock increased to 280 birds in January but departed in February, the last record from the area being eleven at Hathersage on 18th.

In 1974/75 up to 30 birds were reported from 20 localities, mainly in the city suburbs, and a flock of 50 was at Wadsley Cemetery on 14th December. Although over 1,000 birds were present in the country they mostly stayed in the north-east (45). Since then, the only large flock occurred in February 1977 when there were 70-80 in a suburban garden at Nether Edge (MH).

Most records are in the period mid-November to February, although a few have occurred as early as October, the earliest being three flying north-north-west at Big Moor on 22nd October 1979 (RAF) which was the only record during that winter period. There is evidence of a very small spring passage in some years, with one at Edale on 25th April 1965 (NWH) the latest record.

Ringing recoveries from 1970/71 indicate that the invading birds arrived via Scotland, as one had been ringed in Aberdeen that October. Throughout the winter there was apparently a great deal of movement to and from many areas in the north midlands; birds ringed in Sheffield were later recovered in Glossop and Stalybridge (124). Return to a more normal pattern of movement in subsequent winters is confirmed by a bird ringed at Endcliffe on 15th April 1971 which was controlled in Norway on 18th November 1971.

DIPPER *Cinclus cinclus*

Resident breeder; rivers and streams.

The map shows that the Dipper is distributed along the broader but fast-flowing parts of the rivers in and around the Peak District where, according to the WBS, there is an average of 29-30 pairs on 47km of the seven rivers regularly surveyed. Densities range from one territory per km on the Noe and Wye to one territory on 4km of the Sheaf and Porter. It also breeds on the Little Don, lower Ewden Beck, Alport, Loxley and Barlow Brook.

Dippers were seen but breeding not proven at many moorland streams such as upper Ewden Beck, Burbage Brook, the Ashop above Alport Bridge and the Derwent above Slippery Stones. In such areas the birds probably occupy larger territories, making breeding evidence harder to find. They have been seen on even the smallest streams, almost on the moorland plateaux, up to 530m (e.g. Bleaklow on 19th October 1982). The lowest altitude at which breeding pairs were found was 100m a.s.l. on Barlow Brook and on the Rivelin and Porter as close to the city centre as Malin Bridge and Hunter's Bar.

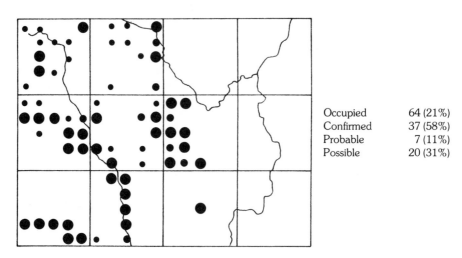

Occupied	64 (21%)
Confirmed	37 (58%)
Probable	7 (11%)
Possible	20 (31%)

In a study of the Derbyshire Dipper population between 1958 and 1968, P. Shooter found that on the major rivers of the Noe, Derwent and Wye, the average density was about one pair per mile of river, i.e. 0.6 pairs per km (*125*). As an example he quotes 13 territories on the Noe and Derwent from Edale to Baslow. In the 1980s this stretch held about 23 pairs - a significant increase - and the average density on WBS rivers was 0.9 territories per km. Since 1974 the total population on all the rivers studied has remained stable at around 30 pairs, annual fluctuations being no more than three pairs. It is estimated that other rivers and streams hold a further 30 or so pairs, giving a total population of *c.*60 pairs. There is no evidence that the recent severe winters have had any adverse effect on numbers breeding, although there are no data relating to the moorland tributary streams where changes should be most apparent. Young have fledged from an average of at least five of the six territories present on 5.6km of the Noe during the years 1975-84.

Local Dippers tend to be highly sedentary, with adults vacating their territories only in times of severe frost or drought, and juveniles moving no more than 6km to occupy adjacent territories. Consequently there are few records away from the traditional breeding areas, exceptions being singles at Blackamoor in September 1970, Redmires in April 1974, Wentworth from December 1974 to May 1975, and Moss Brook in the winter of 1978/79.

WREN *Troglodytes troglodytes*

Resident breeder; woodland, parkland, farmland, suburban gardens, heathland and moorland.

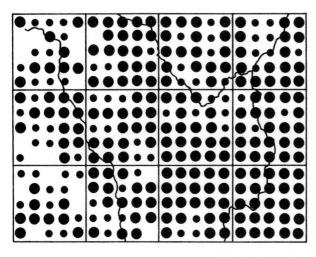

Occupied	282 (94%)
Confirmed	208 (74%)
Probable	74 (26%)
Possible	0

The map confirms that the explosive song of the Wren can be heard almost anywhere in the region, including the most urban parts of the city and many moorland areas. Almost all the tetrads from which it is absent are virtually treeless uplands such as Bleaklow, Margery Hill, Pike Lowe, Back Tor, Bradwell Moor, Totley Moss and East Moor.

In 1976 Sharrock commented that "the Wren is perhaps the commonest nesting bird throughout Britain and Ireland today" (*19*). However, Sheffield data suggest that even during the mid-1970s it was the scarcest of several 'common' species such as Robin, Blackbird, Blue Tit and Willow Warbler. For example, it was absent from eight of the 36 city parks studied in 1975-76 (*120*); only the 14th most frequent visitor to gardens and the eighth most widely reported garden nesting species (*119*). However, the Wren was one of the three commonest species in Little Matlock Wood (max. 29 pairs), Blackbrook Wood

205

(max. 19 pairs), Whiteley Wood (15 pairs), and in the conifers of Swinden Plantation (max. 16 pairs). In the years following severe winters the local CBC population averaged only 42 pairs, and numbers were reduced by 67% in 1979. Since then, the population appears to have increased to a fairly high level: c.70 singing males were counted in one km² of the Shirebrook Valley in 1985 and birds are found in almost every moorland clough except on the highest plateaux.

Wrens maintain territories throughout the year and so are usually seen in ones or twos. However, several birds may roost together for warmth in winter; e.g. a party of ten were disturbed from a Woodpigeon nest near Broomhead, one evening in December 1976.

DUNNOCK *Prunella modularis*
Resident breeder; woodland, parkland, farmland, suburban gardens and heathland.

Occupied	277 (92%)
Confirmed	213 (77%)
Probable	61 (22%)
Possible	3 (1%)

The Dunnock is a very widespread bird occurring in almost all tetrads except those on the treeless plateaux such as Kinder, Bleaklow, Margery Hill and Bradwell Moor. Although it does occur in many of the moorland cloughs, the large number of squares to the west of Sheffield where breeding was not confirmed suggests that it is less common on higher ground, presumably because there is reduced cover. This is supported by the fact that of all the CBC areas, Swinden Plantation (a woodland on the moorland fringe) was the one with the least number of Dunnocks - only one pair occasionally established a territory there. On average, four to seven pairs were present in each of the other CBC areas, making it one of the ten commonest species at all these localities. At Breck Farm in 1970-73, ten pairs were located on average, but more recently there have been only four pairs.

The map shows that the Dunnock breeds in even the most urban areas. It is one of the few species found in the industrial north-east of the city, quickly exploiting even small areas of wasteland provided there is some cover. It was recorded as a common resident in all but one of the city parks surveyed in 1975-76, and was found to be the fifth commonest visitor to Sheffield gardens. In 1973-74 a total of 27 nests were reported from gardens, making it the sixth most numerous garden breeding bird.

The fact that none have been recovered more than 19km from where ringed indicates that the Dunnock is very sedentary. However, birds are occasionally seen at migration watch-points, apparently on autumn passage, e.g. three south at Concord Park on 28th September 1982 and one south at Mickleden on 10th October 1981. Larger than normal numbers have also been recorded at lowland localities in winter, e.g. 16 at Tinsley S.F. on 8th January 1983. It is not known whether these observations result from local movement or continental immigration.

ROBIN *Erithacus rubecula*

Resident breeder, winter visitor; woodland, parkland, farmland and suburban gardens.

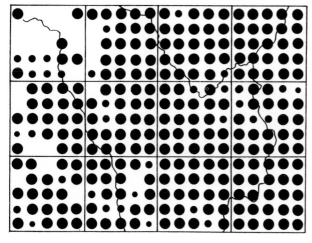

Occupied	275 (92%)
Confirmed	241 (88%)
Probable	29 (11%)
Possible	5 (2%)

The Robin is one of the commonest birds in the area. Not only was it found in almost every tetrad but it has proved to be the commonest bird of deciduous woodland, being one of the four most numerous species in every woodland area studied. It is obviously outnumbered by the Meadow Pipit in moorland areas, the Skylark on lowland farms and the Chaffinch in coniferous woodland, but it is abundant in a greater range of habitats than any of these species. It is fifth commonest on the upland Tor Farm, fourth in the conifers of Swinden Plantation and eighth on the lowland Breck Farm near Staveley. Also, it was found to be the seventh most abundant breeding bird of gardens and was located in all but four of the Sheffield parks in 1975-76.

The most favoured habitat seems to be the mature woodlands of mainly oak and elm on the western edge of the city. An average of 24-26 pairs was found in Whiteley Woods and the Limb Valley where it was the commonest species, and Little Matlock Wood where it was second only to Blue Tit.

Numbers at the upland and farmland CBC areas crashed in 1979, to a total of 9 pairs from 25 in 1978, but in the lower woodlands of the Limb Valley and Ecclesall Woods the population remained stable at 44 pairs. A previous drop had occurred at Tor Farm where in 1975 there were 21 pairs but the subsequent population fluctuated between four and eleven pairs until 1983 when it rose to 15.

Colour ringing of Robins in Beeley Woods and at Breck Farm has shown that the birds are strongly territorial throughout the year, but in periods of hard weather they move to local food sources, i.e. along the River Don or around the farm buildings, in the respective cases of the woodland or farmland birds (ABG and GPM, pers. comm.). One caught while feeding with the resident birds at Breck Farm, on 25th January 1984, proved to be a second year bird which had been ringed 950km away at Nidingen in Sweden on 24th April 1983. All other records have been less than 5km from the ringing site apart from two birds from Breck Farm which were recovered the following summer in Holland and near Bridlington.

NIGHTINGALE *Luscinia megarhynchos*

Scarce visitor.

The Nightingale undoubtedly bred in the area during the nineteenth century, albeit sparsely. Allis (4) notes that they were "occasionally heard near Sheffield", whilst at the sale of Stoke Hall, Grindleford, in 1846 the auctioneer commented that "the Nightingales sing so loud that they disturb the occupants" (21). J. Baldwin Young, writing from Richmond Park, Sheffield, in 1900 stated that "two or three pairs usually nest every year" (5). However, during this century it has certainly become very scarce, although it does still breed east of our area. A breeding pair was reported at Wath Wood in 1944 (21) and in the same year a male was present in the lower Ewden Valley from 25th April to 3rd June. Since then the only substantiated record occurred on 5th May 1978 when Mrs Dixon heard and tape-recorded a Nightingale singing outside her window overlooking Graves Park, Sheffield (DH). There have been claims that the species has occurred at one locality in a few years during the 1970s.

BLACK REDSTART *Phoenicurus ochruros*

Migrant breeder, passage visitor; urban and industrial areas, gritstone edges.

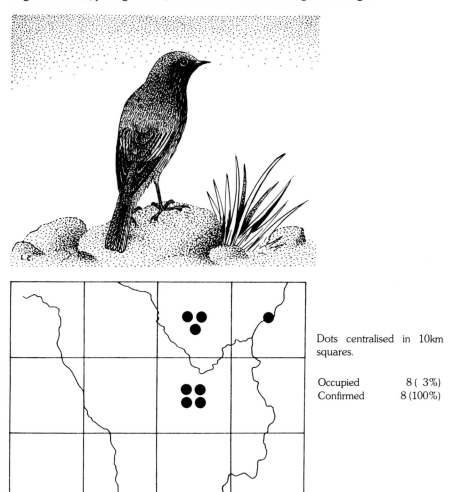

Dots centralised in 10km squares.

Occupied   8 (3%)
Confirmed   8 (100%)

Apart from a male feeding young near Rotherham in 1946, the first evidence of Black Redstarts breeding in the Sheffield area came in 1973 with a singing male, followed by a recently fledged juvenile killed by traffic in the city. There were no records in 1974 but in 1975 two broods were successfully reared from a nest on an occupied building in the city, a female deserted 3 infertile eggs and two additional singing males were reported. The number of pairs in the city increased annually to nine in 1979 but subsequently declined (as shown in the following table), for no apparent reason.

P   209

Year	75	76	77	78	79	80	81	82	83
Min. no. of breeding females	2	3	5	6	9	8	6	4	4

The map shows that eight squares were occupied during the *Atlas* period. All were in industrial or urban Sheffield but have not been accurately plotted to avoid the risk of disturbance at breeding sites of this rare species. Nests are commonly in factories, power stations or dilapidated buildings, but the most surprising was a successful pair using an old Blackbird nest high above a circular saw in a well-used carpenter's workshop. Some birds have two broods and in 1979 bigamy was noted, with a male serving two females in nests 30m apart (*127*).

Birds arrive at the breeding sites in April and are sometimes seen en route in the city suburbs in late March or early April. Passage birds have been recorded in most years since 1970 in rural or moorland localities, particularly on gritstone edges. There have been a few winter records since 1978 when one was at Wincobank on 20th February and another at Grimesthorpe in December. These were most notable in 1982/83 when singles were at Unstone on 18th-23rd November and in Upper Derwentdale on 14th November and 17th December, the only records outside the city, and an immature male stayed around City Farm, Heeley, in January and February 1983.

REDSTART *Phoenicurus phoenicurus*

Migrant breeder, passage visitor; woodland.

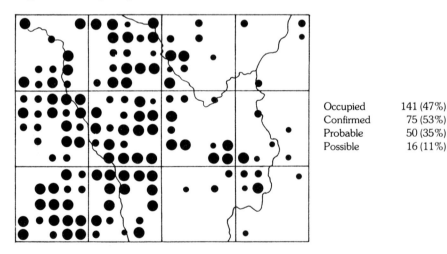

Occupied	141 (47%)
Confirmed	75 (53%)
Probable	50 (35%)
Possible	16 (11%)

The Redstart is most widespread to the west of Sheffield where it occurs in almost every tetrad containing deciduous woodland or scrub, and also in a few places where coniferous woodland borders on to moorland. It is particularly numerous in areas of relict hanging oak woodland as exemplified by Padley Gorge (15 singing males in 1980 and 1983) and in the extensive woodlands of Upper Derwentdale, where the population was estimated to be at

210

least 30 pairs in 1982 (NO). Other details of breeding numbers include 17 singing males along the Wye (1982), eight pairs around Broomhead (1979), six singing males along 1.5km of Alport Dale (1985) and five pairs in the dry limestone valley of Peter Dale (1978). Up to six pairs (average three) have bred in the census area at Swinden Plantation, making it the ninth commonest species there. Two pairs breed at Tor Farm where there were ten in 1967, and there were none at Blackbrook Wood in 1976-78 compared with the three or four pairs which bred in 1964-67. This is the only local evidence of the fall in population which occurred from 1969 due to prolonged drought in the Sahel, the Redstart's wintering grounds. It is still fairly common in the north, e.g. in Wharncliffe Woods and the Ewden Valley, but scarce in city woodlands such as Ecclesall.

To the east of Sheffield there is a small population in the Moss Valley (six pairs in 1979) and breeding was confirmed at Renishaw. Singing birds have been found at Tankersley, Wentworth, Denaby Wood, Canklow Wood, Treeton and Clowne where the first record was not until 1977 (JR).

The first sightings of the year are usually in the middle fortnight of April, although the earliest record accepted is 31st March 1975 when a female was in woodland in the Moss Valley (DJG). Passage birds have been found in spring at non-breeding localities, including Gleadless, Beighton, Moorgate and Clifton Park (Rotherham), Thrybergh Banks and Bolehill Flash.

Interesting reports include a male which joined a Pied Wagtail roost at Old Whittington S.F. on 25th July 1975, and singles found dead in late September in suburban Sheffield (1976 and 1981) and Dronfield (1982). At Tinsley S.F. the species was not recorded until April 1977 but subsequently has been found to be a regular spring and autumn migrant.

A few birds usually linger, at least until mid-September,and there have been three later records to mid-October (at Frecheville, Thrybergh and Midhopestones). A very late report was of one at Redmires on 3rd November 1981 (KC, PAA).

A bird ringed as a *pullus* at Ladybower on 6th June 1971 was recovered at Norwich on 22nd April 1974.

WHINCHAT *Saxicola rubetra*

Migrant breeder, passage visitor; heathland, moorland, farmland and wasteland.

The Whinchat is widely distributed, but is absent from those tetrads which lack areas of unkempt long vegetation. This would explain the gaps in its distribution: in the city itself and in the extensively cultivated farmland areas of Chapeltown, Dronfield, Chesterfield, Clowne and Whiston. The pastures between Loxley and Deepcar and on the limestone plateaux are also too closely cropped to support this species. It does breed in small numbers on the fringes and in the cloughs of the gritstone moors; e.g. in 1984 three pairs were present in a clough on Derwent Moors (where breeding was not reported in the *Atlas* years, probably due to lack of coverage). It is locally numerous, especially in areas of Bracken-covered slopes such as in the Little Don Valley where 13 nests were located in 1979. Other favoured

211

areas include White Edge and East Moor, where there were nine and seven pairs in 1976. To the east of Sheffield it proved to be surprisingly widespread, especially in the valleys of the Rother and Don where wastelands and wet meadows provide the necessary habitat.

During the national *Atlas* Whinchats were not recorded at all in SK49 (Rotherham) or SK47 (Staveley) where they are now fairly widely distributed. This may be due to poor observer coverage of the industrial wastelands. However, the breeding of Whinchats at Tinsley S.F. and Tinsley Park Golf Course in 1978 was a genuine spread to areas where nesting had not previously been recorded.

The timing of the spring arrival is very variable, as this species is apparently more dependant than most on the occurrence of suitable winds (i.e. southerlies). Typically, most do not arrive until May, but there are usually a few sightings in April or even the last week of March. In 1979 none arrived until the second week of May, having been delayed by a succession of northerly winds since early April. In 1976 one was present at Sheffield Parkway from 23rd to 26th February (RT), and either this or another bird was seen near Ulley on 7th March (RT, DB). This was only the second February record of Whinchat in the British Isles and is perhaps attributable to the prevailing calm, warm, foggy weather which had also brought a Wheatear to Breck Farm on 26th and a Yellow Wagtail to Staveley S.F. on 21st.

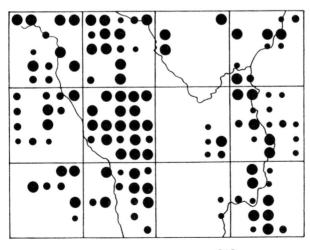

Occupied	127 (42%)
Confirmed	65 (51%)
Probable	33 (26%)
Possible	29 (23%)

Birds are recorded during spring and autumn passage at many localities in South Yorkshire, including some where they do not breed, such as Loxley, Crookesmoor, Shirecliffe, Sheffield Parkway and Harthill. Parties of up to eleven have been recorded (at Padley in May and Redmires in July), with the largest number 14 at Tinsley S.F. The number of sightings declines during September but one or two are usually reported in October, the latest being one at Big Moor on 17th in 1976.

STONECHAT *Saxicola torquata*

Casual breeder, winter/passage visitor; heathland, moorland and wasteland.

Although according to Nelson (5), Stonechats nested annually near Sheffield until 1880, the only breeding record this century until 1968 was at Tinsley Park in 1932-33 (21). In 1968 a pair with young was seen at an upland site in South Yorkshire. This was followed by single breeding records in 1970 and 1972, but the species was still a scarce winter/passage visitor until 1973 when there was an unprecedented number of sightings from more than 20 localities, mainly on the western moors from September onwards. In 1974 two pairs were seen feeding young at an upland site and two other summering birds were recorded (72). The following year three pairs successfully reared

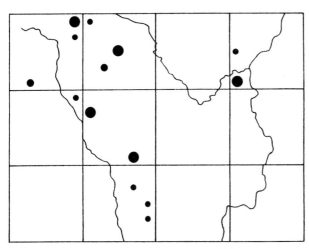

Occupied	14 (5%)
Confirmed	5 (36%)
Probable	2 (14%)
Possible	7 (50%)

at least five broods at widely scattered moorland sites, and many reports were received in autumn from 35 localities throughout the area, including 13 in three parties between Agden and Strines on 11th October. Strangely, after this date there was no evidence of breeding in the uplands until 1981, although birds were seen in suitable habitat in the 1978 breeding season. However, breeding did occur at Tinsley S.F. in 1976 when one pair raised two broods, and 1977 when only one brood fledged.

The high level of sightings outside the breeding season continued until the hard weather of early 1979. That appeared to have a catastrophic effect: there were only four subsequent records that year and a total of only seven in 1980 with no evidence of breeding. Since then there has been a partial recovery and one or two pairs have bred successfully each year at upland localities. At the time of writing however, both winter and passage numbers are still well down on the period 1974-78.

WHEATEAR *Oenanthe oenanthe*

Migrant breeder, passage visitor; moorland cloughs and gritstone edges.

Frederick J Watson

The map shows clearly that Wheatears are most widespread in the region of Carboniferous Limestone to the south-west of Sheffield. They also breed, rather more locally, in gritstone areas, especially where there are rocky gullies or rock-strewn slopes as found in moorland cloughs. The gritstone edges of Derwent (where there were nine males in 1977), Burbage and Froggatt are particularly favoured. To the east of Sheffield there were several instances of birds seen in suitable habitat in the *Atlas* years, although most sightings doubtless involved birds on passage. The only records of Wheatears breeding away from the upland areas are at Tinsley in 1980 (DH) and at Staveley in a few years during the 1950s when it bred in an area of heather, and on rough ground once in the 1960s (RAF pers. comm.). In addition, a pair were seen displaying at Thrybergh Banks on 21st May 1978.

The first sightings are often in the third week of March, but in the years 1976-78 were much earlier. The only February record was one at Breck Farm on 26th in 1976, coinciding with an early Whinchat in Sheffield. In the following years, single birds were seen near Sheffield Parkway on 5th March 1977 and Totley on 4th March 1978. By early April loose parties of up to eight birds may be present on breeding grounds, and territories are rapidly established. There was an exceptional record of 36 near Redmires on 9th April 1951 (DRW). Passage continues into May; e.g. at Thrybergh Resr in 1982 the peak occurred on 5th May when nine birds were present.

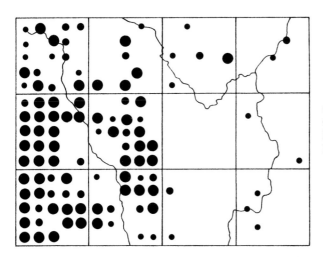

Occupied	109 (36%)
Confirmed	59 (54%)
Probable	24 (22%)
Possible	26 (24%)

Passage birds are sometimes seen in city suburbs, such as a pair in a Bents Green garden (1975), and singles in a Beauchief garden (1983) and the Botanical Gardens (1984), all in May. One which died after hitting a window in Chapeltown on 12th May 1981 was found to be of the Greenland race *O. o. leucorrhoa*. Birds showing the characteristics of this race have been reported on at least 13 occasions from ten localities, all in the first half of May. There have also been autumn records but due to the difficulty of racial identification at this time such reports are open to question.

Post-breeding gatherings often occur at upland sites including Ughill (maximum 20 on 14th August 1977) and Barbrook (20-25 from 23rd July to mid-August 1980). Return passage is noted mainly from mid-July to mid-September, with birds noted at a wide variety of localities, including over 20 in the lowlands where parties have reached double figures at Thrybergh Resr and Breck Farm. Most Wheatears have left the area by the end of September but there are usually a few sightings in October, the latest often being in the last week of the month. There has been only one November record - a single at Thrybergh on 7th and 8th in 1982 (SJH *et al*).

A bird wintered in 1959/60 at Swinton where it was trapped on 12th December and stayed until 5th February (DDOS), a most unusual event.

RING OUZEL *Turdus torquatus*

Migrant breeder, passage visitor; moorland cloughs and gritstone edges.

The distribution of the Ring Ouzel is entirely restricted to the Peak District. Dixon *(8)* quoted flocks of up to 200 arriving in upper Rivelin Valley in early spring and H.C.B. Bowles stated that probably 20-30 pairs used to breed at Abney Moor in the 1930s *(20)*. There has therefore been a dramatic decline in the population as birds have rarely been seen at either of these localities in the last decade or more. The distribution map suggests the species has contracted further during the 1970s, although it is likely that some pairs were overlooked. It was absent from all but seven squares south of Grindleford, with breeding confirmed in only three tetrads (Curbar, Gardom's and Froggatt Edges). This area includes White and Baslow Edges, many rocky outcrops around Grindleford and Baslow, and Bretton Clough where it had been recorded in 1973-74. Furthermore, there were no records at all from SK17 (Tideswell) and SK37 (Chesterfield) where Ring Ouzels were found during the national *Atlas* survey, albeit sparingly.

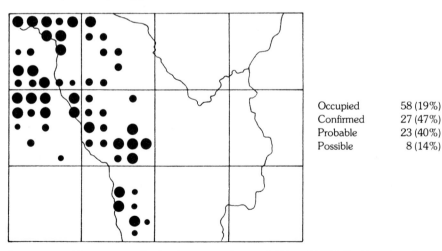

Occupied	58 (19%)
Confirmed	27 (47%)
Probable	23 (40%)
Possible	8 (14%)

In a survey of the species in Derbyshire, carried out in 1973 and 1974, D. Alsop found pairs breeding at altitudes from 200m to 540m a.s.l., the average being 330m *(128)*. He describes their favoured habitat as rocky broken steep slopes with well-defined cloughs or

216

gulleys and running water, with adjacent pastureland to provide a supply of earthworms. He suggests that the Woodlands Valley has the densest population in Derbyshire (nine pairs counted in the Snake area in 1974) but surprisingly few pairs were found around Westend, Alport, Kinder and Howden, numbers perhaps being limited by a lack of food. Alsop estimated the total Derbyshire population to be 200-250 pairs. As the western side of the gritstone plateau not in our area may hold more birds than the north-eastern Yorkshire section which is in the area, and there may have been a slight decline, the Sheffield population is likely to be in the order of 150-200 pairs.

A favourite haunt is in the valley of Burbage Brook where there were six pairs in 1973 but in more recent years there have been no more than three pairs recorded. This apparent decline may be attributable to human disturbance or possibly to a notable increase in Blackbirds in that area. The map shows Ring Ouzels in two areas of Carboniferous Limestone, at Bradwell and near Winnat's Pass. Another, in the limestone valley of Coombs Dale on 10th April 1974, was presumably a passage migrant.

The first arrivals invariably occur before the end of March, by which time birds have been reported from many localities. The earliest sighting was of a male at Mam Tor on 2nd March 1976 (ABG), the year of early Whinchat and Wheatear, and a week before the next earliest record. During April more birds continue to arrive (e.g. five at High Bradfield on 15th April 1980 had flown in from the south-east) and are sometimes found in small parties (max. 30 in Ashop Valley on 9th April 1977 (AS) and c.20 roosting at Alport Castles on 10th April 1984); some territories are not occupied until the end of that month. Between late March and the end of April spring migrants have been seen at several lowland localities including Marsh Lane, Graves and Endcliffe Parks, Tinsley S.F. and Thrybergh Banks.

Autumn passage is most obvious during September when parties may occur at favoured localities (e.g. twelve at Barbrook in 1974, 15 at Dore in 1972 and 25 at Burbage on 23rd September 1973), often feeding on Bilberry, Crowberry and Rowan. Visible migrants may be observed then at Redmires at dawn (e.g. up to four birds on five dates in 1981). Such birds have gone from most areas by the end of September but there are frequently a few October records. These may involve birds of continental origin; e.g. two arrived with Redwings at Woodhead on 18th October 1975, and a spate of records in late October 1975, including twelve at Burbage on 31st (BAM, MSu), coincided with an unprecedented Redwing invasion in Scotland (45). Birds are also seen occasionally at lowland sites in the latter half of October, e.g. at Staveley S.F. (1969), Wentworth (1970) and Wadsley (1982). There have been three November records: at Barbrook on 5th (1962), Edale on 6th (1971) and Burbage on 16th (1979), which was perhaps the same bird as one seen there on 9th December 1979 (MB & JBE). The only 'true' winter bird was a male seen in Upper Derwentdale on 7th January 1983 (TPA, CPa) - the species does winter in south-west Britain.

BLACKBIRD *Turdus merula*

Resident/migrant breeder, winter visitor; woodland, parkland, farmland and suburban areas.

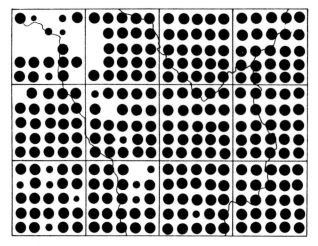

Occupied	286 (95%)
Confirmed	270 (94%)
Probable	13 (5%)
Possible	3 (1%)

The Blackbird is both abundant and widespread, occurring in almost as many tetrads as the Skylark. The only squares in which it was not recorded were those on the treeless gritstone plateaux of Kinder, Bleaklow, Margery Hill, Back Tor and part of Stanage Edge. However, it does breed at altitudes up to 375m in moorland cloughs. It has been found to be one of the seven commonest species at every CBC site. At Breck Farm it is second only to Skylark in abundance with an average of eight pairs, although prior to 1973 an average of 19 pairs were present. At Tor Farm up to 19 pairs have bred, making it second only to Chaffinch, although since 1978 the average has fallen to only twelve pairs. In the deciduous woodlands censused, Little Matlock Wood averaged 23 pairs, Limb Valley 15, and Blackbrook Wood and Ecclesall Woods 14 each, but there were only six pairs in Whiteley Woods (compared with 24 pairs of Robin). In the conifers of Swinden Plantation it was the seventh commonest bird with an average of five pairs.

The Blackbird was found in all the Sheffield parks in 1975-76 and was the most commonly reported garden breeding bird, accounting for almost a quarter of all nests located (119). It even nests successfully in the city centre, e.g. by the City Hall and in the Peace Gardens in 1982. Interesting breeding records include:- three young fledged from a nest on the ground at Tinsley S.F. in 1978; a pair with a nest on the track-rod ends of a car in daily use at Brinsworth in 1977; a pair still feeding young in a nest at Ecclesall on 29th March after two days of snow; and, most surprisingly, a female found incubating four eggs on 4th January 1980 in the Christmas tree in Rotherham town centre - the nest failed. In the same year, many Blackbirds (and thrushes) had late broods, which were possibly their third, because of the abundance of food such as worms, resulting from the wet summer. In 1985 a nest containing 15 eggs, apparently a second clutch all laid by one hen, was found in a Chesterfield garden; the bird deserted, probably due to disturbance from photographers.

Flocks may occur in autumn, especially at localities on the edge of the moors such as Agden, Redmires and Rivelin where the largest flock was of 60 on 27th October 1975. These birds may be of the same origin as those which appear erratically during dawn migration watches. At Redmires small numbers are seen flying south or west on many dates in September and October, with the main movement from mid-October to early November when migrating parties of up to 38 birds have occurred. On 19th October 1981 a small 'fall' was indicated by the presence of 38 birds in a plantation at Redmires. These are probably some of the Scandinavian birds which are known to spend the winter here; birds ringed in Sheffield, the majority of which are first winter birds, have been subsequently recovered in Sweden (3), Finland (3), Norway (3), Denmark (4) and Germany (4).

Supporting evidence for the continental origin of many wintering Blackbirds is that they are often most numerous when Fieldfare and Redwing are abundant. For example, in December 1982 and January 1983 parties of 50-65 birds were seen near Dronfield, in the Hope and Ewden Valleys, and at Owler Lee, Ravenfield Park and Listerdale, and 231 were counted in the Moss Valley on 7th December (DJG). A large influx of Blackbirds was noted on the Yorkshire coast from 24th October to 6th November 1982. One first-year bird ringed at Rivelin Valley on 27th November 1980 was recovered four years later in Wicklow, Eire.

In contrast, the resident birds appear to be highly sedentary as 89% of recoveries of birds ringed locally in the breeding season have only moved a short distance in the area, although one Sheffield juvenile was retrapped the following winter in Staffordshire 75km away. Three young birds ringed at Poolsbrook in October 1978 were all found dead at Staveley, 2km away, between 31st December 1983 and 22nd April 1984, a remarkable coincidence.

The largest numbers are usually counted at nocturnal roosts, with maxima of 200 at Holbrook on 14th December 1980; 160 at High Moor on 20th November 1983; 150 at Rivelin on 2nd January 1980; 100 at the City Botanical Gardens from October 19th to the year end; and 100 at Troway on 1st December 1983.

During severe weather Blackbirds become very scarce in woodlands but are then more frequently seen in gardens where only House Sparrow and Starling are more numerous. In the cold December of 1981, 50 were found inside a farm out-building in the Moss Valley, and one died frozen stiff in the fork of a tree at Shuttlewood where a flock of 66 was subsequently seen.

FIELDFARE *Turdus pilaris*

Casual breeder, winter/passage visitor; parkland, farmland and moorland.

Despite its scarcity as a breeding bird nationally, Sheffield has had a remarkable number of summer records of Fieldfare since 1973. Full details were given by Frost and Shooter (*129*) for the southern Pennines, most of the records coming from the Sheffield area.

The first potential breeding record was in 1967 when one bird was present at Barbrook throughout July, but there were no more until three separate reports of singles in 1973. However, a pair with three juveniles had been seen below Stanage Edge around the start of the decade but not reported (TM). Records have since come from up to four sites in the western half of the area in every year (to 1983) except 1978. All breeding data for years outside 1975/1980 are shown as open circles on the *Atlas* map. In five years breeding was confirmed for single pairs, all at different localities, namely Leash Fen (1974), Edale (1975), Wharncliffe (1976), Moscar (1980) and Ladybower (1981), and an unlined nest abandoned at Foolow in 1980. Only the Edale, Moscar and Ladybower birds were known to be successful.

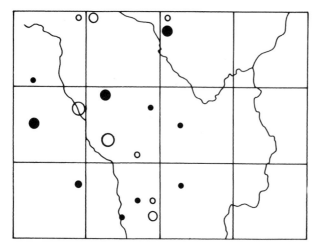

Occupied	13 (4%)
Confirmed	3 (23%)
Probable	1 (8%)
Possible	9 (69%)

Open circles refer to breeding records outside the *Atlas* years.

The first migrants usually appear in mid-September, often a little in advance of the first Redwing. Birds are occasionally seen earlier in the month or even in late August but the main influx does not occur until late October and early November, coinciding with the peak Redwing passage. As many as several thousands may then be seen moving in a southerly or westerly direction at migration watchpoints, and many roost in heather, e.g. 2,000 at Broomhead on 23rd October 1982.

Flocks numbering up to several hundreds are commonly seen feeding on berries late in the year. When the supply of berries is exhausted, the birds move onto fields and rough pasture, often in large flocks. In some winters they are particularly numerous, and an exceptionally large roost formed at High Moor in 1983, with 10-12,000 present in January and early February. Pronounced movements are sometimes observed in the mid-winter period, presumably associated with the onset of hard weather in Europe. On 12th December 1983 a total of 4,300 was recorded flying over five localities. Most of our wintering birds leave when conditions are extremely harsh, as in January 1979, but some remain in the suburbs and small flocks may then be seen feeding in urban areas, even in the centre of Sheffield.

Return passage is evident from mid-March to mid-April. Roosting again occurs on moorlands, with 3,000 on Big Moor on 5th April 1973 an exceptional number. Flocks are sometimes seen in late April and early May, e.g. 500 at Chatsworth on 25th April 1982, 300 at Cheedale on 29th April 1978 and 35 in the Moss Valley on 4th May 1979. A party of 15 at Upper Whiston on 18th May 1980 (PRB) was unusually late. Ringing indicates their likely destination to be north-east Europe as birds have been recovered in Sweden, Finland and Poland.

SONG THRUSH *Turdus philomelos*

Resident breeder, winter visitor; woodland, parkland, farmland and suburban gardens.

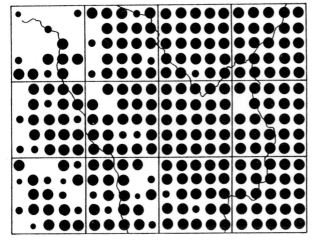

Occupied	271 (90%)
Confirmed	239 (88%)
Probable	27 (10%)
Possible	5 (2%)

The Song Thrush is very widespread, occurring in all areas except the high plateaux of the gritstone and limestone. Its absence from a greater number of upland squares suggests that it is less able to cope with high altitude conditions than are species such as Blackbird, Wren and Robin. Its apparent absence from the area between Darnall and Handsworth on the distribution map is probably an oversight.

Analysis of CBC data shows that although twice as common as the Mistle Thrush it is far less numerous than the Blackbird, which out-numbers it by about four to one. The average of eight pairs in Little Matlock Wood make it the sixth commonest bird there, but none of the other study plots support, on average, more than four pairs. There is evidence that Song Thrushes have declined at Blackbrook Wood, Breck Farm and Tor Farm. It was located in

221

all but two of Sheffield's parks in the 1975-76 survey (*120*) and was found to be the eleventh most numerous garden visitor, and fifth most commonly reported garden breeding bird (*119*). An unusually late breeding record was of a pair feeding young at Tinsley S.F. on 12th October 1983 (KC).

Upland areas such as Redmires are vacated in autumn, when small numbers (up to ten per day) may be seen during dawn migration watches between September and early November, with a peak in mid-October. These southerly or westerly movements are often associated with passages of Fieldfares and Redwings and coincide with influxes of Song Thrushes on to the east coast of Britain. Therefore, such birds may be of the continental race *T. p. philomelos*, and further evidence of this is provided by the recovery in France of a bird ringed six years earlier at Staveley on 2nd November 1970. A young bird ringed at Tinsley S.F. on 3rd October 1981 was recovered ten weeks later in Dublin. Also at this time flocks of up to 30 birds occur in lowland areas and 50 were at Poolsbrook on 8th October 1977. An exceptionally large flock of 150, at Wentworth on 22nd October 1980 (JPS, PJ), could well have been continental migrants.

REDWING *Turdus iliacus*
Winter/passage visitor; farmland, parkland, woodland.

The first Redwing of the winter are usually reported in the last week of September; birds heard over Barlborough on 3rd September 1977 (SJR) were exceptionally early. Many birds migrate during the night when their thin flight calls reveal their presence but not their numbers. However, the pattern of events can still be seen at dawn: small numbers (no more than 50 birds) usually occur on several dates in the first half of October, increasing to several hundred on many dates up to mid-November. The largest movements have been westerly in October; strangely, two were early in the month with by far the greatest, 7,500 at Mickleden on 6th in 1984, and 1,090 at Redmires on 12th in 1979. On 29th October 1983 a total of over 2,000 were counted at three localities.

The abundance of Redwing at different times during the winter varies according to the severity of the weather both here and elsewhere in Europe. In a typical year, large numbers arrive in autumn and some remain in conspicuous, though locally distributed, flocks until the first spell of really cold weather, which may not be until January or February. In such conditions flocks cease to be reported, although small parties may occur within the city and surrounding towns, feeding on lawns and in shrubberies. Exceptionally, e.g. in February 1976, they even feed on roadside verges and central reservations in the busy centres of Sheffield and Rotherham. However, most birds usually move on, perhaps even leaving the British Isles completely.

A marked exception to this pattern occurred in the winter of 1976-77 when there were far more birds than usual in autumn following an unprecedented influx on the east coast of Britain (45), and then in January there was an increase rather than a decrease, due to a further influx from the continent where conditions were exceptionally harsh. The pattern was also less obvious in those years when very few birds arrived in autumn, such as 1974 and 1978.

Although feeding flocks of up to 400 birds may occur, the largest gatherings are usually at roosts, such as in the Hawthorns at Renishaw, Loxley and Rivelin where there was a maximum of 2,500 in December 1979. In 1983 there were 2,000 feeding in several flocks in the Hope Valley on 2nd January, and a huge thrush roost at High Moor held between 2,500 and 3,500 in January and early February, numbers declining thereafter to none by the end of March.

Reports increase in March and April, due to birds on return passage, e.g. 240 in Graves Park on 8th April 1984. Song is often heard from flocks at this time. Most birds have gone by mid-April, although parties of up to 200 may occur later in the month. There have been only six May records in the last ten years; the latest was one at Redmires on 6th May 1979 but in 1982 a bird was seen at the River Ashop on 18th May (DWY). There have been at least two summer reports of singing males which may have been breeding, or, more likely, were simply 'summering', and one was seen at Ladybower on two dates in June 1976 (SJ).

Ringing returns show that birds may migrate to different parts of Europe in subsequent winters, e.g. Belgium, western France, Italy and Iberia (124).

MISTLE THRUSH *Turdus viscivorus*

Resident breeder, passage visitor; woodland, parkland, scrub and suburban gardens.

The map shows the Mistle Thrush has an even greater aversion to the higher plateaux than has the Song Thrush. This is especially striking in the Carboniferous Limestone areas where it is almost completely restricted to the Dales themselves. It is also apparently scarce in the areas of Magnesian Limestone around Bramley and Clowne. Although widespread elsewhere, its requirement of a rather large territory restricts its density, and only one to three pairs were found on each of the CBC plots where it was recorded every year. The only evidence of higher densities comes from areas on the moorland fringe such as Redmires (22 pairs in 1976) and Langsett (35 pairs in 1978).

In the city it is sufficiently widespread to be found in 31 of the 36 parks in 1975-76 and in 1977 a pair even nested on a window ledge near Sheffield Town Hall. The Mistle Thrush quickly exploits derelict land and so is now common in the north-east of the city; e.g. feeding young in an abandoned building at Canal Wharf in 1985. According to the Garden Birds Survey it was the eleventh commonest breeding bird and the fourteenth commonest visitor (*119*). However, there appears to have been a subsequent decline in some suburban areas, perhaps due to predation by the expanding Magpie population.

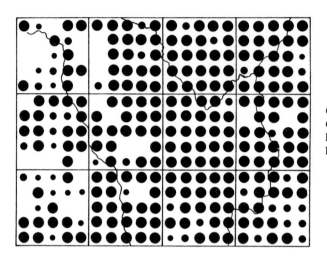

Occupied	271 (90%)
Confirmed	224 (83%)
Probable	30 (11%)
Possible	17 (6%)

Many breeding sites, especially those on higher ground, are deserted by mid-July as the birds form post-breeding flocks. Hence parties of 20-100 birds may occur during July and August, with upland pastures the most favoured habitat. These birds may be of different origin from those which are seen almost daily during dawn migration watches from early September onwards.

At Redmires, where movement is usually westerly, peak passage occurs from mid-September to early October; the maximum count was 240 on 3rd October 1980 but daily counts are usually much lower; e.g. the maximum in 1981 was 34, with 63 in 1982. Such birds presumably contribute to the increase in the size and number of feeding flocks which is evident at this time. Several flocks of 100 or more have been reported, including 180 at Baslow on 27th September 1973, and 'several hundred' at Rivelin in October 1980. After the beginning of November there are usually no further reports of migrating parties or feeding flocks, although 52 were at Chatsworth on 31st December 1980 and 30 flew west at Redmires on 12th January 1976. The origin of the passage birds is unknown, but likely to be northern Britain as influxes are not apparent on the Yorkshire coast.

An early breeding record was of a pair feeding young in the nest at Ulley on 7th February 1980. A bird ringed as a nestling in Hathersage in 1981 was killed by a cat on 20th January 1982 in Gloucestershire, 188km to the south-west.

GRASSHOPPER WARBLER *Locustella naevia*

Migrant breeder, passage visitor; heathland, farmland and wasteland.

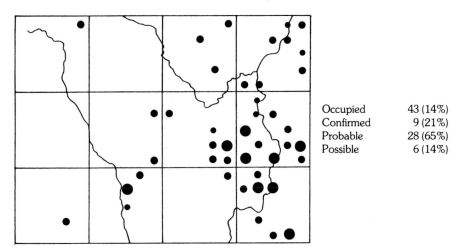

Occupied	43 (14%)
Confirmed	9 (21%)
Probable	28 (65%)
Possible	6 (14%)

The map represents a composite picture of Grasshopper Warbler occurrences over six years rather than its distribution in any one year, since it is usually reported from only about a dozen sites annually. Clearly, this species is more likely to be present at lowland localities where there are more areas of its favoured habitat, which tends to be waste or marshy ground with unkempt vegetation. It will sometimes briefly colonise young conifer plantations, but there have been many such areas in the Peak District which were not occupied during the *Atlas* period.

Reports usually refer to single males performing their reeling song, often in only one year, although some localities have attracted birds for several successive years, e.g. up to four singing birds at Barrow Hill and Renishaw and up to three at Harthill and Thrybergh Banks. Another regular site, Tinsley S.F., has not been occupied since 1976 when a fire destroyed the preferred area.

The first individuals may arrive in April (earliest - 12th, 1981 and 82), but it is usually mid-May before several have been located. In most years the last bird is reported in early August, with the latest one singing in a Shiregreen allotment on 25th in 1976 (DH).

SEDGE WARBLER *Acrocephalus schoenobaenus*

Migrant breeder, passage visitor; flashes, marshes, wetlands and wasteland.

The *Atlas* has shown that the Sedge Warbler is surprisingly widespread to the east of Sheffield. Clearly, it is not only present at most lowland marshland but has also colonised drier habitats including, on occasions, industrial wastelands, and in June 1985 a field of rape. The only reports from higher ground were of singing males in the Hope Valley and at

Underbank Resr, although during the national *Atlas* singing birds were also located in the Baslow 10km square. There were no reports in 1975-80 from the many millponds in the Don, Loxley, Rivelin and Porter Valleys, although singles were in the Rivelin Valley in May 1981 and 1982.

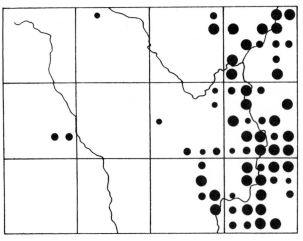

Occupied	65 (22%)
Confirmed	34 (52%)
Probable	22 (34%)
Possible	9 (14%)

Since all the areas of reed or marsh around Sheffield are relatively small, most occupied tetrads support only one or two pairs. However, larger numbers of singing males have been counted at Harthill (13), Thrybergh Banks (10), Tinsley S.F. (8), Catcliffe Flash (7), Old Denaby (6), and Killamarsh (5 in 1976, before open-cast mining destroyed the site).

First reports often occur before the end of April (earliest at Tinsley S.F. on 6th in 1982), but many sites may remain unoccupied until at least mid-May. Some of the birds which occur at Hackenthorpe and Tinsley S.F. in August and September are presumably on passage, as with individuals which have been seen at Barbrook Resr, Graves Park, Woolley Wood and in a Chapeltown garden. There are usually at least a few sightings during September, especially at Tinsley S.F., and there have been two October records - at Tinsley on 8th in 1978 and Gleadless on 20th in 1977.

Ringing recoveries have shown that birds reared at Tinsley S.F. return there in subsequent years. Birds ringed at Poolsbrook in August 1976 and 1981 were recovered 305km south at Radipole Lake, Dorset.

MARSH WARBLER *Acrocephalus palustris*

Scarce visitor.

The only records are of singing males at Tinsley S.F. on 7-9th May 1978 (CRM, DH), and at a locality in the south-east from 9th June 1985 until at least 16th (AA *et al*). Continental migrants were exceptionally numerous in the British Isles during both these springs.

REED WARBLER *Acrocephalus scirpaceus*

Migrant breeder, passage visitor; flashes and marshes.

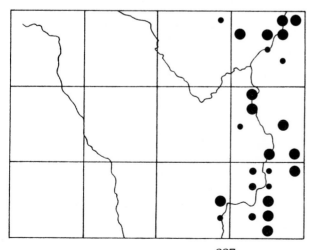

Occupied	26 (9%)
Confirmed	14 (54%)
Probable	3 (12%)
Possible	9 (35%)

The Reed Warbler was always regarded as a rather scarce breeding bird in Sheffield, restricted to a handful of sites. However, the map shows that it has probably bred in at least 17 localities to the east, suggesting that its favoured habitat of reed-beds (especially *Phragmites*, although *Typha* will also be utilised) is not such a rare commodity as was once thought. Suitable, albeit small, reed-beds are evidently found beside some lakes (Wentworth, Renishaw), reservoirs (Harthill), sewage farms (Old Whittington) and, especially subsidence flashes including Treeton, Catcliffe, Old Denaby, Thrybergh Banks and several sites discreetly hidden amongst industrial areas, housing estates and wasteland in the Don and Rother Valleys. Numbers of singing males counted at favoured localities include nine near Staveley in 1979 and 1980, five at Poolsbrook in 1976 and Catcliffe in 1973, six at Thrybergh Banks in 1982 and seven at Old Denaby in 1985.

The first spring reports are invariably in the first fortnight of May, (earliest - 1st, 1977 at Thrybergh Banks). Ringing results show the birds have a fidelity to their natal area, returning in succeeding breeding seasons. Two five-year olds were controlled at Poolsbrook in 1981, having originally been ringed in their first year at Attenborough (Notts) and Coventry in 1976. Careful watching and mist-netting at Tinsley S.F. has shown that this species may occur on passage, at least in late summer and autumn, in areas where there are no reed-beds. In July 1981, for example, one or two birds occurred there on five dates, and were found in both Elder scrub and Willow carr. In recent years there have been annual sightings of one or two in September, the latest being at Thrybergh Resr on 22nd and 29th September 1984. An exceptionally late bird, in a weak condition, was closely observed on 22nd October 1982 in scrub at Orgreave Coking Plant (PLB).

MARMORA'S WARBLER *Sylvia sarda*

Vagrant.

A male of this localised Mediterranean species was found singing in Mickleden Beck on 15th May 1982 (GL), the same date as a Red-footed Falcon arrived at Potteric Carr, Doncaster, and the day before a probable Montagu's Harrier flew north over Alport Castles. It built a nest during the two days immediately after its discovery, and continued to sing throughout its two-month stay, having clearly established a territory. It was last seen on 24th July. As it was the first ever to be recorded in Britain, many hundreds of birdwatchers came to see it.

The record has been accepted by the *British Birds* Rarities Committee and the species has been admitted to the British list, category A, by the British Ornithologists' Union.

LESSER WHITETHROAT *Sylvia curruca*

Migrant breeder, passage visitor; farmland, scrub and hedgerows.

The Lesser Whitethroat is another species which has proved to be more widespread than expected. It is interesting to note that during the national *Atlas* there were no reports of singing males in the western half of the area, and none were located in the Treeton 10km square where, in the 1975-80 *Atlas*, birds were found in 16 tetrads. This skulking species is easily missed, unless the song is known, and therefore it was probably overlooked

previously, particularly in the wasteland areas where it often occurs. It is most abundant to the south-east of Sheffield where there are still dense hedgerows and Hawthorn thickets, especially on railway embankments. Such habitats are more scarce to the west but there are some suitable areas in the Rivelin, Loxley, Derwent and Porter Valleys, and in certain limestone dales including Coombs Dale where one male sang from a Gorse thicket. Singing males have also been reported from Millhouses Park, the Botanical Gardens, and even a garden in Rawmarsh and bushes at Sheffield Polytechnic near the city centre, as well as from a young conifer plantation near Pilsley.

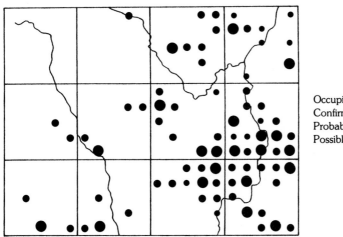

Occupied	78 (26%)
Confirmed	21 (27%)
Probable	46 (59%)
Possible	11 (14%)

The first birds usually arrive in the last week of April or the first week of May, the earliest being one at Hackenthorpe on 17th April 1974. At Tinsley S.F., where breeding was suspected in 1980 and certainly occurred in 1985, it is primarily a passage migrant, e.g. occurring almost daily from 11th to 18th September 1980. Such passage birds have been reported from many other areas, mainly to the east (e.g. nine at Poolsbrook on 2nd August 1980) but occasionally from higher localities such as Ramsley Moor (on 28th August 1975). Several birds usually linger into September, the latest being singles on 29th September at Old Whittington S.F. and Breck Farm in 1979 and Rivelin Valley in 1982.

One locally ringed bird was controlled five years later 295km north in East Lothian, whereas another was controlled two years later only 12km away.

229

WHITETHROAT *Sylvia communis*

Migrant breeder, passage visitor; farmland, heathland and scrub.

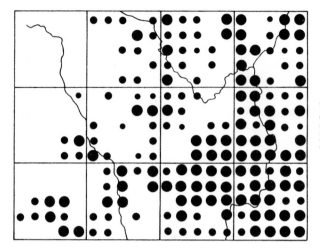

Occupied	177 (59%)
Confirmed	89 (50%)
Probable	78 (44%)
Possible	10 (6%)

The Whitethroat is considerably more widespread and abundant to the east of Sheffield where there are more hedgerows and more areas of wasteground with scrub or Gorse. Whitethroats also occur, but are relatively scarce, in the valleys of the Don and its tributaries, the Little Don, Ewden, Loxley, Rivelin and Porter. Within the city the Whitethroat has encroached into urban areas as far as Malin Bridge, Shirecliffe, Bingham Park, Gleadless and Tinsley S.F. It is well distributed in the Derwent Valley south of Bamford and in many of the limestone dales.

The dramatic reduction in the Whitethroat population between the summers of 1968 and 1969, due to prolonged drought in the Sahel, has been well documented nationally but not locally. Frost (*20*) states that probably more than three-quarters of the usual territories were vacant in 1969. The population recovered partially during the 1970s, e.g. at Breck Farm in the early '70s birds appeared briefly without establishing territories, but by 1977 six pairs were present and at least three pairs have bred in every subsequent year. 1977 was apparently a very good year for this species in Sheffield since 32 singing males were counted in the Moss Valley, and there were over 20 at Thrybergh Banks. The Rivelin Valley holds at least 15 pairs in most years, but a count of four pairs in the Hope Valley in 1976 is more typical of the numbers in the upland valleys. However, the population in the 1980s is still well below that of the 1960s.

The first spring migrants usually arrive in the last week of April although the earliest was on 13th April 1985 (at Dronfield S.F.). In autumn it is a regular passage migrant at Hackenthorpe, Tinsley, Renishaw (max. 24 on 28th July 1979) and Staveley (max. 35 on 2nd August 1980). A few usually remain until mid-September, and there have been two recorded in October at Tinsley S.F. - on 4th in 1983 and 8th in 1978.

230

GARDEN WARBLER *Sylvia borin*

Migrant breeder; passage visitor; scrub and woodland margins.

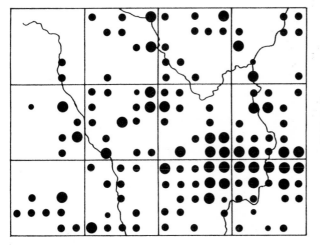

Occupied	137 (46%)
Confirmed	38 (28%)
Probable	92 (67%)
Possible	7 (5%)

The Garden Warbler is widely distributed, favouring deciduous woodland margins and unkempt areas of tall shrubs and bushes. Hence it is found in many of the river valleys, particularly the Moss, Wye and Rivelin, but is scarce in mature woodlands unless glades or clearings are present. It appears to have become more numerous in the present decade, so that the breeding map probably understates the present distribution, at least in the north of the area. However, it is more selective in its habitat requirements than the Blackcap, which is additionally found in scrub and thicker undergrowth as well as closed canopy woodland. Despite its name, this species is rarely found in gardens, or urban areas, although two singing males were recorded between Granville College and Sheffield Midland Station on 3rd June 1975. It was reported from only six of the areas covered by the Survey of City Parks.

This warbler is one of the latest arrivals in spring with only occasional reports in late April, the earliest being one in the Porter Valley on 16th in 1982. The main influx occurs from early May onwards but can be delayed until the latter half of the month in some years. Whilst much less numerous than the Blackcap, it is not uncommon; e.g. 35 singing males were reported in 1982 and six were singing in Rivelin Valley on 2nd June 1983. However, it is rarely recorded after the breeding season due to its skulking nature, which it shares with most *sylvia* warblers. Small numbers are seen or trapped at localities such as Tinsley S.F. and Hackenthorpe. Most of these are in September, and occasionally in October, the latest being one at Barrow Hill on 20th October 1984. An even later bird was killed flying into a city centre window on 31st October 1979.

BLACKCAP *Sylvia atricapilla*

Migrant breeder, passage/winter visitor; deciduous/mixed woodland, scrub and suburban gardens.

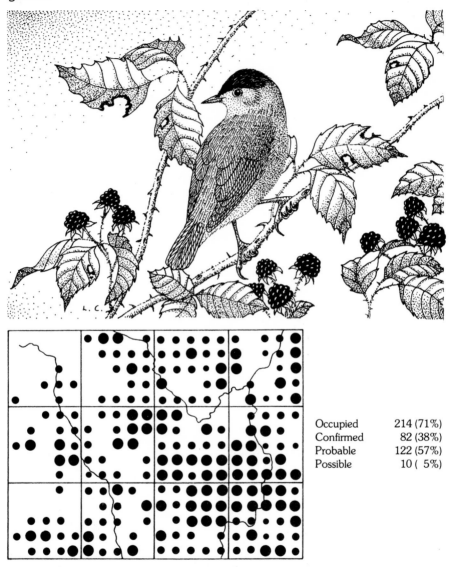

Occupied	214 (71%)
Confirmed	82 (38%)
Probable	122 (57%)
Possible	10 (5%)

Amongst the warblers the Blackcap is second only to the Willow Warbler in both abundance and the extent of its distribution in the area. The map shows it is absent only from the largely treeless gritstone and limestone plateaux and from heavily built-up and industrialised areas.

A few deciduous trees or tall bushes with nearby scrub or undergrowth is its basic habitat requirement. However, it is by no means as numerous as the Willow Warbler and appears to be restricted to the lower ground since it rarely occurs above 400m a.s.l. The highest number of territories recorded at the CBC sites is only five (at Little Matlock Wood), but reports such as ten singing males at Woolley Wood on 8th May 1981 indicate that it is one of the commonest summer visitors. It was reported from 16 Sheffield parks in 1975-76 (*120*).

Although predominantly a summer migrant, the Blackcap does winter in small numbers, and does so much more commonly than the Chiffchaff. This makes it difficult to determine the start and finish of migration. An influx is usually noted in mid-April with passage continuing throughout the month and into May, as illustrated by a female trapped in breeding condition at Unstone on 22nd May 1982 which had been ringed at Spurn Point eleven days previously. Post-breeding dispersal can be seen in late July and August. At Tinsley S.F. up to 15 birds have been recorded on autumn passage; five were trapped there on 3rd October 1981 and two remained until 17th. Birds are recorded throughout the winter, mainly from suburban gardens, often at bird-tables. Reports have been much more frequent during the last ten years, although whether this is a genuine increase in wintering birds or merely more observer interest is unclear. Birds are usually seen at 10-15 localities, in ones and twos, but there were five in the Botanical Gardens in 1977/78 and at least 20 individuals were in the area from January to March 1983. The origin of these is unknown but all those caught and ringed have been first winter birds. A female ringed at Dronfield S.F. on 27th December 1977 was killed by a cat on 23rd April 1978 at Sutton Coldfield (West Midlands.) 82km away.

WOOD WARBLER *Phylloscopus sibilatrix*

Migrant breeder; deciduous woodland.

233

The Wood Warbler breeds exclusively in mature woodland, favouring Beech and particularly Oak including even small copses within mainly coniferous woods (e.g. at Langsett) and wooded moorland cloughs (e.g. Ewden Beck). The map shows that its distribution is largely to the west, particularly along the river valleys, and the southerly fringes of the city, i.e. from Limb Valley to the Moss Valley. Numbers appear to have increased in the last ten years, so that in the favoured areas of Padley Gorge, Upper Derwentdale, Wyming Brook, the upper Don Valley and the Moss Valley, it is not uncommon to hear six to eight singing males. Indeed, the species is commoner in such areas than the Chiffchaff, possibly because it requires less ground cover.

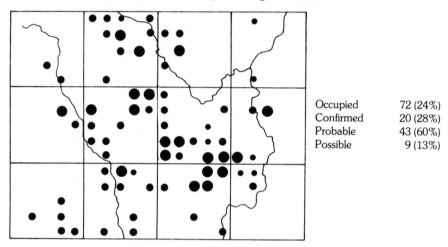

Occupied	72 (24%)
Confirmed	20 (28%)
Probable	43 (60%)
Possible	9 (13%)

The apparent absence of Wood Warblers from the north-east, as reflected by the breeding map, may be false. Careful observation at Woolley Wood has shown that it occurs regularly, at least on spring passage. For example, in 1983 at least twelve individuals were seen between 26th April and 8th May, with a maximum of four on 2nd. This period represents the normal arrival time, although in some years it is not reported until early May. The earliest record was of one in the Moss Valley on 20th April 1975. Once the males stop singing in late June, the species is rarely recorded. There have been only five sightings of singles in August, with the latest at Thrybergh Banks on 23rd in 1981.

One ringed as a *pullus* in Ecclesall Woods in 1962 was recovered in Italy in August 1964.

CHIFFCHAFF *Phylloscopus collybita*

Migrant breeder, passage/winter visitor; deciduous woodland and scrub.

The Chiffchaff is a widespread but not abundant breeder, preferring areas with tall deciduous trees and well developed undergrowth. Hence it is found in the major deciduous woodlands, mature parklands and well-wooded dales. The distribution map is perhaps surprisingly similar to that of the Garden Warbler; the most notable differences being that the latter is more strongly represented in the east of the area whilst the Chiffchaff occupies

234

more of the city tetrads in SK38, including 13 city parks in 1975-76 (*120*). In the west it is largely confined to the Derwent Valley and a few of the limestone dales. It is not numerous anywhere, with no more than three pairs breeding at any CBC site.

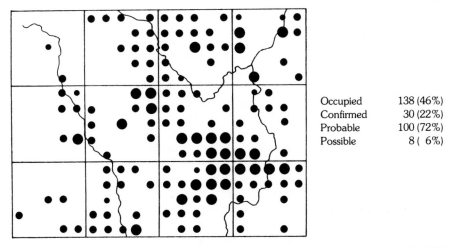

Occupied	138 (46%)
Confirmed	30 (22%)
Probable	100 (72%)
Possible	8 (6%)

The species is one of the earliest migrants in spring, mainly coming from southern Europe. It is regularly seen during the last week of March, although passage peaks in April in the scrub and hedgerows of eastern localities such as Tinsley S.F. Birds are seen away from breeding habitat in July, perhaps indicating dispersal and possibly the start of return passage, and this situation continues into September. There are usually a few reports from the east in late September and even early October, but late passage is confused by the presence of small numbers of wintering birds. In most winters there are a few records, particularly from areas of scrub and carr in the north-east or around Dronfield; but numbers fluctuate, for example there were no reports (unusually) in 1981/82 whereas at least six birds were seen in December 1982.

WILLOW WARBLER *Phylloscopus trochilus*

Migrant breeder, passage visitor; woodland, scattered trees and scrub.

As the map illustrates, the Willow Warbler is found throughout the area, from industrial parts of the city to all but the barest moorland or Carboniferous Limestone pasture. It is by far the most abundant warbler, merely requiring a few bushes or trees with associated ground cover for nesting, but is most numerous in deciduous or mixed woodland. An indication of its abundance is given by counts made in 1976 when there were at least 73 singing males in the Moss Valley on 22nd April; 54 territories located at Redmires and 66 found on three CBC plots - more than for any other species. It was seen in 23 of the 36 Sheffield parks surveyed in 1975-76, although at some of these it was only a passage visitor (*120*).

In spring the main influx usually occurs in the third week of April and is often very marked, with few or no birds on one day and many singing males on the next. On 17th April 1982 *c.*180 were counted in Monsal Dale (JWW). However, there is usually at least one sighting in the first week of April and occasionally one in March, the earliest record being one at Tinsley S.F. on 20th in 1982. Upland sites may not be occupied until early May in some years, e.g. at Redmires in 1976 the influx was noted on 2nd May.

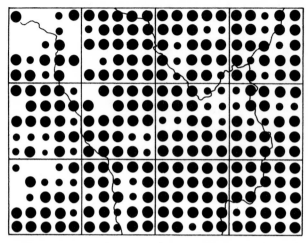

Occupied	283 (94%)
Confirmed	226 (80%)
Probable	56 (20%)
Possible	1 (0.5%)

Autumn passage can be detected at localities such as Tinsley S.F. where up to 50 birds may be seen (compared with only a handful breeding). This continues until mid-September, with a few later stragglers (including birds singing in October in some years), the latest being one at Malin Bridge on 20th in 1974. Although the species has not been identified in the winter, its presence should not be ruled out because a *phylloscopus* caught at Hackenthorpe on 14th November 1976 was identified by wing formula as a Willow Warbler (ML).

An adult ringed at Hathersage on 5th July was recovered at Cadiz, Spain, on 6th April 1984. A leucistic bird was at Ladybower on 11th July 1981. Strangest of all, a bird thought to be this species was present at Hackenthorpe in the 1980-82 breeding seasons and sang songs characteristic of both Willow Warbler and Chiffchaff, one following on from the other in random order (RAF, in press)!

GOLDCREST *Regulus regulus*

Resident breeder, passage/winter visitor; woodland.

The Goldcrest is abundant and widely distributed, occurring primarily in coniferous woodland and to a lesser extent in mixed and pure deciduous woods. It certainly breeds in many of the areas which on the map show evidence of only probable breeding. This indicates the difficulty of locating nests and the ease with which singing males can be detected. There is a considerable north-western bias in the distribution of the Goldcrest, which is a reflection of the amount of suitable nesting habitat in the form of large areas of conifer plantations within this region. Goldcrests probably reach their highest local densities here and may be found in virtually every area of coniferous woodland. During the *Atlas* survey, birds probably nested in Black Clough (SK1098) at *c.*350m a.s.l. while further evidence of probable breeding was obtained in the upper Ashop Valley at *c.*400m a.s.l. In the Sheffield area at least, the distribution of the Goldcrest appears to be limited by habitat rather than altitude. All the blank tetrads in SK18 correspond to tracts of open moorland or treeless pasture. Most of the south-west is devoid of substantial woodlands of any type and is especially lacking in conifers. Within the Wye Valley Goldcrests breed in the mixed woodland around Monsal Dale but are absent from the purely deciduous woods further up the valley. To the east the amount of suitable habitat increases and its distribution becomes more continuous.

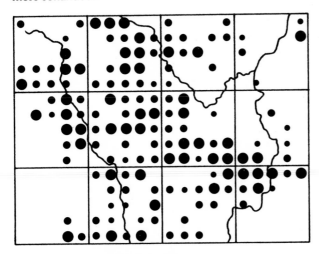

Occupied	147 (49%)
Confirmed	51 (35%)
Probable	76 (52%)
Possible	20 (13%)

Although the Goldcrest occurs in the suburbs of Sheffield to the west and south, it is absent from much of the city, Chesterfield and Rotherham. The bird is rare to the north-east where the few wooded areas are largely deciduous. A similar situation is to be found in the south-east, with the exception of the Moss Valley where it is locally common in mixed woodland.

The numbers of Goldcrests breeding in Sheffield have undoubtedly increased as a result of extensive planting of coniferous trees, such as Spruce. In such plantations the bird can achieve remarkably high densities with up to 320 pairs per km² being recorded in other parts of England (*19*). In many of our plantations the Goldcrest, along wih the Chaffinch and Coal Tit, forms a large proportion of the birds present. The species may well have been only a local breeder in the previous century when the great majority of woodlands were deciduous.

In autumn there is an increase in numbers in suburban woodlands including areas where few are likely to breed, e.g. the city Botanical Gardens and Catcliffe Flash. As these are occasionally accompanied by Firecrests, most are probably migrants from Scandinavia. They may remain throughout the winter and in cold weather be accompanied by more local birds as many of the woods on the moorland edges are largely deserted then. Birds are also recorded in suburban gardens where sightings have become more frequent in recent winters. Such reports are generally from areas to the west of the city, e.g. Stannington, Millhouses and Ecclesall, together with a few from the east, such as Rotherham. Flocks of birds are occasionally recorded at this time of year, sometimes in the company of various tit species. Thirty were recorded together in December 1975 at Redmires and over 50 were present at Broomhead in November 1980.

FIRECREST *Regulus ignicapillus*

Infrequent visitor; woodland, hedgerows and scrub.

This striking little bird was first recorded in 1878 when a specimen was obtained in Endcliffe Woods (5). It was not noted again until 1974 when a male was located in Ewden Valley on 26th October. In the ensuing ten years a further 23 have been seen. However, 14 of these were in only two years - 1975 and 1982 - all other years having no more than two sightings. In the peak year of 1975, when eight were seen, there were only another six inland records in the remainder of Yorkshire and Derbyshire.

The great majority of birds have been recorded in the period October to early April, indicating that they are migrants from continental Europe. Three exceptional records - two in 1975, on 30th August at Wyming Brook and 11th September at Dore, and one at Longshaw on 12th September 1981 - could have been of more local origin as Firecrests have bred in south Derbyshire and north Nottinghamshire in recent years.

Firecrests have been seen in a wide variety of localities throughout the area, including the city Botanical Gardens, but usually remain for no more than two or three days. The longest stay was at Catcliffe from 4th to 12th December 1982; although earlier in that year one was seen at Renishaw on 31st January and 6th March, indicating that it may have spent more than a month in the area. The most recent record was of a singing male at Tinsley S.F. on 7th May 1985 (CRM).

SPOTTED FLYCATCHER *Muscicapa striata*

Migrant breeder, passage visitor; woodland, parkland and suburban gardens.

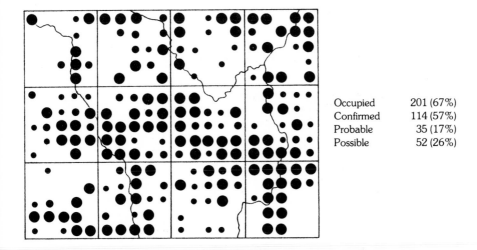

Occupied	201 (67%)
Confirmed	114 (57%)
Probable	35 (17%)
Possible	52 (26%)

The Spotted Flycatcher is a widespread species. The most obvious areas where it is absent, or at least very scarce, are the gritstone and limestone plateaux (including the Magnesian Limestone between Bolsover and Clowne), the built-up areas in the northern part of the city, and, more surprisingly, the wooded valleys between Chesterfield and Owler Bar, and between Ecclesfield and Tankersley. It occurs where there are mature trees bordering open spaces, such as woodland clearings and margins, and rivers. It is particularly numerous in the limestone dales, the Hope Valley, and large parkland areas such as Renishaw and Chatsworth where there were 12 to 15 pairs in 1983. Twelve pairs were present in the Redmires area in 1977 but this was unusual (KC). However, in many tetrads it is represented by only one or two pairs which may not be present annually. Indeed, it was not regularly recorded in any of the CBC study areas, although it has bred at least once in Little Matlock Wood and nested at Tor Farm until 1975, but not subsequently. In 1975-76 it was recorded in ten of Sheffield's parks, breeding at Graves Park (six pairs in 1981), Bowden Housteads Wood, Psalter Lane Cemetery and Middlewood (*120*). It has also bred in large suburban gardens in Rotherham and Sheffield, including at Broomhall in the inner city.

The first birds usually arrive in the first ten days of May, although there have been a few April records, the earliest being two at Hathersage S.F. on 23rd in 1982 (JDM, JC). In autumn it has been seen in a Gleadless garden (up to three in August 1966), at Thrybergh Banks and at Tinsley S.F. where a thorough watch in 1980 showed that up to 15 birds were present during August. Most individuals have left by mid-September, although there are occasional sightings up to early October, with the latest one at Grenoside on 6th in 1978.

RED-BREASTED FLYCATCHER *Ficedula parva.*

Vagrant.

One was seen feeding in Birches and Alders beside a stream near Bradfield on 18th October 1981 (DG,PJF). There were several on the east coast at that time but inland records are rare.

PIED FLYCATCHER *Ficedula hypoleuca*

Migrant breeder, passage visitor; deciduous woodland.

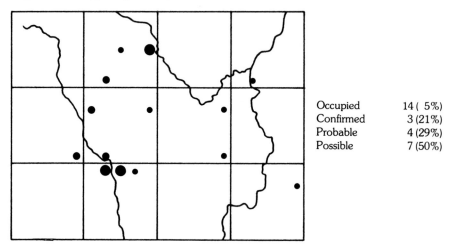

Occupied	14 (5%)
Confirmed	3 (21%)
Probable	4 (29%)
Possible	7 (50%)

The Pied Flycatcher is a very localised breeding species, virtually restricted to hanging oak and birch woodland. The only regular site is Padley Gorge, where it nests mainly in boxes erected for it. It does breed sporadically elsewhere to the west and north-west of Sheffield, particularly in the Derwent and Don valleys, and a pair was seen on 14th May 1974 at Kiveton Park, on the eastern edge of the area.

Fortunes have fluctuated at Padley over the last 20 years. The known stable breeding population has been five or six pairs, and up to three additional singing males have been present. The number of fledglings reared has usually been in the twenties, despite stolen clutches and vandalised nest-boxes. However, in the late 1960s and early 1970s, only two or three pairs were known to have bred, whereas in the 1980s there has been an increase in the population, which has also been reflected at another site, as follows:-

Year		1980	1981	1982	1983	1984
No. of Breeding	at Padley	6	9	8	7	14
Females	at Site A			1	2	9

Spring passage birds have been recorded from mid-April onwards at a variety of localities, including a number to the east. The earliest date is 11th April (1966 and 1981), although prior to the main review period a singing male was reported near Sheffield on 26th March

1950 (AFT). However, most birds do not arrive until the last week of April or early May. Immediately after fledging, the birds become very elusive and soon leave the breeding locality. Surprisingly few are reported on return passage in July and August. September records are rare, the most notable being one at Tinsley S.F. from 8th to 13th, 1980 (CRM); the remains of a male killed by a Sparrowhawk in the Moss Valley on 10th, 1978 (DJG); and the latest, one near Peak Forest on 20th, 1983 (DJG).

BEARDED TIT *Panurus biarmicus*

Scarce visitor.

The first record for the area was a pair in a *phragmites* reed-bed at Bolsover from 15th February to 4th March 1978 (RAF) when the male was caught and ringed (ML). Two birds occurred in the autumn of the same year, at Staveley on 7-9th October (AC), and at least two were at Bolsover on 20th January 1984 (RAF).

LONG-TAILED TIT *Aegithalos caudatus*

Resident breeder; woodland, heathland, parkland, hedgerows and scrub.

Tit flock

IDR. '85.

The high proportion of tetrads in which Long-tailed Tits were seen but no further breeding evidence obtained gives the misleading impression that this species is rather locally distributed, especially to the west of Sheffield. However, although it is absent from large expanses of high ground on both gritstone and limestone, and from the built-up northern half of the city, it is otherwise fairly widespread. Its requirements for dense bushes to hide its relatively bulky nest leads to a preference for areas of Gorse or Hawthorn scrub which are found mainly on the gentle valley slopes, railway enbankments and waste ground to the south and east. To the west of Sheffield such habitat is confined to the river valleys and this is

S

reflected in the bird's distribution. In 1975-76 it was recorded in 15 of Sheffield's parks including areas of garden allotments (*120*). Pairs have been found at every CBC site except Swinden Plantation, but not annually.

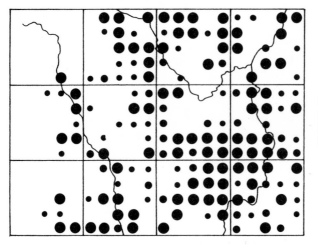

Occupied	163 (54%)
Confirmed	87 (53%)
Probable	28 (17%)
Possible	48 (29%)

Foraging flocks, often of 20 or more birds, may be found in winter, especially along hedgerows and beside rivers. Such parties occasionally pass through suburban gardens, but more unusual records include twelve flying over Hunter's Bar and eight on the University campus, both in October in suburban Sheffield, and eight on Big Moor, 400m from any trees or bushes in December 1977. The largest flock was of 50 birds at Agden on 8th December 1974.

Long-tailed Tits are badly affected by prolonged cold weather and it is noticeable that all large parties are reported between September and December before cold spells take their toll. However, numbers appeared to be good at the end of 1982, despite the preceding hard winter, with 54 in four parties in Upper Moss Valley, 49 in Linacre Woods and 32 at Stonely Wood, Gleadless.

MARSH TIT *Parus palustris*

Resident breeder; deciduous woodland and parkland.

The Marsh Tit is a scarce bird in the area except in the Carboniferous Limestone dales where it is locally common. It is also regularly seen in the Derwent Valley from Chatsworth to Hathersage. It appears to breed exclusively in mature deciduous woodland or where there are scattered trees. Records did come from other parts of the area during the *Atlas* years but as the species is frequently confused with the Willow Tit, there is no definite evidence of even probable breeding from elsewhere. As it does breed to the north-east and south-east just outside the area, it is not inconceivable that the occasional pair may be found in the north or east of the Sheffield area.

242

Outside the breeding season individual birds or small parties are found, often associating with other tit species, both in breeding areas and further afield. For example in December 1982 one was ringed at Holmesfield and a year later one visited a garden at Mosborough.

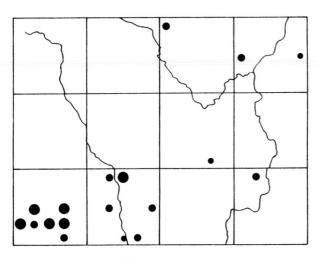

Occupied	18 (6%)
Confirmed	6 (33%)
Probable	9 (50%)
Possible	3 (17%)

WILLOW TIT *Parus montanus*

Resident breeder; woodland, scrub, wasteland and carr.

The breeding map indicates that the Willow Tit is widespread throughout the eastern half of the area, but to the west is confined to the lower ground, mainly in the valleys of the Don, Little Don, Ewden, Loxley, Rivelin, Porter and middle reaches of the Derwent. It is typically found in scrub, tall hedgerows and trees or woodland near to water. It is therefore surprisingly scarce in the Peak District dales and there is almost no overlap with the Marsh Tit.

243

The species is widespread within the city, being found in all but four of the urban and suburban tetrads. This is particularly reflected in the results of the Survey of City Parks when Willow Tits were located in 17 of the 36 sites (*120*). However, it is not numerous; e.g. the only CBC site at which it was regularly recorded was Little Matlock Wood where two or three pairs usually bred.

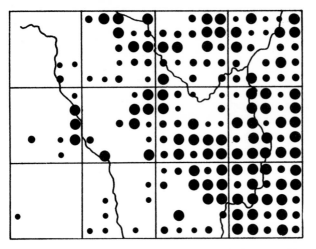

Occupied 176 (59%)
Confirmed 84 (48%)
Probable 54 (31%)
Possible 38 (22%)

Outside the breeding season it is commonly found in tit flocks but rarely in numbers exceeding five or six, although parties of 15-16 were recorded at Norwood in March 1975 and the Moss Valley in January 1976. There are frequent reports from gardens and urban areas including two birds which fed on toast in a factory yard at Attercliffe in January 1976.

A bird ringed at Hackenthorpe in 1973 was retrapped there six and a half years later, illustrating both the sedentary nature of the species and the remarkable age to which some individuals survive.

COAL TIT *Parus ater*

Resident breeder; coniferous and mixed woodland.

The Coal Tit is very much a bird of coniferous woodland, occurring abundantly in the extensive plantations of the Peak District. It is not, however, confined to areas of conifers since up to two pairs nest annually in Little Matlock Wood where all the trees are broad-leaved, and at least some of the pairs in the limestone dales occur in Ash woodland. It is absent from the gritstone and much of the Carboniferous Limestone plateau. The north-eastern half of the city is almost devoid of breeding Coal Tits and there is a curious absence in the triangle formed by Staveley, Chesterfield and Bolsover.

Unfortunately there have been no CBC studies giving the density of Coal Tits in those coniferous woodlands where they are most numerous, although a small plantation in the Limb Valley held up to seven pairs. At other CBC sites up to three pairs have been recorded, although it is absent from census plots at Breck Farm and Whiteley Woods.

Outside the breeding season it is more widespread and has been reported from a variety of localities including Tinsley S.F., Harthill and Attercliffe. One, presumably moving through, was recorded at 500m a.s.l. on moorland at Langsett on 29th September 1980. Dawn migration watches at Redmires have shown that in certain years (e.g. 1981) Coal Tits regularly fly high over the moors, heading south-west, on clear October mornings.

It was a regular winter visitor to a minority of gardens in 1973-74 (*119*) and occurred in 19 of Sheffield's parks in 1975-76 (*120*). In winter, birds usually occur singly or in small numbers, often amongst flocks of other tit species. However, flocks of up to 60 birds have been reported; Derwentdale is a favoured locality with a maximum there of 70 on 20th December 1975.

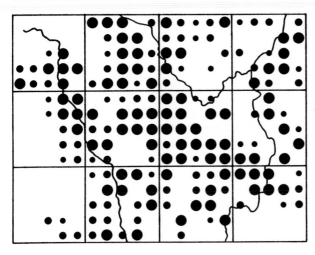

Occupied	176 (59%)
Confirmed	89 (51%)
Probable	57 (32%)
Possible	30 (17%)

BLUE TIT *Parus caeruleus*

Resident breeder; woodland, parkland, farmland and suburban areas.

The Blue Tit is abundant and is found in even the most industrial of habitats. In the upland Peak District it is still widespread but absent from the highest altitudes where there are few or no trees. It seems to have been more successful than the Great Tit in colonising areas on the fringes of the open moors and is therefore present in a greater number of upland tetrads.

245

The results of CBC studies suggest that this species shares, with the Robin, the distinction of being the commonest bird of the deciduous woodlands. It was found to be the most abundant bird in Little Matlock Wood (averaging 28 pairs), Whiteley Woods (24 pairs) and Ecclesall Woods (23 pairs). As expected for such a small resident bird, the population is badly affected by severe winters. For example, in 1979 numbers were a third fewer at Tor Farm and Limb Valley, although in Ecclesall Woods there was little effect, possibly because of proximity to garden bird tables. The availability of food in suburban gardens during the winter months certainly helps this species and accounts for the influx of birds into such areas during protracted periods of severe weather. Recovery is also aided by large broods after hard winters, e.g. up to 15 in 1979.

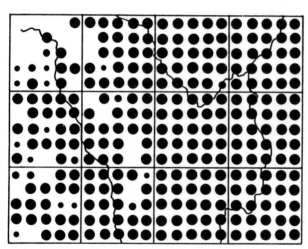

Occupied	277 (92%)
Confirmed	256 (92%)
Probable	8 (3%)
Possible	13 (5%)

Blue Tits were found in all but one of Sheffield's 36 parks in 1975-76 (*120*). In the Garden Bird Survey of 1973-74, 52 nests were located -indeed, only Blackbird and House Sparrow were more abundant (*119*). Many have been ringed, e.g. 119 at Ramsley Moor on three dates in late summer 1983, and the species shares with Greenfinch the distinction of over 5,000 being ringed by the Sorby/Breck Ringing Group in the period 1968-1979. The vast majority of ringing returns are of short movements (*124*).

Outside the breeding season Blue Tits often form small flocks and may wander to unexpected places, including town shopping centres and the highest moorland (e.g. two at

600m on Kinder Scout on 2nd October 1977). The number seen during dawn migration watches varies from year to year but in autumn flocks of up to 25 birds occasionally gather on the fringes of Redmires plantations before circling high overhead and departing south-west. Such movements are always on calm, clear mornings, usually in October (KC). Two locally ringed birds have been recovered in Lancashire - in 1980 after moving 72km and in 1984 after moving 73km. Flocks of 50 or more are noteworthy, and in the last ten years there have been four reports of over 100 birds together, the maximum being 250 at Chatsworth on 26th August 1977 (counted as they flew across a gap in a conifer plantation - RAF).

GREAT TIT *Parus major*

Resident breeder; woodland, parkland, farmland and suburban areas.

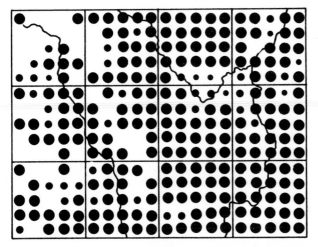

Occupied	262 (87%)
Confirmed	223 (85%)
Probable	32 (12%)
Possible	7 (3%)

The Great Tit is a common resident, found wherever there are woods or hedgerows. It is absent from the tree-less gritstone plateau and the bare fields of the Carboniferous Limestone. It seems scarce in the north-east of Sheffield and absent from industrial areas.

Great Tits were reported from 28 of Sheffield's 36 parks during 1975-76 (*120*) but in 1973-74 only five nests were located in gardens (*119*). In each of the well-studied deciduous woodlands it was found to be one of the seven commonest species, with up to 23 pairs in Ecclesall Woods where only the Blue Tit was more abundant.

Outside the breeding season this species becomes more nomadic and is more likely to be found in moorland cloughs (e.g. 15 near Langsett in March 1976) or even on open moorland (e.g. one in Bracken on Broomhead moor, 400m a.s.l.). It also occurs more frequently in gardens, being the seventh commonest visitor in the 1973-74 survey (*119*). Although a few Great Tits commonly occur amongst flocks of other tit species, parties of more than 20 are unusual, and 55-60 at Hathersage on 18th December 1980, Longshaw on 19th February 1981 and Derwent on 29th January 1983, were exceptional numbers.

247

NUTHATCH *Sitta europaea*

Resident breeder; woodland and parkland.

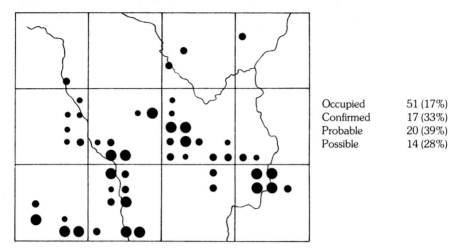

Occupied	51 (17%)
Confirmed	17 (33%)
Probable	20 (39%)
Possible	14 (28%)

In Sheffield the Nuthatch is approaching the northern limit of its range within the British Isles, as shown by the national *Atlas* map (*19*). Sharrock states that the discontinuity of breeding records between the North Midlands and North Yorkshire may be due to industrial atmospheric pollution (*19*). The Sheffield region lies on the southern edge of this discontinuity and the distribution of the Nuthatch within the area is sparse and scattered. During the last century, however, it was even less widespread. Whitlock (*7*) states that it was "rare in the Peak" whilst according to Nelson it was occasionally met with and nested sparingly.

The species is very scarce north of the city centre with no definite breeding records from the local *Atlas* years. The four probable breeding records are from woodlands in Derwentdale, Beeley Wood, Greno Wood and Wentworth Park. Nesting may also have occurred near Ladybower and in the Loxley Valley. To the south of the city, the bird is commoner but still very local, with the main concentrations along the Derwent and Wye Valleys in the south-west and in the Renishaw area in the south-east. Not all apparently suitable wooded areas along the Derwent contain Nuthatches, although in the Padley and Chatsworth areas they are relatively common with several pairs present annually. The main breeding site in the south-east is Renishaw Park, parts of which are in all four tetrads in which breeding was proven in SK47. Several pairs are also present along the Moss Valley and in the areas of mixed woodland to the east of Dronfield, but the species is rare in the Chesterfield area. Within the city boundary, the Nuthatch is found in several of the larger parks containing mature, deciduous trees. During 1975-80, breeding was proven in Ecclesall Woods, Endcliffe Park, Whiteley Woods and the Rivelin Valley. The estimated population in Ecclesall Woods in 1976 was 6-12 pairs. Evidence of probable breeding elsewhere in the city was obtained from the Limb Valley and from Graves Park.

Since the breeding survey, the Nuthatch has definitely nested in Beeley Wood, Woolley Wood and in Graves Park where two or three pairs are now present, indicating a continuation of the colonisation documented for Derbyshire by Rodgers (*130*). Here, Nuthatches first appeared in Chatsworth in 1960 and bred for the first time at Padley in 1963 and in Monsal Dale in 1965. By 1970, the species was well established at the latter site and had also reached Hathersage. Further expansion northwards up the Derwent Valley has occurred since the time of the national *Atlas* (1968-1972), as far as Derwent Reservoir, but it is still surprisingly scarce in the Hope Valley.

The Nuthatch is basically sedentary although records indicate that some birds wander from the breeding areas. Single birds were reported from Ughill in 1974 and from Redmires in June 1982, both roughly five kilometres from the nearest known breeding site in the Rivelin Valley. In hard weather, birds are recorded feeding at garden bird tables in areas close to nesting woods, e.g. at Hathersage and in the south-west suburbs of the city.

TREECREEPER *Certhia familiaris*

Resident breeder; woodland and parkland.

The widespread distribution of the Treecreeper in the Sheffield area is a reflection of its wide choice of woodland habitat. Unlike the Nuthatch, which has a much more restricted distribution, the Treecreeper breeds in purely coniferous woodland as well as mixed and deciduous woods, and even in parks and large gardens. During 1975-80, the species was recorded in 165 tetrads (55%) but, if the squares in which there is little or no woodland are excluded (*c.*50, mostly moorland and urban/ industrial areas), the Treecreeper was recorded in approximately two-thirds of all the remaining tetrads. The breeding season begins early, the main song period being from February to early April, and this factor may have contributed to the under-recording of this species as the bird becomes much more difficult to locate later in the season when the majority of woodlands were checked.

In the west and north-west of the area, the Treecreeper is mainly confined to the river valleys, where it breeds in the many commercial stands of conifers planted around the reservoirs. The main limiting factor in this type of habitat is the availability of nest-sites. In the south-west, much of the land is treeless pasture and this is reflected in the lack of Treecreepers in most of SK17, with the exception of the wooded Wye Valley in the south. Further east, the distribution is more or less continuous with two major exceptions: the north and north-east of the city, where the main land-uses are housing and heavy industry, and a

249

broad strip of land along the southern edge of the region covering Bolsover and Chesterfield where, although the amount of woodland is small, the almost total lack of records seems surprising. Elsewhere in the area, the Treecreeper is present in the majority of woodlands, including some of the smaller coppices provided they are not too isolated. In the Survey of City Parks the species was found to be widespread and occurred only 1.5km from the city centre, in Norfolk Park. This distribution is emphasised by the *Atlas* results which show the Treecreeper in all parts of the city with the exception of the city centre, Attercliffe, Tinsley, Parson Cross, Wadsley and Ringinglow.

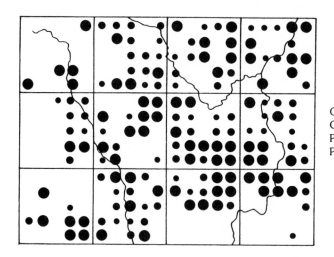

Occupied	165 (55%)
Confirmed	79 (48%)
Probable	53 (32%)
Possible	33 (20%)

In winter, the majority of woods still contain Treecreepers although the more exposed, high altitude, woodlands are deserted in hard weather. At this time of year, Treecreepers often consort with roving flocks of tits and they have been shown to be one of the commonest non-tit species present in such flocks (*131*)

Past records of Treecreepers are rather few in number as the species is often overlooked or ignored, although it would seem that numbers in the Sheffield area have been fairly stable in recent years. In 1979, fewer reports than normal were received, suggesting that numbers declined during the severe weather of the previous winter. Very few counts of birds in the breeding season have been made, although nine singing males were located in Padley Wood on 26th April 1975. Perhaps the most outstanding record concerns the movement of between 75 and 100 birds through a small wood at Chatsworth on 19th August 1977 (PT), a remarkable concentration for a species which, according to Witherby (*9*), rarely occurs in groups larger than family parties.

GOLDEN ORIOLE *Oriolus oriolus*

Scarce visitor.

The first record of this species is of one heard in Wyedale on 14th August 1980 (JPG). The next was an immature male which sang for an hour in the grounds of Thundercliffe Grange, Rotherham, on 31st May 1983 (JPS), the day after the first Avocets were seen in the area. One was seen at Filey (North Yorkshire) on the same date. A female or immature male was seen in willows bordering the River Doe Lea at Poolsbrook on 28th May 1984 (RAF) when the area's first spring Mediterranean Gull was present.

RED-BACKED SHRIKE *Lanius collurio*

Scarce visitor.

This species bred in the area in the 19th century and, sporadically, up to 1942 10-15km further south in Derbyshire (*20*), and yet there was not a single record this century until 26th October 1976 when an adult male was seen at Taddington (JAC). This bird was also unusual in being so late in the year. There have been several unconfirmed reports since that date but the only other substantiated record was of a female perched by the side of the road at Strines on 12th and 13th June 1980 (IF,DH).

GREAT GREY SHRIKE *Lanius excubitor*

Winter/passage visitor; heathland, scrub, sewage farms and farmland.

The status of this species as a scarce passage migrant and irregular winter visitor appears to have been unchanged this century until the 1970s (*72*). Numbers increased in th early part of the decade, as shown in Table 5, and over 15 birds were seen at up to 25 localities during the winters 1974/75 and 1975/76. After this there was a marked decline to only a few visiting in the first half of the 1980s, with 1982/83 the peak winter when eight birds were recorded.

251

Table 5 - Number of apparently different birds
recorded per winter.

Year	72/73	73/74	74/75	75/76	76/77	77/78
No. of birds	3+	c12	c17	c20	7	10
Year	78/79	79/80	80/81	81/82	82/83	83/84
No. of birds	1	6	2	3	8	4

Most Shrikes are transients and so there have been records from many places where there are scattered trees or bushes or overgrown hedgerows, including at least two suburban gardens. The first birds are normally seen in October, the earliest being 30th September (1972 and 1984). In good years more arrive in November and possibly December. They are usually solitary but two are occasionally seen together. A few individuals may establish winter territories in which they can regularly be seen for at least part of the day. There is then the possibility of hearing the unusual but characteristic song, as at Brough on 27th December 1983 and Strines on 14th April 1977. Examples of winter territories are: a disused railway line at Killamarsh (30th December 1970 to 27th February 1971); Hawthorn scrub around Elsecar S.F. and Resr (6th December 1970 to 14th February 1971); birch scrub in the Leash Fen - Ramsley Resr area (21st October to 4th November 1973); scattered deciduous trees and bushes along small rivers - Porter Valley (26th February to 1st April 1974) and Ewden Valley (13th October 1974 to February 1985); and scattered Scots Pine and Larch on moorland edge at Strines (12th March to 15th April 1977).

Shrikes recorded within the Sheffield region have been seen to kill Twite and Robin, eat a lizard species and impale a Short-tailed Vole on a thorn. The remains of four Short-tailed Vole, three Common Lizard, two small birds and at least 21 insects, mainly beetles, were found in a batch of pellets (132).

Departure normally ranges from mid-March to mid-April but in 1983 a bird was at Barbrook from 25th April to 3rd May.

JAY *Garrulus glandarius*

Resident breeder, passage/winter visitor; woodland and scrub.

The Jay is primarily a widespread but local resident breeder. Occurring more exclusively in woodland than any other British crow, the Jay's distribution reflects, to a large extent, the distribution of this type of habitat, particularly in the west. The bird is secretive in the breeding season and the nest hard to find, resulting in a low proportion of tetrads in which breeding was proven. The lack of a widely-used song also made probable breeding difficult to ascertain, resulting in a high number of possible breeding records.

The incidence of the Jay in the west of the area is primarily influenced by river valleys, as these contain the majority of woodlands. This effect is most striking in the Derwent Valley where the bird occurs from Howden Resr in the north to Chatsworth in the south, but it is largely absent from the treeless moors and limestone plateau on either side. Jays are also common in SK29 where they inhabit the large areas of coniferous plantations in the valleys of the Little Don, Ewden and Loxley rivers. Over much of the remaining area, the Jay's distribution is more or less continuous except where woodland is lacking. Thus it is absent from the centre and the industrial north-east of Sheffield, much of Rotherham and from the Bolsover area in the south-east. It is common in the well-wooded country to the north of Sheffield, in the Moss Valley, and in a large proportion of the western and southern city suburbs, breeding as close to the city as the Botanical Gardens.

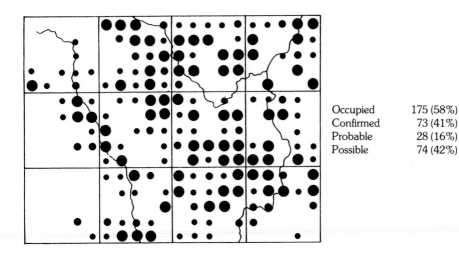

Occupied	175 (58%)
Confirmed	73 (41%)
Probable	28 (16%)
Possible	74 (42%)

During this century the Jay's population has undoubtedly increased in the western half of the area, with the advent of commercial afforestation. In the last 15 years Goshawks may have controlled the numbers in certain woodlands, as the Jay is a favoured prey of at least some of these raptors. Nevertheless, it appears to be becoming more and more common, with increasing reports away from woodland and especially in suburban gardens, particularly in winter.

There are usually several reports of parties in the winter months. These are normally not very large, with the highest number 25 at Midhope on 15th October 1977. Most such reports are from the north-west where the Jay achieves relatively high densities. The only flock reported outside the period October to February involved 21 at Langsett on 7th August 1976 (PR).

In 1983, following the failure of the acorn crop in continental Europe, large numbers were observed flying in off the sea and the British Isles was the focus of a massive invasion. Large flocks throughout Britain were reflected within the Sheffield area, and unprecedented numbers moved through the region from mid-September to late October. Between 13th September and 27th October, 164 birds were counted moving south-west or west over Concord Park, peaking at 58 on 6th October. Also in October, 31 flew west over Hallam Moors on 2nd, whilst visible movement over a built-up area near Dronfield involved 35 birds flying south in one hour on 11th. Ten were in Norfolk Park on 2nd November.

MAGPIE *Pica pica*

Resident breeder; woodland, scrub, farmland and suburban areas.

The Magpie is probably one of Sheffield's most conspicuous and controversial breeding species. It breeds throughout the area, being absent only from the higher gritstone moors, the open pasture of the Carboniferous Limestone plateau and some areas of heavy industry in the Don Valley. Magpies are typically found in areas of open grassland with some tree-cover for nesting. However, since the 1940s the occurrence of urban nesting Magpies has increased (*19*), a trend which is reflected in Sheffield where the results of three separate surveys of the breeding population show an increase in breeding density from 1.4 pairs per km² in 1946 (*133*) to 4.2 pairs per km² in 1976 (*134*) and 5.0 pairs per km² in 1981 (*135*). This increase appears to have occurred in response to several factors including:- (a) low levels of persecution within towns; (b) an increase in roost-site availability due to extensive tree-planting programmes within Sheffield following the Second World War; (c) an opportunistic diet which, together with an efficient food-hoarding behaviour, enables Magpies to exploit the large quantities of food provided for garden birds.

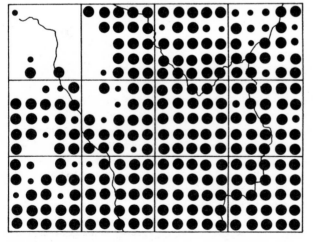

Occupied	265 (88%)
Confirmed	232 (88%)
Probable	14 (5%)
Possible	19 (7%)

Within Sheffield the highest density of Magpies can be found in the south-west of the city and along the numerous upland valleys, where densities of up to 27 pairs per km² have been recorded. An example of the latter is the Rivelin Valley which has traditionally supported a large Magpie population (*8*). Dr T. Birkhead initiated a long-term study of the behaviour of this population in 1976, using individually colour-ringed birds. This has revealed that breeding pairs have a high rate of survival, are strongly territorial and are highly sedentary. Furthermore, most young birds appear to nest within 500m of their parent's nest. The longest movement recorded to date is of a nestling which was ringed at Ramsley Moor and found dead a year later at Ladybower - a movement of only 18km.

Non-breeding birds often form discreet flocks which are most conspicuous in the winter months in adverse weather conditions. Numbers may then increase to 60 birds, albeit rarely, but more typically are between five and fifteen. Non-breeding birds also collect in large communal roosts which are used year after year. These are usually most conspicuous in December and January when several roosts have contained over 100 birds, e.g. at Rivelin Hagg and Great Hollins Wood.

Not surprisingly, there is no evidence of any regular movement or passage.

JACKDAW *Corvus monedula*

Resident breeder; woodland, farmland, quarries and suburban areas.

The Jackdaw is widespread and numerous, breeding in a variety of sites, which accounts for its occurrence in most of the area. From the distribution map it is apparent that there are two major areas from which the Jackdaw is completely absent, namely the gritstone moorlands in the north-west and the heavily urbanised and industrialised north-east where there is little potential breeding habitat. The reason for its absence from further east, around Thurcroft and Bramley, is harder to explain but may also be due to a lack of suitable nest-sites as much of the land is under the plough and there are few wooded areas.

Inside the city boundary, Jackdaws are confined largely to the suburbs in the south and west where the housing density is lower than in the east and where the greater proportion of parkland and open areas provides a more suitable breeding habitat. In the south-west the species is common in the limestone dales, where many pairs breed on the cliffs, and in the Hope and lower Derwent Valleys where nests on buildings are common. In the south-east,

255

the bird is common in SK47 which contains significantly more woodland than areas from which it is absent further north. Jackdaws are also common north of Sheffield in the Don Valley and the lower parts of its tributaries, and in much of the wooded farmland to the east, across to Wentworth.

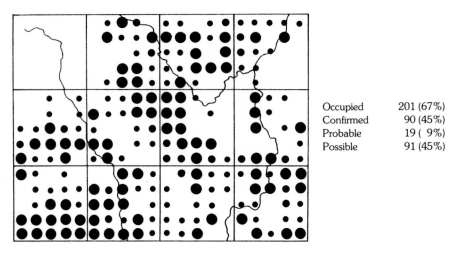

Occupied	201 (67%)
Confirmed	90 (45%)
Probable	19 (9%)
Possible	91 (45%)

There is some evidence of a small-scale migration in a south-westerly direction in autumn in most years, with maximum counts at Redmires of 44 on 3rd October 1982 and 63 on 27th October 1983.

In the winter months, Jackdaws form sizeable feeding flocks and roosts from November to February, with the largest numbers all being reported from the south-east. They usually associate with Rooks at this time, and it is very difficult to estimate the numbers of each in large flocks. The favourite localities are the Holmesfield/Cordwell Valley and Renishaw areas where mid-winter roosts of up to 5,000/6,000 corvids regularly occur. Perhaps half of these birds may be Jackdaws. A flock of 2,000 was recorded at Breck Farm on 22nd February 1979 and 500-600 were reported from Moss Valley and Linacre in 1983. Smaller flocks, usually numbering less than a hundred birds, occur in the south-west, but there were 900 corvids, mainly Jackdaws, at Wardlow on 30th December 1983 and 300 at Peter Dale on 30th January 1982. Although most of these birds may be of local origin, one ringed at Barrow Hill on 22nd February 1978 was recovered on Humberside, 89km to the east, on 10th April 1980.

ROOK *Corvus frugilegus*

Resident breeder; woodland and farmland.

Of all the birds breeding in Sheffield, the Rook is probably the easiest to census, due to its habit of nesting in conspicuous colonies. It has been the subject of five local breeding surveys (in 1965, 1970/71, 1975, 1980 and 1985) and is the only common species for which a reasonably accurate estimate of breeding numbers can be given. It is abundant and widespread, occurring over most of the region with the exception of the gritstone moorlands in the west. The Rook was recorded in two-thirds of all tetrads surveyed but if those which contain predominantly moorland habitat are excluded, this proportion rises to approximately 80%. The number of possible breeding records is high and over-estimates the Rook's distribution, especially in the east, as few rookeries are likely to have been overlooked. The records of definite breeding give a much more accurate picture of the bird's distribution and the map shown corresponds well with the map of rookeries given by Gosney (*136*).

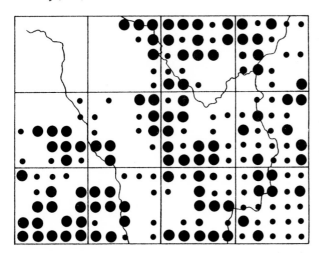

Occupied	197 (66%)
Confirmed	98 (50%)
Probable	4 (2%)
Possible	95 (48%)

Away from the moorlands the breeding colonies are widely distributed although some local concentrations occur. Wentworth, Stocksbridge, the south-western edge of the city, Calver, Bamford and Renishaw are all sites with several rookeries in a relatively small area. There are now no colonies in the north-east of Sheffield, nor in much of the land around Rotherham, Conisbrough, Bolsover and Clowne. These are all areas with few deciduous woodlands or copses. The species is common on the Carboniferous Limestone in the south-west where, although there are few extensively wooded areas, there are many lines and small copses of mature trees, which Roocks prefer to larger woods. They will even nest on electricity pylons - 49 nests were found in 1985 on one large pylon near Stocksbridge - and floodlight towers, e.g. 6 nests at Arkwright Colliery in 1985. A curious phenomenon in the distribution of colonies noticed by Gosney (*136*) is their high incidence on, or very close to, the edge of the Millstone Grit region (24 colonies within 1km of the boundary) while there are very few rookeries actually on the main gritstone area. The reason for this is not known. Rookeries are found over a wide range of altitudes in Sheffield, ranging from around 30 metres a.s.l. in the lower Don Valley to 360m at Tideswell, with the majority of colonies between 100 and 250 metres.

Analysis of the rookery census results indicates the population was static from 1965 to 1971, then increased from 3,901 (104 colonies) to 4,442 pairs (128 colonies) in 1985. However, this may be misleading for two reasons. Firstly, observer coverage has improved during these years, e.g. a thorough search in 1985 of some areas where rookeries had not previously been found, revealed the presence of an extra six, holding 385 nests, most of which are likely to have existed for some years. The other problem is that recent checks have shown that numbers change during the season at some sites, e.g. due to late starters and tree-felling. Culling by shooting also occurs and can be substantial at certain larger rookeries. The overall picture is probably one of slow decline, associated with changes in land-use, and a considerable redistribution of colonies (e.g. in 1985 only two were located in SK49 but there were 13 in SK28, compared to 10 and 8 in 1975)

The size of colonies varies greatly, from one to c.230 nests (at Wentworth in 1985), with a mean size of 37.5 in 1965 and 32.3 in 1985. The breeding density over the whole area averaged 3.7 pairs per km^2 in 1975, which becomes 4.0 pairs per km^2 if SK19 is excluded. This indicates that Rook densities are similar to the national average of 3.9 pairs per km^2 (137). Much higher local concentrations occur, such as (in 1985) 353 nests (7 colonies) along 4km of the Little Don Valley around Stocksbridge and 299 (4 colonies) in a 1km transect of the limestone plateau at Peak Forest.

In winter, Rooks congregate into large flocks for feeding and roosting and some sites hold large roosts each year. Of these, Renishaw is probably one of the largest and most regular. Counts in the region of 5,000 birds have been made almost annually and 7,500 were reported in February 1980. Other large roosts occur at Wentworth, where a maximum of 7,000 corvids (mostly Rooks) was present in September 1978, and Smeekley Woods. Flocks of over a thousand birds are recorded in the vicinity of the roosts, e.g. in the Owler Bar/Leash Fen/Holmesfield area, and in a few other localities such as Ringinglow and the Moss Valley. Numbers begin to build up in late summer, e.g. 1,000 at Wentworth in mid-July 1978, and remain high until the end of February or early March when dispersal back to the colonies begins.

A bird breeding at Barlborough in May 1980 had been ringed as a *pullus* 63km away in Lincolnshire.

CARRION CROW *Corvus corone*

Resident breeder, passage/winter visitor; farmland, moorland and built up areas.

The Carrion Crow is very widespread, as the map shows, being found in virtually all habitats from open moorland to urban and industrial areas. The large number of possible breeding records results from the conspicuous nature of the bird, having few natural predators, in its wide ranging search for food.

There are few gaps in the breeding distribution of this species and some of these may be due to incomplete surveying. It is sparse on certain moorlands, due to either absence of trees for nesting or persecution by keepers. There are several squares to the north of Sheffield where it was probably overlooked but the relative scarcity in the north-east and south-east corners of the area is likely to be more real. The bird is common within the city and breeds close to the city centre, e.g. in Weston Park and near Bramall Lane.

Outside the breeding season, feeding flocks are reported, usually from areas of farmland. The largest concentrations occur in the winter months from November to February. The only site regularly to hold a large flock at this time of year is at Holmesfield, where up to 200 birds have been present. Nearby Linacre also held over 200 birds in December 1974 and a roost of c. 175 was present at Longshaw in the same winter. In 1982/83 up to 170 were in the Moss Valley in December and two flocks at Harthill on 3rd February contained 408 Carrion Crows. Flocks of less than a hundred have been reported from the Porter and Rother Valleys, Renishaw, Midhope and Redmires.

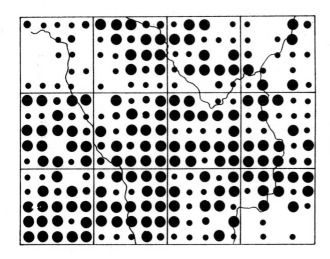

Occupied	262 (87%)
Confirmed	142 (54%)
Probable	28 (11%)
Possible	92 (35%)

There have been 24 records of Hooded Crow *C.c.cornix* since 1960 and with one exception, concerning a Carrion/Hooded hybrid at Staveley in June 1969, all the dates are between October and April inclusive. Just over a half are in October and November, the time at which continental birds arrive on the east coast. Occurrences are somewhat erratic, with no birds recorded in some years while in the autumns of 1975 and 1976 there were minor influxes into the region, with six and five records respectively. As there has been only one record in the present decade (on 11th January 1981), the status of this sub-species has perhaps changed to that of a scarce visitor.

As might be expected from a bird which breeds in such a wide variety of habitats, the localities in which Hooded Crows have been recorded are widespread with no particularly favoured sites. There is a slight bias to the west which is perhaps surprising as presumably most birds are immigrants from the continent. Thrybergh Resr and Leash Fen are the only sites where the Hooded Crow has been recorded more than once: there are three reports from both localities. On 11th October 1975 there were probably two birds present in the area as sightings occurred at Bleaklow and Hathersage.

RAVEN *Corvus corax*

Scarce visitor.

Although locally common prior to the nineteenth century, the Raven was eradicated from most of England by persecution during the Victorian era (*138*). This was undoubtedly the period when it disappeared as a breeding bird from much of the Sheffield region, and nesting occurred at only isolated sites in the Dark Peak and possibly one site in the limestone dales. The last known breeding sites were Howden Chest in 1863 and Alport Castles a year or two earlier. During the present century its status has been very much that of a scarce visitor to the uplands. In 1966 a pair appeared in the Bleaklow area and bred at Alport Castles in 1967-68. These were, however, thought to have been released and a wild origin appears unlikely (*20*).

In 1968 there were four reports away from Alport with birds recorded at Dungworth (2nd April), Ladybower (two on 19th June), Redmires (20th July) and Dronfield Woodhouse (11th November). Single birds were seen at Ladybower on 22nd January 1969 and Eyam Moor on 19th April 1970. Since 1970 there have been only six acceptable records of what are likely to be wild birds. Singles were reported from Ladybower on 29th July 1975, Longstone Edge on 21st March 1977, Upper Derwentdale on 6th March 1977, 9th April 1983, 1st June 1984, and the Little Don Valley on 13th May 1985 (JL). All were presumably wandering birds and there seems little likelihood of a further nesting attempt in the near future.

STARLING *Sturnus vulgaris*

Resident/Migrant breeder, winter visitor; urban areas, farmland and woodland.

The Starling is a common breeding bird over much of the area and is the fifth most widespread nesting species. All the squares from which it is absent are confined to the upland regions where there is little suitable breeding habitat, as are all instances of possible or probable breeding, except one. Breeding has occurred in a wide range of habitats from urban buildings and woodlands to quarries, crags and hedgerow trees. Local results show interesting variations in breeding densities according to habitat. Suburban woodland in Sheffield may hold densities equivalent to 66 pairs per km², upland moorland-fringe woodland 20 pairs per km², upland farmland 8 pairs per km², and lowland industrial farmland 5 pairs per km². This conforms well with the densities quoted by Sharrock (*19*).

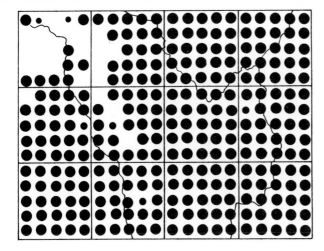

Occupied	278 (93%)
Confirmed	272 (98%)
Probable	4 (1%)
Possible	2 (1%)

British Starlings have been shown to be largely sedentary (*139*) and conforming to this, all recoveries of birds ringed locally in the breeding season have been within 50km (*124*). However, large numbers of continental birds winter in the area and 25 winter-ringed recoveries have occurred in eastern Europe and the U.S.S.R. Much westerly movement of Starlings over the area is apparent in October and November; for example 5,000 birds passed over Redmires in 75 minutes on 1st November 1980 and 3,600 in two hours on 6th November 1983.

Starlings are notable for the formation of large roosts in the non-breeding season. In the summer, big flocks of mainly juveniles are to be found on pastures and moorlands particularly to the west of Sheffield, and associated roosts are often quite large. In the winter the population is swollen by continental immigrants and a number of roosting sites are used. A survey of local Starling roosts conducted in 1979-1980 revealed 19 to 27 definitely or probably used roosts, although the situation was found to be very fluid, with only a proportion of these in use at any one time (*140*). The largest was at Catcliffe and held 50,000 birds at peak; two other roosts held populations of between 10,000 and 20,000, nine were between 1,000 and 10,000 and eleven between 1 and 1,000 birds. All but two were in the eastern half of the area. Most roosts peaked in numbers in either July/August or October; these probably correspond to the presence of juvenile birds and migrants, respectively.

Urban roosting was first recorded in the city in 1978, although the peak count was only 2,000 in 1979. The roost at Wentworth Park, which held 250,000 birds in 1973, had ceased by 1979. With these two exceptions the winter roost situation has remained similar in pattern, though not in detail, throughout the 1970s and up to the present. In 1983 the largest roost located was at Bow Bridge in Rotherham where there were 25,000 on 18th October rising to 50,000 by 22nd November. Earlier in the year a roost of 10,000 was located at High Moor in January which increased to 15,000 by March.

HOUSE SPARROW *Passer domesticus*

Resident breeder; urban areas and farmland.

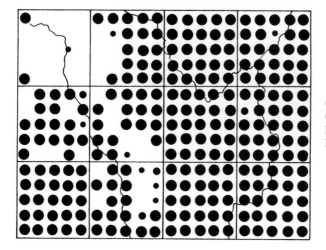

Occupied	255 (85%)
Confirmed	243 (95%)
Probable	4 (2%)
Possible	8 (3%)

The House Sparrow is widespread and abundant throughout most built-up areas and is absent only from open moorland and the more exposed areas of the Carboniferous Limestone plateau. It is even found in the isolated buildings near the entrance to the Woodhead Tunnel in the extreme north-west. By exploiting the urban environment this species can evidently start breeding at an earlier date than its close relative the Tree Sparrow.

Post-breeding flocks are reported from the end of June (max. 400 at Kilnhurst on 25th June 1982), but most frequently in August when concentrations of several hundred birds are not uncommon on farmland associated with urban areas. The peak count was 450 in the Moss Valley on 9th August 1976. Numbers increase during the autumn period when over 1,450 were counted at Thrybergh Resr on 14th September 1983; 1,000 birds were at Killamarsh on 20th October 1973, 500 at Ravenfield on 16th September 1974 and 450 at Harthill on 22nd October 1974. The dispersal of birds from these flocks may explain the small but annual south-westerly passage of birds over the Southern Pennines. These movements occur in September and October, usually in association with high pressure systems, i.e. on clear, calm days. Ringing recoveries from the 1970s suggest that at least some of these birds are involved in movements of more than a local nature.

Reports of large flocks during the winter months are few; 450 birds at Wentworth on 18th January 1975 and 300 at Ravensfield on 14th January 1979 being exceptional. This may simply reflect that in a largely urban environment food is broadly dispersed.

TREE SPARROW *Passer montanus*

Resident breeder, passage/winter visitor; woodland, farmland and parkland.

The Tree Sparrow is widespread and locally common. With the exception of some upland areas it may be found wherever suitable nesting habitat occurs. This hole-nesting species regularly uses trees, buildings and walls with suitable cavities. It is often to be found in association with farmland where 'weed' seeds provide a readily available source of food. Nationally, there appears to be a trend for Tree Sparrows to prefer areas of low rainfall (*19*) and this may be reflected locally. It is largely absent from the heavily industrialised and built-up areas of Sheffield, but within the city parks, Smith (*20*) considered it to be more numerous than was generally believed, and it probably breeds in most wooded areas. It will nest in boxes in suburban gardens on the edge of parkland. The highest breeding concentrations are to be found in the lowlands to the south-east of Sheffield. Post-breeding flocks are rarely reported, the maximum being 80 at Elsecar on 5th August 1981.

Occupied	197 (66%)
Confirmed	125 (63%)
Probable	23 (12%)
Possible	49 (25%)

263

At present little is known about the autumn passage, although the species is recorded annually on visible migration watches. At Redmires small parties flying to the west and south-west are not uncommon during September and October. Similar movements have also been recorded over Concord Park and Tinsley S.F.

The largest concentrations are usually found during the winter months, but numbers vary annually, a feature which may, in part, reflect fluctuations in breeding success. In October and December 1977, 500 birds were present at Breck Farm, Barrow Hill, feeding on Kale. Elsewhere, 240 were in the Moss Valley on 8th November 1975, whilst flocks of c. 100 birds are not uncommon. The distribution of winter flocks probably reflects the main breeding areas and the major food sources.

CHAFFINCH *Fringilla coelebs*

Resident/partial migrant breeder, passage/winter visitor; woodland, parkland and farmland.

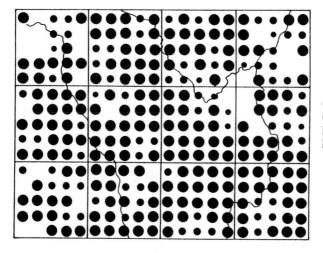

Occupied	274 (91%)
Confirmed	200 (73%)
Probable	65 (24%)
Possible	9 (3%)

A widespread and locally abundant species, the Chaffinch is absent only from open moorland in the north-west and the industrial and built-up areas to the north-east of both Sheffield and Rotherham. It is even found in small patches of Mountain Ash in moorland cloughs. It was recorded in most urban woodland and some ornamental parks, although it was usually less numerous than the Greenfinch.

Local CBC data indicate that in the upland conifers there can be considerable annual fluctuation in the breeding population; e.g. at Swinden Plantation the breeding density of 0.25 pairs per ha in 1975 had more than doubled by 1979 to 0.6 pairs per ha. However, in the mixed habitat of Tor Farm and the Limb Valley the population has remained stable at a density of 0.35 pairs per ha.

Post-breeding movements prior to the autumn moult are recorded in most years from mid-July to mid-August 1981. At this time small feeding flocks are occasionally reported, although they rarely exceed 100 birds. A second and more substantial passage occurs from mid-September to mid-November. During this period over 400 birds per hour have been counted at Redmires on several dates with a peak of 800 birds moving west on the evening of 26th and the morning of 27th October 1984. In the autumn of 1981 over 4,000 passed though in a west to south-westerly direction (KC). Transitory feeding flocks are not uncommon during the migration period, the largest being 300 at Lodge Moor. Many of these passage birds and winter visitors are undoubtedly of continental origin as birds ringed locally during this period have been recovered in spring in the Netherlands, Fair Isle, Denmark and Norway.

During the winter months the largest concentrations are usually found at roosts. Approximately 1,500 birds were present at Chatsworth Park during November and December 1977, but more typically, roosts of a few hundred birds are recorded annually from both upland and lowland localities. Large flocks may also be found feeding on arable farmland and, in some years, on Beech mast, often in association with other finches, particularly Brambling and Greenfinch. They peak in December when 600 were at Broomhead Hall on 4th in 1981, and 500 at Wentworth on 16th in 1978 and Ecclesfield on 26th in 1980.

BRAMBLING *Fringilla montifringilla*

Winter/passage visitor; farmland, woodland and parkland.

The Brambling is a locally common winter visitor whose numbers fluctuate widely from year to year. Large influxes occurred during the winters of 1965/66, 1971/72, 1976/77 and 1980/81. Within any one year the largest concentrations usually occur shortly after the main autumn influx, the biggest flock being 1,000 at Barlborough Park on 18th November 1965. Similar concentrations may also be found in early spring along the moorland fringe, where in April 1,000 birds occurred at Broomhead Hall in 1983 and well over this number gathered in Beech woodland at Strines Dike in the early morning of 14th in 1977 (JH). In most years flocks of several hundred birds are often seen in association with arable farmland or Beech mast. Reports from suburban areas include 500 at Beauchief on 19th March 1981 and at Stannington on 9th November 1973,

265

whilst sightings in gardens continue to increase and birds have been seen feeding on hop-waste in the Botanical Gardens and Ecclesall Woods.

The earliest autumn record is of three birds in the Moss Valley on 18th September 1976. More typically the first birds are not reported until late September or during the first two weeks of October. Bramblings are regularly recorded on visible migration watches until mid-November, although the rate of movement rarely exceeds 100 birds per hour. Large numbers have been ringed locally, including 341 during a prolonged cold spell in 1972/73. One ringed at Breck Farm in February 1969 was controlled in Lappi, Finland, in July 1970, the most northerly British recovery (124). Most birds have usually departed by May. Flocks of 150 birds at Woolley Woods on 2nd May 1981 and 100 at Redmires on 7th May 1977 were exceptional. The latest record is of a pair at Hackenthorpe on 16th May 1981.

Summer records are few and refer to single males at Gleadless on 12th June 1969, and in an Ecclesall garden on 23rd August 1980. At Redmires in June and July 1978 a bird defended a territory throughout the summer apparently without a mate. On 18th June 1983 a male was found in Padley Gorge; it sang daily until 2nd July and attempted to mate with a breeding female Chaffinch, departing when she started to feed young (141). A singing male was subsequently located at Ingbirchworth, just north of our area, staying from 12th July to 1st August (DJS et al). It is notable that this followed the first proof of breeding in England - in Northamptonshire in 1981 (Brit.B).

GREENFINCH Carduelis chloris

Resident breeder, winter/passage visitor; woodland, parkland, farmland, wasteland and suburban gardens.

The Greenfinch breeds throughout the area wherever hedgerows, open woodland, ornamental gardens and scrubland occur. It is absent only from areas of open moorland and the dry-stone walled pasture-land of the Carboniferous Limestone plateau. Within the city parks and woodlands it is the most abundant of the breeding finches, occurring in 31 of the 36 areas studied. However, numbers are low at all CBC sites, with usually no more than one or two pairs breeding at any one site. Post-breeding flocks rarely exceed 100 birds although larger numbers are occasionally reported, including the exceptional record of 900 at Bramley in August 1977 (DJG).

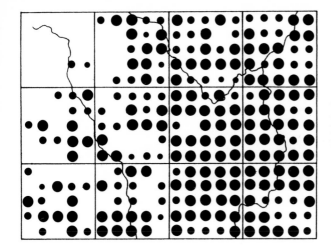

Occupied	235 (78%)
Confirmed	147 (62%)
Probable	79 (34%)
Possible	9 (4%)

The largest concentrations of Greenfinch have been reported during the autumn months with 1,000 at Thrybergh Woods on 6th October 1975 and Marsh Lane on 2nd October 1976. The dispersal of these flocks may contribute to the passage of birds observed annually at several moorland localities. At Redmires the passage begins in late September and may continue until late November. Peak movements at this locality include 260 west in 75 minutes on 23rd November 1980 and 221 west in 60 minutes on 13th October 1980. The number of birds involved in these movements fluctuates between years. These observations support the recent idea that the Greenfinch is a partial migrant in the northern and eastern part of its British range where birds undergo a westerly and southerly migration in November and December. Both the distances moved and the number of birds involved in these movements is positively correlated with the population density (142)

During the winter months the Greenfinch is a common visitor to suburban gardens and wasteland, where flock size is small but turnover high; e.g. 677 were ringed in the 1972/73 winter. Concentrations are commonly found on the outskirts of the city, often in association with arable farmland. Therefore it is not surprising that the largest flocks have been recorded from the lowlands. Maxima include 900 at Barrow Hill on 9th January 1974 and 750 at Beighton on 26th February 1976. Flocks of up to 300 birds are more widely distributed including occasional records from the moors.

Ringing returns of interest include a bird killed by a cat on 2nd May 1983 only 2km away from where it had been ringed over seven years earlier (on 28th February 1976). In contrast, one controlled on the Isle of Man on 29th October 1983 had been ringed 243km away at Breck Farm (on 1st August 1982).

GOLDFINCH *Carduelis carduelis*

Resident/migrant breeder, passage visitor; farmland, heathland, parks, scrub and wasteland.

The Goldfinch is a widespread breeding species and is found throughout the area except on open moorland and parts of the Carboniferous Limestone plateau. There is no evidence to suggest that its distribution to the east of Sheffield is still patchy, as suggested by Smith (21). The map indicates that it may be less common to the north of the city where there is a lower proportion of confirmed breeding records. It also appears to be thinly distributed in parts of the south such as the Cordwell Valley, but it may have been overlooked. The Goldfinch is not uncommon in urban districts where flocks of up to 100 birds have occurred during the autumn. Males have been reported singing in the city centre and pairs have nested at the Pond Street entrance to the Sheffield Polytechnic.

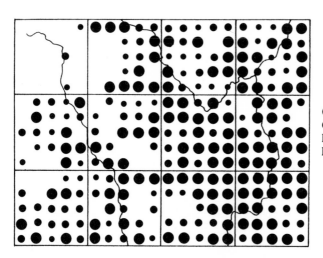

Occupied	243 (81%)
Confirmed	127 (52%)
Probable	77 (32%)
Possible	39 (16%)

Autumn passage is not visually evident until September and continues into November in most years. During this period small flocks are regularly seen moving at migration watchpoints including Tinsley S.F. Large flocks are sometimes reported at this time, e.g. 120 at Whiston Meadows on 3rd October 1980. 1979 was an exceptional year with 200 birds in the Moss Valley in late September and 600 at Grindleford on 28th October (GPM). During the autumn and winter months wasteland, rough pasture, open scrubland and the limestone dales are favoured habitats where thistle seeds, a preferred food, are often abundant.

By mid-November the majority of birds have left the area, presumably wintering further south or even on the continent. Several locally ringed birds have been recovered during the winter in France, Spain and Portugal, and on Bardsey Island in spring. However, small numbers may remain through the winter, with maxima of c.60 at Millhouses, on 12th December 1976, and in the Moss Valley on 4th January 1975. The winter of 1974/75 was unusually mild and a flock of c.25 Goldfinch stayed on Broomhead Moors, at an altitude of 300m.

From February onwards numbers slowly increase as migrant birds return. During March and April 1977, c.75 were at Renishaw feeding on Alder seeds, but in most years the major influx does not occur until mid-April and early May when flocks of up to 50 birds are commonly seen.

SISKIN *Carduelis spinus*

Resident breeder, passage/winter visitor; woodland, parkland and suburban gardens.

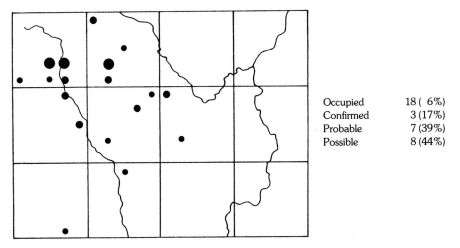

Occupied	18 (6%)
Confirmed	3 (17%)
Probable	7 (39%)
Possible	8 (44%)

Although formerly known only as a winter visitor, the Siskin is now a regular breeder in coniferous plantations. The first indication of possible nesting was a female at Holmesfield in June 1965. This was followed by records of summering birds in each year from 1970 to 1973. In 1974 breeding was confirmed when two pairs were seen feeding young on 21st July at Strines, South Yorkshire (72). Following a slight setback in 1975, when there were no breeding records, the population has continued to increase. In 1977 three pairs bred at Strines, whilst the first breeding record for Derbyshire was substantiated when a nest was located in Derwentdale. The population spread from the extensive coniferous plantations to smaller mature coniferous stands on the moorland fringe, e.g. first breeding at Chatsworth in 1980. By 1982, 10-15 pairs were breeding in Derwentdale and smaller numbers occurred in several other Derbyshire woodlands. In South Yorkshire numbers have shown a constant increase and few mature conifer plantations are now without nesting Siskin. A typical breeding population may now number between 50 and 100 pairs in the Peak District.

Large influxes into the area are often reported in September and October, when a small but widespread south-westerly and westerly passage has been reported, of typically less than 100 birds per day. However, the largest concentrations do not usually occur until the winter months. The size of the winter population varies greatly between years. Exceptional winters were 1979/80 and 1984/85 when large flocks were reported throughout the area. These included 200 at Chatsworth on 23rd December 1979 and 6th February 1980, 150 at Broomhead on 7th February 1980 and 120 in the Porter Valley on 17th November 1979. There were 200 in Upper Derwentdale in late 1984, increasing to up to 450 in early 1985, and smaller flocks of 100 or more in the extensive coniferous woodlands in South Yorkshire.

The preferred winter habitat appears to be alongside rivers wherever Alder is plentiful and in coniferous woodland in which Larch is common. Thus flocks of c.50 birds are regularly reported from the Derwent Valley, Wyming Brook, Strines, the Moss Valley and Woolley Woods.

Since the mid-1970s the Siskin has become a regular visitor to garden bird-feeders in many parts of the city, showing a strong preference for red plastic bags containing peanuts. One ringed in a Walkley garden on 4th March 1981 was retrapped at Darnaway Forest (Grampian) two years later and found dead at Nairn (Highland) on 18th July 1983. Another caught in Sheffield in winter had been ringed in Inverness the previous July.

LINNET *Carduelis cannabina*

Resident/migrant breeder, winter/passage visitor; heathland, farmland and wasteland.

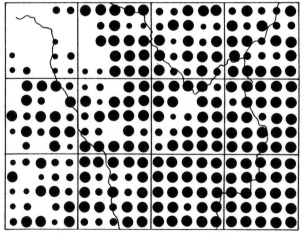

Occupied	263 (88%)
Confirmed	177 (67%)
Probable	61 (23%)
Possible	23 (9%)

The Linnet is the most widely distributed of the breeding finches. It is absent only from the High Peak and adjacent areas of open moorland, although scarce on the more exposed areas of the Carboniferous Limestone plateau. It favours areas of scrub, hedgerows and heathland with easy access to its preferred food, the seeds of 'weeds'. Where such conditions prevail, Linnets will nest in small colonies, the location of which often moves from year to year. Thus breeding numbers at CBC sites may fluctuate annually, e.g. between one and ten pairs at Breck Farm and one and seven pairs at Tor Farm.

Post-breeding flocks can be seen from July onwards; e.g. there were 200 birds in the Moss Valley on 2nd July 1977 and at Redmires on 17th July 1974. The frequency with which these occur reaches a peak in September when over 500 birds have been reported from Breck Farm, Killamarsh and Tinsley S.F., with a maximum of 675 at Abney on 17th September 1971.

Autumn passage usually starts in mid-September and continues into mid-October. During this period over 1300 birds were counted flying south over Redmires in 1981. Peak rates of movement are typically in the last week of September when maxima include 340 in two hours on 30th September 1982. Recoveries of locally ringed Linnets suggest that at least some winter on the continent in France and Spain. The maximum concentration was a flock of 800 at Barrow Hill on 4th October 1980. By November most birds have departed from the area, the maximum flock recorded in this month being c.40, at Alport on 17th November 1979.

Winter records are infrequent, although large flocks are occasionally reported from the lowlands. Maxima include 250 at Barrow Hill in the winter of 1980 and 200 at Wadsley Common on 17th December 1978. Ringing returns from the former locality suggest that many of these birds may be of local origin.

Return movement is evident from February onwards, reaching a peak in April and early May, when parties can regularly be seen moving to the north-west over the moorland fringe. During this period flocks of 350 birds have been recorded in the Moss Valley, whilst on 5th May 1979 1,000 were seen at Wardlow (PAA).

TWITE *Carduelis flavirostris*

Migrant breeder, passage visitor; moorland, rough pasture and wasteland.

The Twite has a thinly scattered breeding population which, with the exception of a small number on the Carboniferous Limestone plateau, is restricted to the higher altitude moorland fringe where heather and Purple Moor Grass, a staple food, often coincide. Through much of its range it replaces the Linnet, although overlap occurs in some areas, especially where Bracken is present. During the period 1960-71 only three breeding sites were listed for the Sheffield area (*143*). By 1977 the number had increased to ten and the *Atlas* added a further 20 probable breeding localities. It appears that during the 1970s the Twite recolonised many of its former breeding haunts (*72*).

Post-breeding flocks are recorded from late July, being most frequently reported in August, although peak counts often occur later in the autumn. Maxima are 400 at Big Moor in October 1973, 200 on Hallam Moor on 21st September 1976 and 140 at Barbrook on 25th

July 1976. The latest date for a large flock is 10th November 1971 when 100 birds were still on Burbage Moor. Unfortunately, if the size of the post-breeding flock reflects the year's breeding success there is little cause for optimism, as recently numbers have rarely exceeded 50 birds. This decline has been particularly marked in Yorkshire on Hallam Moor where in 1970-76 the mean of the largest annual flock was 100 birds, whereas during the period 1977-82 the mean peak flock size fell to only eight birds.

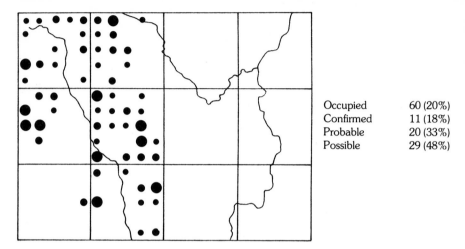

Occupied	60 (20%)
Confirmed	11 (18%)
Probable	20 (33%)
Possible	29 (48%)

Autumn passage is ill-defined; visible migration watches have provided little evidence of any regular movements either along or across the southern Pennines. It seems likely that the local birds undergo an easterly movement to the East coast. This behaviour would account for the large number of records from the lowlands during the autumn months, although it is surprising that the largest lowland flock is one of only five birds at Breck Farm in 1974. At Concord Park a total of 16 (up to four a day), mainly moving south, were noted on five dates from 1st to 20th October 1983, with a similar picture in 1984 when 23 were seen between 14th October and 4th November.

During the winter months there are usually a few isolated reports, involving small numbers of birds, from both upland and lowland localities. There were two notable flocks in December 1984: 14 at Bradwell Ponds on 16th and twelve at Froggatt Edge on 31st. Birds may return to the breeding grounds as early as the first half of March.

REDPOLL *Carduelis flammea*

Resident/migrant breeder, winter/passage visitor; woodland, wasteland and farmland.

The Redpoll is a widespread but thinly distributed species and is absent only from areas of open moorland and the Carboniferous Limestone plateau. Within the urban habitat it is not uncommon, with the exception of the heavily industrialised areas to the north-east of the city. It may be found in small loose colonies in scrubland, hedgerows, overgrown allotments and young conifer plantations. Breeding is difficult to confirm due to the small, discretely

272

hidden nest and the wide ranging behaviour of the adults during the breeding season. Several pairs nest amongst Willow carr at Tinsley S.F. and one nest was located a metre above ground level (DH).

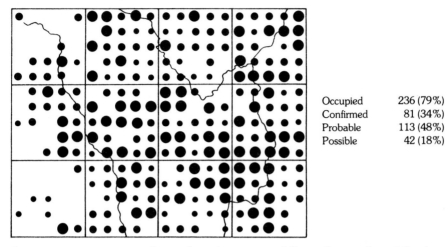

Occupied	236 (79%)
Confirmed	81 (34%)
Probable	113 (48%)
Possible	42 (18%)

Autumn passage is usually evident between mid-September and mid-October. Observations at Redmires suggest that the number of birds can fluctuate markedly between years. In the autumn of 1980 passage was heavy with peak movements on 24th September when 350 birds flew west in three hours. In contrast, 1981 proved to be an exceptionally poor year with movements rarely exceeding ten birds per hour. It is of interest to note that during the winter of 1981 records were unusually scarce. Recoveries of birds ringed locally indicate that many of these passage birds are moving from their breeding grounds in the north of England. Many winter on the continent, where recoveries have been received from Holland, Belgium, Germany, France and northern Italy.

In the lowlands large winter flocks are seen most frequently in November and December. Elsewhere they are recorded in all winter months, especially in woodland areas with a high density of Birch or Alder, the seeds of which are an important food source. Winter maxima include 200-400 in late November 1984 at Wyming Brook, 300 at the same locality from 10th-31st December 1974, and 250 at Wharncliffe on 24th October 1975 and 24th February 1976. During the last decade the winter population has increased, as prior to the 1970s there were no records of flocks greater than 50 birds.

Spring passage begins in early March, and continues into mid-May when flocks of 100 birds are not uncommon.

The Scandinavian race *C. f. flammea*, the Mealy Redpoll, has also been recorded, outside the breeding season, on at least 13 occasions prior to the 1984/85 winter. It is usually seen singly or in small parties, mostly in the lowlands. The largest party was six at Millhouses on 13th April 1974. There appears to have been a marked influx in the most recent winter (1984/85), probably associated with a large influx of Siskin, but details have yet to be collated.

TWO-BARRED CROSSBILL Loxia leucoptera

Scarce visitor.

A male of this species was reported from Strines on 30th October 1982 in company with 45 Crossbills and two Parrot Crossbills (DHu). Unfortunately, a clear view of the individual was not obtained and the record is still under consideration by the *British Birds* Rarities Committee. This was the first evidence of a remarkable invasion of crossbills into the area. The species was not identified again until 9th January 1983 when what was presumably the same bird was found in Upper Derwentdale where it apparently remained until at least 27th February (DH, DHu *et al*). This was the only British record in 1982/83.

CROSSBILL Loxia curvirostra

Casual breeder, summer/passage visitor; coniferous woodland.

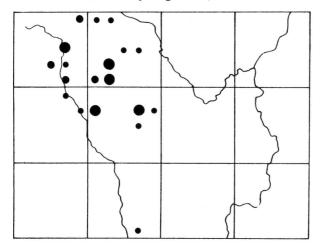

Occupied	19 (6%)
Confirmed	5 (26%)
Probable	4 (21%)
Possible	10 (53%)

The Crossbill is an annual visitor to the coniferous woodland of the gritstone valleys, and is particularly attracted to Larch plantations. In most years it is only seen in small parties, but sometimes there are larger invasions. These invariably occur in late June to early August, or in late October to December. In the first decade of the review period, invasions occurred in the summer of 1962 (e.g. 56 at Longshaw in July), 1963 and 1966. Then in 1972 there were 32 at Langsett and 65 at Ladybower, on 9th July, and up to 60 at Hathersage and Wyming Brook in August. Latterly, invasions have been predominantly in late autumn, with 1976, 1980 and 1982 the principal years. There has been an increase in numbers in the 1980s, which is detailed below. Most of the summer arrivals usually overwinter and depart in February or March, presumably to their northern breeding grounds.

Breeding reports were very sparse until 1981. The first was at Longshaw in 1958 (TM), followed by lone pairs feeding young at Strines on 19th May 1973 and near Ladybower in 1977 when there was also evidence of breeding at two other sites. In the period 1978 to 1980 at least one or two pairs bred annually in Peak District woodlands. An invasion began in mid-November 1980 and numbers increased gradually so that by February 1981 parties of up to 20 were to be found in almost any plantation on the gritstone, and there were at least 50 birds at Strines. Many of these stayed to breed, which was unprecedented and presumably attributable to a particularly favourable cone crop. Breeding records came from Langsett (at least two sites), Midhope, Ewden, Strines, Derwentdale and Wyming Brook, involving at least 100 pairs (DH, PKG). In June parties of up to 50, including many juveniles, were evident but subsequently left the area.

There were very few reports in the latter half of 1981, or indeed in 1982 until 24th October when twelve were seen at Midhope, followed by 30 flying south-west at Redmires on 28th. These heralded a major sudden invasion; by early November there were probably at least 200 birds scattered in parties of up to 40 throughout the western coniferous plantations, and a few were even seen in Larch elsewhere, e.g. in the lower Moss Valley. The presence of small numbers of accompanying Parrot Crossbills indicated a Scandinavian origin. Many stayed into early February but most departed later in the month. A few remained to breed in several plantations, but only small numbers were reported subsequently. The 1984 season was the lowest year for breeding Crossbills in the 1980s, with evidence of not more than one to two pairs. Numbers were low in the following winter but there was another invasion in early July 1985 when parties were seen at several localities and included c. 100 at Strines (TM).

PARROT CROSSBILL *Loxia pytyopsittacus*

Scarce visitor.

On 11th/12th October 1982 there were five records of single Parrot Crossbills on the Lincolnshire and Humberside coast, three of which died. These, together with one in Norfolk on 16th/17th October, were the first evidence of what was to be a major invasion by this species. Parrot Crossbills became apparent at three sites in the northern Peak from 30th October. On this date seven were identified at Howden and two at Strines (DHu), and on the following day there were two at Wyming Brook (PAA). A total of at least 45 individuals were eventually identified in company with very large numbers of (Common) Crossbill. They were evidently attracted to the area by the abundant Larch cone crop, having left Scandinavia due to the failure of the cone crop there.

In the plantations around Howden Resr, Upper Derwentdale, there were four males and three females on 30th October with 60/70 Crossbill. Numbers increased until by 15th November there were 25: ten males, eleven females and four immatures. These remained in the area until at least 10th January 1983. There were 20 present on 3rd February, after which most departed leaving a single male on 13th.

At Hollingdale plantation, Strines, there were two males on 30th October, increasing to seven males and three females by 11th November. These were possibly joined by a further pair and the 10-12 birds remained until 10th January. Numbers then increased and at least 20 were last recorded on 27th February (PKG,DH). Presumably the later influx was of birds from Derwentdale.

At Wyming Brook 14 were present on 2nd November, including six males, but no more than eight were seen (four males) at any one time after this. They were regularly present until 20th February, and were seen flying west to roost at Redmires on 5th January. The last sighting was of five on 23rd February.

Almost coinciding with the departure of these birds, a few were recorded at Swinden plantation, Langsett (*144*). At least one male accompanied 31 Crossbills on 5th February and two pairs were seen on 23rd February. Identification was difficult as the birds tended to be secretive but up to eleven were thought to be present. One or two pairs were seen courtship feeding; at least three singing males were reported, and nest-building occurred at two separate sites on 13th March and 2nd April. The behaviour subsequently suggested attempted breeding by at least one pair in a Scots Pine. A family party of seven active birds was reported on 7th May of which two were juveniles, and a begging juvenile was fed by a female on two occasions. However, the presence of breeding Crossbills in that locality at the same time may have caused a confusion of identification, so that breeding by Parrot Crossbills is not considered to have been confirmed.

What makes the events all the more remarkable is that the only other records of the species that winter, apart from the five coastal birds in October, were 13 on Scottish islands, two in Durham, twelve at Winskley (North Yorkshire) from 29th January to 24th February, and seven in Norfolk in October. The first confirmed breeding record for the British Isles was in Norfolk in 1984.

BULLFINCH *Pyrrhula pyrrhula*

Resident breeder/passage visitor; woodland, wasteland, parks, gardens and farmland.

The Bullfinch is a widespread, highly sedentary species. The high proportion of possible breeding records probably reflects the secretive behaviour of this species during the breeding season rather than a thinly distributed population. It is absent only from areas of open moorland, the Carboniferous Limestone plateau and isolated urban areas including the city centre. It was recorded in 26 out of 36 city parks, and nesting occurred in all wooded areas in these localities (*120*). However, the population density is low, as shown by the sparsity of the species at local CBC sites except Little Matlock Wood where there were five pairs (in 12.5 hectares) in 1975.

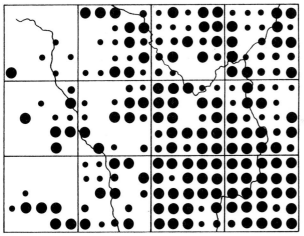

Occupied	212 (71%)
Confirmed	126 (59%)
Probable	34 (16%)
Possible	52 (25%)

The higher ground may be deserted in cold weather, and although return is not well documented, in 1982 it was noted that a few pairs reappeared in Upper Derwentale in late April. It is rare to see more than a handful of birds together. Small flocks of up to 20 birds do form in some winters, and there have been two records of flocks of 30: at Barrow Hill on 8th December 1973 and Langsett on 23rd January 1977.

An indication of the sedentary nature of Bullfinches is illustrated by the recovery of a bird ringed in its first year at Rivelin in December 1978 four and a half years later only 4km away. Surprisingly, one ring was found in the pellet of a Short-eared Owl.

HAWFINCH *Coccothraustes coccothraustes*

Resident breeder; deciduous woodland, parkland and Hawthorn scrub.

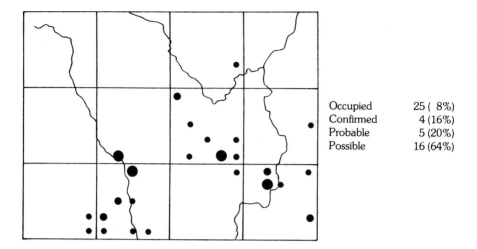

Occupied	25 (8%)
Confirmed	4 (16%)
Probable	5 (20%)
Possible	16 (64%)

The Hawfinch is an uncommon and secretive species, breeding almost exclusively in mature deciduous woodland. The map indicates that it is to be found mainly in the lower Derwent Valley and in the south-east of the area. It is, however, undoubtedly overlooked and probably breeds regularly in several of the Carboniferous Limestone dales and in woodland to the north-east of Sheffield where in recent years up to three pairs have nested. Hawfinches are scarce in the north-west, although there was evidence of breeding in Upper Derwentdale in 1982 and a male was seen feeding at Losehill Hall, in the Hope Valley, in September 1984. Colonial nesting has not been recorded in the area and indeed, only isolated nests have been located. Breeding pairs may well be more widespread than previously suspected, particularly within woodlands which form part of the Sheffield City Parks.

Outside the breeding season small flocks occur, particularly in woodland with large amounts of Hornbeam. Numbers fluctuate from year to year, with up to 30 recorded in the winter of 1980/81 in a woodland within the city boundary, and 20 present there in the winter of 1984/85. Feeding parties are also seen occasionally in Hawthorn, e.g. on the Carboniferous Limestone in early spring 1980. Only two major roosting sites have been found, although there may well be others. At the larger roost, within the Peak District, there were 35 birds in 1977 and at least 50 on 23rd December 1979, but in subsequent years numbers have been smaller with 17 in February 1982 the maximum recorded.

DARK-EYED JUNCO *Junco hyemalis*

Vagrant.

On 3rd January 1977 near Thrybergh Banks a male Dark-eyed (formerly called Slate-coloured) Junco was clearly seen perched in a Hawthorn bush with House Sparrows. It appeared to be in poor condition, but after a few minutes it flew southwards over Thrybergh village (JH). This record, the first for Yorkshire, was accepted by the *British Birds* Rarities Committee as the ninth British and Irish record, and the first in January.

LAPLAND BUNTING *Calcarius lapponicus*

Scarce passage visitor.

The first Lapland Bunting was seen at Big Moor on 26th October 1966. There have been a further ten records accepted since then, all of singles in the autumn, although four could have referred to the same bird as they were all from Big Moor in the period 7th November to 1st December 1981. There were reports from two other localities in 1981, the only year when more than one bird was recorded.

All but two reports have come from the gritstone moors, with Big Moor the favoured locality, the exceptions being Stannington in 1982 and Concord Park in 1983. Most birds have been seen or heard in flight during the period mid-October to mid-November, with exceptions on 27th September 1973 and 1st December 1981.

SNOW BUNTING *Plectrophenax nivalis*

Winter/passage visitor; moorland and farmland.

There have been one or two records of Snow Buntings in most years since 1960, particularly of single passage migrants in November at upland localities such as Barbrook Resr. All have been between 16th October and 25th March. However, it is likely that the species is overlooked as few birdwatchers walk the higher moors in winter where it is said to occur annually in small numbers (e.g. from Kinder to Win Hill (RWe)).

In the early to mid-1960s (and in the years prior to the review period) Totley Moss was the favoured site, the birds frequenting an area which was burnt in 1959. A flock of c.36 was there on 27th December 1965 with 32 on 9th January 1966 (RAF). After that the largest parties reported were in the mid-1970s. Eight were on the South Yorkshire moors from 7-10th February 1975, in a year when the exceptionally large number of records in Yorkshire was reflected locally with no fewer than 14 separate sightings in the winters of 1974/75 and 1975/76. On 7th January 1976 a flock of 40-50 was on moorland above Redmires Resr (PAA).

Upland records have subsequently been few until 1984/85 when five birds were seen on Howden Moors in December, four on Langsett Moors in January and several singles were reported. There had been few records from the lowlands until recent years. However, increased coverage has resulted in occasional sightings of singles at localities such as Concord Park, Thrybergh Resr and Rother Valley C.P.

YELLOWHAMMER *Emberiza citrinella*

Resident breeder, partial migrant; farmland, wasteland and heathland.

The Yellowhammer is a locally common species and nests in areas of farmland and heathland. It is absent from open moorland, the limestone plateau and much of urban, suburban and industrial Sheffield and Rotherham. At Breck Farm results show a reduction in the breeding population from 13 pairs in 1970 to only five pairs during the late 1970s. This trend appears to be reflected in some other parts of the area, but winter flock sizes have not declined and the breeding population at Tor Farm has merely fluctuated in the range three to ten pairs.

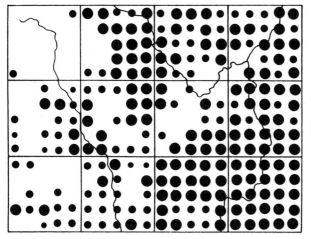

Occupied	226 (75%)
Confirmed	138 (61%)
Probable	82 (36%)
Possible	6 (3%)

Small post-breeding flocks are reported from August onwards, but the formation of larger flocks does not usually occur until November. During the winter, large flocks are regularly recorded in the south-east, with maxima of 450 feeding on farmland at Pebley Pond on 20th January 1985, 250 at Staveley in 1969, 200 in the upper Moss Valley on 19th February 1983, and 180 at Pebley Pond on 10th. In the uplands flocks rarely exceed 100 birds, with 150 at Bradfield on 26th January 1975 the largest. More typically, flocks in double figures may be seen at many localities including Midhope, Ewden Valley and Barrow Hill.

The flocks usually break up by mid-March, when most birds return to their breeding grounds. However, with the onset of adverse weather conditions many birds may be forced to abandon these territories, reforming flocks in areas of high food availability. This was evident in late April 1981, following a period of snow and high wind, when flocks of c.30 birds were recorded from many localities, whilst 55 were present at Grenoside on 25th April.

REED BUNTING *Emberiza schoeniclus*

Resident breeder, passage visitor; rivers, lakes, sewage farms, flashes, wasteland, farmland, moorland and marshy areas.

A locally common breeding species, the Reed Bunting is found both in the lowlands and along the moorland fringe. The map shows it to be absent from much of the open moorland, the limestone region, and urban and industrial Sheffield and Rotherham.

Autumn passage is recorded annually at several moorland localities including Redmires, where, between mid-September and November 1981, in excess of 150 birds flew over to the south and west. During this same period flocks of 80 birds were seen at Ramsley and 35 at Wyming Brook. On 14th October 1973, 123 were counted on Big Moor, a locality which normally holds less than ten birds. In most years the majority of birds have left the upland sites by December, although several large flocks have been recorded on the eastern moors in mid-winter. These include 42 at Leash Fen on 5th December 1976 and c.20 at Ramsley on 16th January 1980.

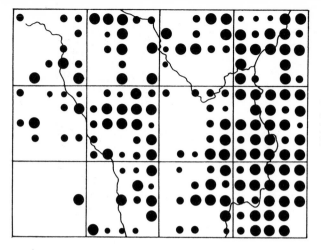

Occupied	178 (59%)
Confirmed	99 (56%)
Probable	56 (31%)
Possible	23 (13%)

An analysis of the monthly ringing totals shows that fewer birds are ringed in November and December than in any other month. This may be because many local birds move away in the autumn, whilst those remaining stay on their breeding grounds until food supplies become depleted. Trapping has also shown that flocks tend to consist of a single sex.

At the traditional roost sites an increase in numbers is usually evident in mid-winter, with numbers reaching a peak in January and February. Maxima include 100 at Bolsover on 8th January 1972, 80 at Staveley on 27th January 1975 and 70 at Old Whittington on 7th February 1973. In recent years the build-up in the winter roosts has been far less impressive and there has been a marked reduction in numbers ringed - from over 100 in most years from 1976 to 1981 to only 16 in 1982 and 15 adults in 1984. This may reflect a fall in the local population, perhaps related to hard weather, or possibly a shift in behaviour as suggested by the increasing number of records from urban gardens. An adult ringed at Poolsbrook on 9th May 1981 was recovered at Stockport, 56km to the west, on 1st January 1982

CORN BUNTING *Miliaria calandra*

Resident breeder; farmland.

The Corn Bunting shows a marked preference for lowland arable farmland, particularly where grain is grown. The only upland area holding a regular but small breeding population is at Greenmoor, 300m a.s.l., but there are occasional reports from Midhope, Redmires and parts of the Carboniferous Limestone plateau. Although widely distributed throughout the lowlands, the species is locally common, being found in loose colonies in certain favoured areas and neglecting apparently similar areas. S. J. Hayhow studied the species in the north-east of the area in 1982 and found densities of approximately two singing males per 100 acres of farmland, with a maximum of eight males in a one km² (*145*). The breeding population in the region appears to have slowly declined during the past thirty years.

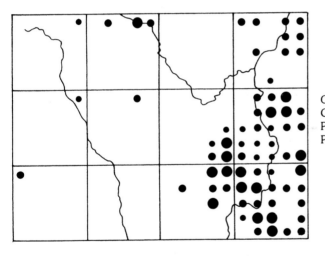

Occupied	69 (23%)
Confirmed	17 (25%)
Probable	38 (55%)
Possible	14 (20%)

The Corn Bunting tends to form flocks of up to 100 birds during the autumn and winter months, with some breeding areas being deserted and flocks often appearing well away from their breeding haunts. The largest concentrations are typically found during the winter and early spring at traditional roost sites, such as Bolsover, which held 270 on 16th February 1976, and Breck Farm where there were 120 on 17th February 1979. In addition up to 60 birds have been recorded roosting at Poolsbrook, Staveley, Harthill, Apperknowle and the Moss Valley.

Appendix 1

Check List of Birds of the Sheffield Area

This list follows the sequence and scientific nomenclature of Professor Dr. K. H. Voous (1977, *List of Recent Holarctic Bird Species*).

The codes in the columns have the following meanings:-

FIRST LETTER(S)

The major status within the Sheffield Area is classified by the letters:

R   resident — present at all seasons.

M   migrant visitor in the breeding season.

W   winter visitor.

P   passage migrant, occurring in greater numbers on migration in spring and/or autumn than in summer or winter.

I   infrequent visitor - has occurred on more than 12 but less than 25 occasions from 1960 to 1984.

S   scarce visitor — not expected but has occurred on 12 occasions or less from 1960 to 1984.

V   vagrant - unexpected, occurring well outside its breeding and/or normal migratory range.

E   escape - presumed to have been a captive bird.

H   historical - only seen before 1960.

FIRST NUMBER

An indication of the current number of pairs breeding, or which have bred since 1970, is given by numerals:-

0   has bred, but does not breed regularly.

1   1-10 pairs.

2   11-100 pairs.

3   101-1,000 pairs.

4   1,001-10,000 pairs.

5   10,001-100,000 pairs.

ASTERISK

The presence of an asterisk shows that the provisional *Atlas* records for the species were included in the computer analysis undertaken at Sheffield University (referred to in Chapter 2).

FIRST INITIALS

The author of the initial account for each species is given by the letters:-

KC	Keith Clarkson.	JH	Jon Hornbuckle.
IF	Ian Francis.	AJM	Tony Morris.
DG	David Gosney.	DSM	David Marshall.
DH	David Herringshaw.		

If there are no initials, the species has not been seen in the area since 1960, and there is thus no account in the systematic list.

OTHER INITIALS

The artist illustrating the species in the systematic list is given by the letters:-

PAA	Paul Ardron	NHR	Norman Richardson.
LC	Les Cornthwaite.	JPS	James Smith.
PL	Paul Leonard.	FJW	Derek Watson.
IDR	Ian Rotherham.		

Non-Passerines

Red-throated Diver *Gavia stellata*	S			IF	PL
Black-throated Diver *G. arctica*	S			IF	PL
Great Northern Diver *G. immer*	S			IF	JPS
Little Grebe *Tachybaptus ruficollis*	R	2	*	IF	
Great Crested Grebe *Podiceps cristatus*	R	1	*	IF	IDR
Red-necked Grebe *P. grisegena*	S			IF	
Slavonian Grebe *P. auritus*	S			IF	
Black-necked Grebe *P. nigricollis*	I	0		IF	
Black-browed Albatross *Diomedea melanophris*	H				
Fulmar *Fulmarus glacialis*	V			IF	
Manx Shearwater *Puffinus puffinus*	V			IF	
Storm Petrel *Hydrobates pelagicus*	V			IF	
Leach's Petrel *Oceanodroma leucorhoa*	V			IF	PL
Gannet *Sula bassana*	S			IF	
Cormorant *Phalacrocorax carbo*	P			IF	
Shag *P. aristotelis*	S			IF	PL
Bittern *Botaurus stellaris*	S			IF	
Little Bittern *Ixobrychus minutus*	V			IF	
Night Heron *Nycticorax nycticorax*	V			IF	
Great White Egret *Egretta alba*	H				
Grey Heron *Ardea cinerea*	R	1		IF	IDR
Spoonbill *Platalea leucorodia*	V			IF	
Mute Swan *Cygnus olor*	R	1	*	IF	PL
Bewick's Swan *C. columbianus*	W			IF	
Whooper Swan *C. cygnus*	W			IF	LC
Bean Goose *Anser fabalis*	V			IF	
Pink-footed Goose *A. brachyrhynchus*	P			IF	PL
White-footed Goose *A. albifrons*	S			IF	
Greylag Goose *A. anser*	I			IF	
Canada Goose *Branta canadensis*	R,W	1	*	IF	PAA
Barnacle Goose *B. leucopsis*	S/E			IF	
Brent Goose *B. bernicla*	V			IF	
Egyptian Goose *Alopochen aegyptiacus*	V/E			IF	
Ruddy Shelduck *Tadorna ferruginea*	E			IF	
Shelduck *T. tadorna*	P			IF	FJW
Mandarin *Aix galericulata*	S/E			IF	
Wigeon *Anas penelope*	W			IF	
Gadwall *A. strepera*	W			IF	
Teal *A. crecca*	R,W	2	*	IF	
Mallard *A. platyrhynchos*	R,W	3/4	*	IF	FJW
Pintail *A. acuta*	P			IF	JPS
Garganey *A. querquedula*	P	0?		IF	
Shoveler *A. clypeata*	P,W	0		IF	PL
Red-crested Pochard *Netta rufina*	V/E			IF	
Pochard *Aythya ferina*	W	0	*	IF	
Ring-necked Duck *A. collaris*	V			IF	
Ferruginous Duck *A. nyroca*	V			IF	
Tufted Duck *A. fuligula*	R,W	2/3	*	IF	LC

Species					
Scaup *A. marila*	P			IF	
Eider *Somateria mollissima*	S			IF	
Long-tailed Duck *Clangula hyemalis*	S			IF	
Common Scoter *Melanitta nigra*	P			IF	
Velvet Scoter *M. fusca*	S			IF	
Goldeneye *Bucephala clangula*	W			IF	FJW
Smew *Mergus albellus*	S			IF	
Red-breasted Merganser *M. serrator*	M,I	1		IF	FJW
Goosander *M. merganser*	W	0		IF	PL
Ruddy Duck *Oxyura jamaicensis*	I/R			JH	FJW
Honey Buzzard *Pernis apivorus*	S			DH	
Red Kite *Milvus milvus*	S			DH	
White-tailed Eagle *Haliaeetus albicilla*	H				
Marsh Harrier *Circus aeruginosus*	S			DH	PL
Hen Harrier *C. cyaneus*	W	0		DH	FJW
Montagu's Harrier *C. pygargus*	S			DH	
Goshawk *Accipiter gentilis*	R	2		DH	
Sparrowhawk *A. nisus*	R	3		DH	PL
Buzzard *Buteo buteo*	P	0		DH	
Rough-legged Buzzard *B. lagopus*	I			DH	FJW
Golden Eagle *Aquila chrysaetos*	H				
Osprey *Pandion haliaetus*	I			DH	
Kestrel *Falco tinnunculus*	R	3	*	DH	
Red-footed Falcon *F. vespertinus*	S			DH	
Merlin *F. columbarius*	R,W	1		DH	PL
Hobby *F. subbuteo*	P			DH	PL
Peregrine *F. peregrinus*	R	1		DH	FJW
Red Grouse *Lagopus lagopus*	R	4	*	DH	FJW
Black Grouse *Tetrao tetrix*	R	0/1		DH	
Red-legged Partridge *Alectoris rufa*	R	3	*	DH	PL
Grey Partridge *Perdix perdix*	R	3	*	DH	
Quail *Coturnix coturnix*	M	0		DH	
Pheasant *Phasianus colchicus*	R	3	*	DH	IDR
Golden Pheasant *Chrysolophus pictus*	S/E			JH	
Water Rail *Rallus aquaticus*	R,W	1		IF	PL
Spotted Crake *Porzana porzana*	S			IF	
Corncrake *Crex crex*	I	0?		IF	
Moorhen *Gallinula chloropus*	R	4	*	JH	PL
Coot *Fulica atra*	R	3	*	IF	IDR
Oystercatcher *Haematopus ostralegus*	P			AJM	NHR
Black-winged Stilt *Himantopus himantopus*	V			AJM	
Avocet *Recurvirostra avosetta*	V			JH	
Stone-curlew *Burhinus oedicnemus*	V			AJM	
Little Ringed Plover *Charadrius dubius*	M	2		AJM	PL
Ringed Plover *C. hiaticula*	P	0		AJM	
Dotterel *C. morinellus*	S			AJM	
Lesser Golden Plover *Pluvialis dominica*	V			JH	
Golden Plover *P. apricaria*	M,W	3	*	AJM	PL
Grey Plover *P. squatarola*	P			AJM	

Lapwing *Vanellus vanellus*	R	3	*	AJM	PL
Knot *Calidris canutus*	P			AJM	
Sanderling *C. alba*	P			AJM	NHR
Little Stint *C. minuta*	P			AJM	
Temminck's Stint *C. temminckii*	S			AJM	
Baird's Sandpiper *C. bairdii*	V			JH	LC
Curlew Sandpiper *C. ferruginea*	P			AJM	
Purple Sandpiper *C. maritima*	S			AJM	
Dunlin *C. alpina*	M,P	2	*	AJM	LC
Buff-breasted Sandpiper *Tryngites subruficollis*	V			AJM	
Ruff *Philomachus pugnax*	P			AJM	FJW
Jack Snipe *Lymnocryptes minimus*	W			AJM	
Snipe *Gallinago gallinago*	R,P	3	*	AJM	
Great Snipe *G. media*	H				
Woodcock *Scolopax rusticola*	R	3	*	AJM	
Black-tailed Godwit *Limosa limosa*	S			AJM	
Bar-tailed Godwit *L. lapponica*	I			AJM	NHR
Whimbrel *Numenius phaeopus*	P			AJM	
Curlew *N. arquata*	M	3	*	AJM	LC
Spotted Redshank *Tringa erythropus*	P			AJM	FJW
Redshank *T. totanus*	R	2	*	AJM	LC
Greenshank *T. nebularia*	P			AJM	FJW
Green Sandpiper *T. ochropus*	P			AJM	
Wood Sandpiper *T. glareola*	P			AJM	FJW
Common Sandpiper *Actitis hypoleucos*	M	2	*	AJM	PL
Turnstone *Arenaria interpres*	P			AJM	
Red-necked Phalarope *Phalaropus lobatus*	S			AJM	PAA
Grey Phalarope *P. fulicarius*	S			AJM	
Pomarine Skua *Stercorarius pomarinus*	H				
Arctic Skua *S. parasiticus*	S			DSM	FJW
Long-tailed Skua *S. longicaudus*	V			DSM	
Mediterranean Gull *Larus melanocephalus*	S			JH	
Little Gull *L. minutus*	I			DSM	
Black-headed Gull *L. ridibundus*	W,R	0	*	DSM	
Common Gull *L. canus*	W			DSM	FJW
Lesser Black-backed Gull *L. fuscus*	P,W			DSM	
Herring Gull *L. argentatus*	W			DSM	NHR
Iceland Gull *L. glaucoides*	I			DSM	
Glaucous Gull *L. hyperboreus*	W			DSM	PL
Great Black-backed Gull *L. marinus*	W			DSM	
Kittiwake *Rissa tridactyla*	P			DSM	
Sandwich Tern *Sterna sandvicensis*	S			DSM	
Common Tern *S. hirundo*	P			DSM	PL
Arctic Tern *S. paradisaea*	P			DSM	
Little Tern *S. albifrons*	S			DSM	
Black Tern *Chlidonias niger*	P			DSM	FJW
White-winged Black Tern *C. leucopterus*	V			DSM	
Guillemot *Uria aalge*	H				
Little Auk *Alle alle*	V			DSM	PL

Species	Status	No.		Code1	Code2
Puffin *Fratercula arctica*	V			DSM	
Pallas's Sandgrouse *Syrrhaptes paradoxus*	H				
Feral Pigeon *Columba livia*	R	3/4	*	DSM	
Stock Dove *C. oenas*	R	3	*	DSM	
Woodpigeon *C. palumbus*	R	4/5	*	DSM	PL
Collared Dove *Streptopelia decaocto*	R	4	*	DSM	
Turtle Dove *S. turtur*	M	3	*	DSM	
Cuckoo *Cuculus canorus*	M	3	*	JH	
Barn Owl *Tyto alba*	R	1		JH	LC
Eagle Owl *Bubo bubo*	V/E			JH	
Little Owl *Athene noctua*	R	3	*	JH	
Tawny Owl *Strix aluco*	R	3	*	JH	PL
Long-eared Owl *Asio otus*	R,W	2		JH	LC
Short-eared Owl *A. flammeus*	M	1		JH	
Nightjar *Caprimulgus europaeus*	M	0		JH	PL
Swift *Apus apus*	M	4	*	JH	IDR
Alpine Swift *A. melba*	H				
Kingfisher *Alcedo atthis*	R	2		JH	PL
Bee-eater *Merops apiaster*	V			JH	
Hoopoe *Upupa epops*	S			JH	
Wryneck *Jynx torquilla*	S			JH	
Green Woodpecker *Picus viridis*	R	2	*	JH	PL
Great Spotted Woodpecker *Dendrocopos major*	R	3	*	JH	
Lesser Spotted Woodpecker *D. minor*	R	1		JH	

Passerines

Species	Status	No.		Code1	Code2
Woodlark *Lullula arborea*	S			JH	
Skylark *Alauda arvensis*	R	4/5	*	DG	PL
Shore Lark *Eremophila alpestris*	S			JH	
Sand Martin *Riparia riparia*	M	2	*	JH	
Swallow *Hirundo rustica*	M	3/4	*	DG	LC
House Martin *Delichon urbica*	M	3	*	DG	IDR
Richard's Pipit *Anthus novaeseelandiae*	V			JH	
Tree Pipit *A. trivialis*	M	3	*	DG	
Meadow Pipit *A. pratensis*	R	5	*	DG	
Rock Pipit *A. spinoletta*	P,W			DG	
Yellow Wagtail *Motacilla flava*	M	2	*	DG	LC
Grey Wagtail *M. cinerea*	R	2/3	*	DG	PL
Pied Wagtail *M. alba*	R	3	*	DG	
Waxwing *Bombycilla garrulus*	W			DG	
Dipper *Cinclus cinclus*	R	2	*	DG	PL
Wren *Troglodytes troglodytes*	R	5	*	DG	
Dunnock *Prunella modularis*	R	4	*	DG	PL
Robin *Erithacus rubecula*	R	5	*	DG	
Nightingale *Luscinia megarhynchos*	S			DG	
Black Redstart *Phoenicurus ochruros*	M	1		JH	LC
Redstart *P. phoenicurus*	M	3	*	DG	
Whinchat *Saxicola rubetra*	M	3	*	DG	JPS
Stonechat *S. torquata*	R,W	1		JH	PL

Wheatear *Oenanthe oenanthe*	M,P	2/3	*	DG	FJW
Ring Ouzel *Turdus torquatus*	M	2	*	DG	PL
Blackbird *T. merula*	R,W	4/5	*	DG	
Fieldfare *T. pilaris*	W	0		JH	
Song Thrush *T. philomelos*	R	4	*	DG	NHR
Redwing *T. iliacus*	W			DG	NHR
Mistle Thrush *T. viscivorus*	R	4	*	DG	
Grasshopper Warbler *Locustella naevia*	M	2	*	DG	
Sedge Warbler *Acrocephalus schoenobaenus*	M	3	*	DG	LC
Marsh Warbler *A. palustris*	S			JH	
Reed Warbler *A. scirpaceus*	M	2	*	DG	
Marmora's Warbler *Sylvia sarda*	V			JH	
Lesser Whitethroat *S. curruca*	M	2/3	*	DG	FJW
Whitethroat *S. communis*	M	3	*	DG	
Garden Warbler *S. borin*	M	3	*	JH	
Blackcap *S. atricapilla*	M	4	*	JH	LC
Wood Warbler *Phylloscopus sibilatrix*	M	3	*	JH	LC
Chiffchaff *P. collybita*	M	3	*	JH	
Willow Warbler *P. trochilus*	M	5	*	JH	
Goldcrest *Regulus regulus*	R	4	*	DSM	
Firecrest *R. ignicapillus*	I			JH	JPS
Spotted Flycatcher *Muscicapa striata*	M	3	*	DG	
Red-breasted Flycatcher *Ficedula parva*	V			JH	
Pied Flycatcher *F. hypoleuca*	M	2		JH	
Bearded Tit *Panurus biarmicus*	S			DG	
Long-tailed Tit *Aegithalos caudatus*	R	3	*	DG	IDR
Marsh Tit *Parus palustris*	R	2	*	JH	IDR
Willow Tit *P. montanus*	R	3	*	JH	
Coal Tit *P. ater*	R	3	*	DG	LC
Blue Tit *P. caeruleus*	R	4	*	DG	PL
Great Tit *P. major*	R	4	*	DG	
Nuthatch *Sitta europaea*	R	2	*	DSM	
Wallcreeper *Tichodroma muraria*	H				
Treecreeper *Certhia familiaris*	R	3	*	DSM	IDR
Golden Oriole *Oriolus oriolus*	S			JH	
Red-backed Shrike *Lanius collurio*	S			JH	
Great Grey Shrike *L. excubitor*	W			JH	PL
Jay *Garrulus glandarius*	R	3	*	DSM	
Magpie *Pica pica*	R	4	*	KC	IDR
Chough *Pyrrhocorax pyrrhocorax*	H				
Jackdaw *Corvus monedula*	R	4	*	DSM	NHR
Rook *C. frugilegus*	R	4	*	DSM	
Carrion Crow *C. corone*	R	3	*	DSM	
Raven *C. corax*	S			DSM	
Starling *Sturnus vulgaris*	R,W	5	*	IF	PAA
House Sparrow *Passer domesticus*	R	5	*	KC	
Tree Sparrow *P. montanus*	R	3	*	KC	LC
Chaffinch *Fringilla coelebs*	R,W	5	*	KC	
Brambling *F. montifringilla*	W			KC	IDR

Greenfinch *Carduelis chloris*	R,W	4	*	KC	FJW
Goldfinch *C. carduelis*	M	3/4	*	KC	PL
Siskin *C. spinus*	R,W	2		KC	
Linnet *C. cannabina*	R	4	*	KC	
Twite *C. flavirostris*	M	2	*	KC	
Redpoll *C. flammea*	R	3	*	KC	
Two-barred Crossbill *Loxia leucoptera*	V			JH	
Crossbill *L. curvirostra*	R,W	1/2		JH	
Parrot Crossbill *L. pytyopsittacus*	V	0?		JH	PAA
Bullfinch *Pyrrhula pyrrhula*	R	3	*	KC	LC
Hawfinch *Coccothraustes coccothraustes*	R	2		KC	
Dark-eyed Junco *Junco hyemalis*	V			JH	
Lapland Bunting *Calcarius lapponicus*	S			KC	
Snow Bunting *Plectrophenax nivalis*	P,W			KC	
Yellowhammer *Emberiza citrinella*	R	3	*	KC	FJW
Cirl Bunting *E. cirlus*	H				
Reed Bunting *E. schoeniclus*	R	3	*	KC	FJW
Corn Bunting *Miliaria calandra*	R	2	*	KC	FJW

Marmora's Warbler

F.J. Watson

Appendix 2
Atlas of Breeding Birds Project

Introduction

Following the success of the 1968-72 national *Atlas* of Breeding Birds (*19*), the SBSG decided to organise a local *Atlas* based on the 2km x 2km squares ('tetrads') of the national grid as recording units. This project was initiated in 1975 and in order to ensure a high level of coverage it was continued until 1980.

Method

The national grid of the Ordnance Survey is an invaluable reference system for the whole of the British Isles. The country is divided into squares 100km x 100km, each of which has a two letter reference. These squares are further subdivided by grid lines at 10km, 1km or smaller intervals depending on the scale.

All the Sheffield area is within the SK 100km square and is covered by the following standard 1:50,000 (1¼ inch to a mile). Ordnance Survey maps: sheets 110, 111, 119 and 120. Each map is divided into 10km x 10km grid squares (the recording unit used in the national *Atlas*) which in turn are sub-divided into smaller squares of 1km x 1km. To have attempted any form of mapping project based upon the 1km squares would not have been feasible. A 2km x 2km square or 'tetrad' was eminently more satisfactory and a well established unit used in similar work elsewhere in Britain. Since each 10km square contains 25 tetrads the Sheffield recording area of twelve 10km squares contains 300 tetrads, which is a manageable number.

The project was launched at SBSG indoor meetings in the spring of 1975. All potential field-workers were given BTO *Atlas* recording cards and an instructional booklet which included definitions of categories of breeding as originally used in the national *Atlas* (*19*). Field meetings were held in that year and the following years, for both instructional and recording purposes.

At the end of each year the results were collated and a detailed report produced for distribution to all contributors. The report, from which results for sensitive species were excluded, indicated the areas which appeared to be well-covered and those which were under-recorded. This subsequently led to surveys in those parts of the region which had rarely been visited by birdwatchers previously.

Although all members of the SBSG were encouraged to join in the project, and many did initially, the number of active participants decreased over the six years. Eventually a hard core 'Atlas team' were responsible for filling in the gaps in the final two years.

Checking the information

At the end of the project provisional maps were produced for every species. At this time the master records were cross-checked by the *Atlas* organisers, D. Gosney and D. Herringshaw, and inaccurate data eliminated.

The Editors of the present publication again reassessed each map before presenting a copy to the contributors responsible for writing the account of that particular species. Additionally, a number of local ornithologists with a special knowledge of either a species or locality were asked to check certain maps to ensure they were as comprehensive and accurate as possible. Any dubious records were removed and omissions added. After considerable deliberation the Editors decided to publish all maps accurately plotted except for Long-eared Owl and Black Redstart, which were 'clumped'. Goshawk and Merlin were considered to be too sensitive for any meaningful maps to be produced. One confirmed record was omitted from the Barn Owl map at the request of the finder of the site. No maps were produced for species such as Quail which are only irregular breeders in the region.

The maps were again rechecked when all the species accounts were edited, and any data removed if considered at all suspect.

The hand-drawn maps were then given to several local ornithologists proficient in graphics who produced final maps using 'Letraset' dots on photocopied base maps. These final maps were checked by the Editors against the hand-drawn maps before delivery to the printer.

Appendix 3
Additions to the Sheffield List since 1960

A **Breeding** (Breeding was confirmed for the following species in the years recorded, except where there is a question mark after the year means breeding was strongly suspected but not proven).

Species	Record	Species	Record
Black-necked Grebe	1982-4	Little Ringed Plover	1960,68-85
Garganey	1982 ?	Ringed Plover	1978-79
Pochard	1979-81	Collared Dove	1963-85
Red-breasted Merganser	1979,82-85	Fieldfare	1974-76,80,81
Goosander	1982,84	Siskin	1974, 76-85
Hen Harrier	1975?,76	Parrot Crossbill	1983?
Goshawk	1965-85		

B **Visiting** (The following species have only been recorded in the Sheffield area in the years stated).

Species	Record	Species	Record
Fulmar	1974,78,80,84	Long-tailed Skua	1978,84
Night Heron	1978	Little Gull	1962,65,69,74,75,78-85
Spoonbill	1975,83	Mediterranean Gull	1981-4
Bean Goose	1976	Iceland Gull	1966-8,71-77,81-85
White-fronted Goose	1970,79,82	Glaucous Gull	1963,1969-85
Greylag Goose	1967,68,70,74,75,78,80-85	White-winged Black Tern	1966
Ring-necked Duck	1982	Shore Lark	1971
Long-tailed Duck	1963,69-75,80,84	Marsh Warbler	1978,85
Ruddy Duck	1979,80,82-85	Marmora's Warbler	1982
Black-winged Stilt	1963	Red-breasted Flycatcher	1981
Avocet	1983,84	Bearded Tit	1978,84
Lesser Golden Plover	1983	Golden Oriole	1980,83,84
Temminck's Stint	1981,84,85	Dark-eyed Junco	1977
Baird's Sandpiper	1983	Two-barred Crossbill	1982,83
Buff-breasted Sandpiper	1975	Parrot Crossbill	1982,83
Black-tailed Godwit	1962,67,75,76,81-83,85	Lapland Bunting	1966,73,78,81-83
Red-necked Phalarope	1981		

The following species have been excluded owing to the likelihood of captive origin:- Egyptian Goose, Barnacle Goose, Ruddy Shelduck, Mandarin, Golden Pheasant, Eagle Owl.

Appendix 4

Species only recorded before 1960

Black-browed Albatross *Diomedea melanophris.*
An exhausted bird was removed from telegraph wires at Staveley in mid-August 1952 and released at Skegness, Lincolnshire *(146).*

Great White Egret *Egretta alba.*
One was reported at Clay Wheel Dam, Wadsley Bridge in 1868 (A.S. Hutchinson).

White-tailed Eagle *Haliaeetus albicilla.*
Immatures were at Derwent from 20th December 1920 to 8th February 1921 and 9-17th March 1939.

Golden Eagle *Aquila chrysaetos.*
A pair bred in Woodlands Valley, Derwent, in 1668. One was seen at Derwent in April 1952 (EHP).

Crake species *Porzana* sp.
A small crake was obtained from Catley Meadows (thought to be at Tinsley Park) in 1883. It was presumably a Little *P. parva* or Baillon's *P. pusilla.*

Great Snipe *Gallinago media.*
One was killed at Bolsover on 12th October 1892 and another at Townhead, Sheffield in 1899.

Pomarine Skua *Stercorarius pomarinus.*
An immature was killed on moorland near Strines in early October 1898.

Guillemot *Uria aalge.*
In November 1890 one was found at Old Dam, Broomhill.

Pallas's Sandgrouse *Syrrhaptes paradoxus.*
In 1863 one was shot near Fox House and another elsewhere in the district. Both birds were probably in flocks which had invaded the country from Central Asia.

Alpine Swift *Apus melba.*
Specimens were obtained from Oughtibridge in 1869 and Langsett on 15th May 1892.

Wallcreeper *Tichodroma muraria.*
One was seen in a rocky area of Upper Ewden on 27th November 1954 by the local keeper J.P. Dearnley.

Chough *Pyrrhocorax pyrrhocorax.*
A pair was seen on the Derbyshire moors in the mid-1800s and one was seen within 10 miles of Sheffield in 1875 by Charles Dixon.

Cirl Bunting *Emberiza cirlus.*
A singing male was reported at Hackenthorpe in 1950 (FNB) and a pair was present in Peter Dale, near Tideswell, on 11th March 1956 (ALH,PS).

Appendix 5

Escaped Species

Birds in this section are those which have obviously escaped from captivity. Others, such as species of wildfowl which may or may not be of wild origin, are included in the systematic list with the appropriate proviso.

Black Swan *Cygnus atratus.*
A pair was introduced onto Birley Hay Dam in 1976 and was resident there until at least 1981. A pair was also seen at Pebley Pond on 2nd February 1983.

Snow Goose *Anser coerulescens.*
One was seen at Queens Park, Chesterfield, in May 1975.

Red-breasted Goose *Branta ruficollis.*
One was present on a mill-pond in the Loxley valley during July 1976.

Muscovy Duck *Cairina moschata.*
Seen regularly and found in 20 tetrads in the breeding atlas survey.

Wood Duck *Aix sponsa.*
A pair was on Birley Hay Dam from August 1976 to the year end, and there were three records of single males on the River Derwent between Bamford and Hathersage in November 1982 and December 1983. A male frequented the Rivers Derwent and Noe in May and June 1985.

Chiloe Wigeon *Anas sibilatrix.*
Reported from nine localities between 1975 and 1984.

Barbary Dove *Streptopelia roseogrisea.*
Singles were seen at Barlborough in December 1980 and Rotherham in October 1983, and two were at Old Denaby in October 1981.

Budgerigar *Melopsittacus undulatus.*
Occasional ones seen in most years.

Cockatiel *Nymphicus hollandicus.*
Seen at three localities in June and October 1978 and April 1982.

Ring-necked Parakeet *Psittacula krameri.*
Recorded at six localities from 1974 to 1983.

African Grey Parrot *Psittacus erithacus.*
One was seen at Jordanthorpe in June 1975.

Monk Parakeet *Myiopsitta monachus.*
Three were seen regularly at a bird table in Ashgate, Chesterfield, through the 1978/79 winter and two there at each end of 1980.

Mackinder's Eagle Owl *Bubo capensis mackinderi.*
One was seen in Derwentdale in January 1983.

Red-winged Blackbird *Agelaius phoeniceus.*
One was at Kimberworth in April 1981.

Canary *Serinus canaria.*
One was seen at Langsett in June 1981.

Bengalese Finch (White-backed Munia) *Lonchura striata.*
One was on waste ground at Walkley in June 1975.

Zebra Finch *Poephila guttata.*
One flew into a building at Loxley in August 1982.

Orange Weaver *Ploceus aurantius.*
A male was at Breck Farm in October 1975 and there are two records of 'weaver species' building nests in the city suburbs in September 1975 and November 1976.

Red Bishop *Euplectes orix.*
One was seen at Staveley in July 1981.

Common Mynah *Acridotheras tristis.*
One was in Upper Derwentdale in July 1976.

Appendix 6

Unacceptable Records

The following records have been published in local reports or bulletins but have either been withdrawn by the observers or not accepted by the editors after consultation with local Recorders.

If the number of birds reported exceeds one, it is given in brackets after the date of the record.

White-fronted Goose	9.12.71 (41 + 30), 24.11.72, 10.1.73 (20), 22.12.73 (5), 23.12.83 (110)
Long-tailed Duck	5.5.58
Honey Buzzard	26.8.76 (2)
Black Grouse	14.3.76 (14), late 1976 (up to 10)
Dotterel	12.5.73 (9)
Whimbrel	23.3.82
Herring Gull	16.4.79 (100)
Swift	21.4.71
Tree Pipit	23.3.72
White Wagtail	1.3.70, 23.10.72, 6.10.73
Redstart	23.3.73
Raven	11.11.73, 16.11.74 (2), 4.5.75

Appendix 7
Species other than birds in the text

A Plants

Both vernacular and scientific names follow those used in Clapham, Tutin and Warburg's *Flora of the British Isles* 2nd Edition (1962). Scientific names of trees not included in the work are from Mitchell's *A Field Guide to the Trees of Britain and Northern Europe* (1974). All 'agricultural' plants are omitted.

Alder	*Alnus glutinosa*
Ash	*Fraxinus excelsior*
Ash, Mountain — see Rowan	
Beech	*Fagus sylvatica*
Bell Heather	*Erica cinerea*
Bent-grass, Common	*Agrostis tenuis*
Bilberry	*Vaccinium myrtillus*
Birch	*Betula pendula/pubescens*
Bog Moss	*Sphagnum* spp.
Bracken	*Pteridium aquilinum*
Cotoneaster	*Cotoneaster frigidus*
Cotton-sedge/grass	*Eriophorum angustifolium/vaginatum*
Cowberry	*Vaccinium vitis-idaea*
Cross-leaved Heath	*Erica tetralix*
Crowberry	*Empetrum nigrum*
Deer Sedge	*Trichoporum cespitosum*
Elder	*Sambucus nigrum*
Elm	*Ulmus glabra/procera/carpinifolia*
Fescues	*Festuca* spp.
Field Maple	*Acer campestre*
Hawthorn	*Crataegus monogyna*
Hazel	*Corylus avellana*
Heather, Common Ling	*Calluna vulgaris*
Holly	*Ilex aquifolium*
Hornbeam	*Carpinus betulus*
Larch	*Larix decidua/kaempferi*
Ling	— see Heather
Moor Grass, Purple	*Molinia caerulea*
Oak, Northern	*Quercus petraea*
Oat Grass	*Arrhenalterum elatius*
Perennial Rye Grass	*Lolium perenne*
Pine	*Pinus* spp.
Pine, Corsican	*Pinus nigra var. maritima* spp. *larico*
Pine, Lodgepole	*Pinus contorta*
Pine, Scots	*Pinus sylvestris*
Reed, Common	*Phragmites communis*
Reedmace, Common	*Typha angustifolia*
Rhododendron	*Rhododendron ponticum*
Rowan	*Sorbus aucuparia*
Spruce, Norway	*Picea abies*

Spruce, Sitka	*Picea sitchensis*
Sycamore	*Acer pseudoplatanus*
Thistle	*Cirsium* spp.
Wavy Hair Grass	*Deschampsia flexuosa*
Willow	*Salix* spp.
Willow, Crack	*Salix fragilis*
Willow, Goat	*Salix caprea*
Yew	*Taxus baccata*

B Animals

Crane-Fly	*Tipulidae* spp.
Earthworm	*Annelida : oligochaeta*
Hare, Mountain	*Lepus timidus*
Lizard, Common	*Lacerta vivipara*
Moth, Northern Eggar	*Lasiocampus quercus callunae*
Mouse, Wood	*Apodemus sylvaticus*
Rabbit	*Oryctolagus cuniculus*
Rat, Brown	*Rattus norvegicus*
Sheep	*Ovis* (domestic)
Shrew, Common	*Sorex araneus*
Shrew, Water	*Neomys fodiens*
Squirrel, Grey	*Sciurus carolinensis*
Squirrel, Red	*Sciurus vulgaris*
Vole, Bank	*Clethrionomys glareolus*
Vole, Field/Short-tailed	*Microtus agrestis*

Little Grebes P.A. Ardron

Appendix 8

Observers initialled in the text

A. Adams
N. W. Addey
D. Amedro (D Am)
S. Anthony
T. P. Appleton
P. A. Ardron
J. S. Armitage
D. Atter
J. W. Atter
F. N. Barker
D. Barr
R. Bartlett (R Ba)
K. Bayes
P. Beaumont
M. A. Beevers
S. Bellinger (S Be)
T. J. Bennett
R. P. Blagden
K. Bower
M. Bowler
S. Boyes
P. L. Brown
G. M. Bullivent
R. Butterfield
T. B. Carter
J. A. Chapman
K. Clarkson
A. Crabtree
J. Crank
R. Cripps
H. Crookes
P. Crooks
D. B. Cutts
J. E. Dale
S. Dobson
J. B. & M. B. Edwards
C. E. Exley
R. Ford
I. Francis
P. J. Freeman
R. A. Frost
P. Garrity
W. E. Gibbs
T. Gibson
P. K. Gill
A. B. Gladwin

D. J. Glaves
P. M. Glaves
D. Gosney
K. R. Gould
T. P. Guest
J. T. Hagarty
S. H. Holliday
A. & B. Hancock
A. Hardcastle (A Ha)
M. Hargreave
J. P. Hartley
D. V. Haslam
R. G. Hawley
S. J. Hayhow
D. Herringshaw
R. Higbid
R. T. Hobson
J. Hornbuckle
A. L. Hunter
D. Hursthouse
C. Jacklin
G. E. Jackson
J. Jackson
S. Jackson
P. Jones
J. Knight
K. Knowles
G. Lee
M. Leonard
P. Leonard
J. Lunn
K. Lynes
P. Marsh
D. S. Marshall
T. Marshall
J. I. Martin
G. P. Mawson
C. R. McKay
J. D. Middleton
P. Milburn
B. A. Moore
A. J. Morris
L. Oldfield
M. G. Oxlade
C. Park (C Pa)
M. Pass

E. H. Peat
C. & M. Perry
A. Platts
R. Platts
J. Prentice
T. Preston
A. Rhodes
A. Roadhouse
P. Roberts
D. Robinson
S. J. Roddis
J. Russell
A. Scougall
R. Simpson
M. A. Smethurst
J. Lintin Smith
J. P. Smith
K. Smith
D. J. Standring
M. F. Stoyle
M. Suggate
W. J. Sutherland
M. E. Taylor
A. Faulkner Taylor
C. Thomson
M. Tong
P. Tooley
R. Twigg
J. P. Uttley
D. Vickers
R. & N. Wareing
F. J. Watson
R. Weeks (R We)
M. Wells
R. Wells
D. Whiteley
D. Williams (D Wil)
R. D. Williams
A. & P. Wilson
D. R. Wilson
J. W. Wilson
J. S. Woodisse
P. Wragg
D. W. Yalden

Appendix 9

Grid references of locations in and near the Sheffield area mentioned in the text.

Four figure grid references are given in accordance with the standard Ordnance Survey system, all in the SK 100km square.

Abney Moor	1879	Broomhall	3386
Agden	2592	Broomhead Hall	2496
Aldwarke S.F.	4494	Broomhead Moor	2295
Alport Dale	1489 to 1292	Broomhead Resr	2695
Alport Castles	1491	Broomhill, Sheffield	3386
Apperknowle	3878	Broomhill Flash	4102
Arkwright	4270	Burbage Brook	2681
Ashford	1969	Burbage Moor	2782
Ashop Dale	1389 to 1090	Canal Basin	3687
Aston	4685	Canklow	4390
Back Tor	1990	Carr Vale	2374
Bamford	2083	Catcliffe Flash	4288
Banner Cross	3284	Chapeltown	3596
Barbrook Resr	2777	Chatsworth	2670
Barlborough	4777	Chee Dale	1273
Barlow	3474	Chesterfield	3730
Barlow Brook	3276	Clowne	4976
Barnside Moor	2298	Concord Park	3792
Barrow Hill	4175	Conisborough	5098
Baslow	2572	Coombs Dale	2274
Beauchief	3381	Cordwell Valley	3076
Beeley Moor	2967	Crooksmoor	3387
Beighton	4483	Curbar Edge	2575
Big Moor	2776	Dale Dike Resr	2491
Bingham Park	3185	Damflask Resr	2790
Birley Carr	3292	Darnall	3988
Birleyhay Dam	3980	Deepcar	2897
Blackamoor	2880	Denaby Wood	4798
Blackbrook Wood	2986	Derwentdale	1790 to 1696
Blackburn Tip	3992	Derwent Resr	1790
Bleaklow (Stones)	1196	Dore	3181
Bolehill Flash	4288	Dronfield	3678
Bolsover	4770	Dronfield Woodhouse	3278
Bolsterstone	2796	Dungworth	2089
Botanical Gardens	3386	East Moor	2970
Bowden Houstead Wood	3986	Ecclesall	3284
Bradfield	2492	Ecclesall Wood	3282
Bradwell	1781	Ecclesfield	3594
Bradwell Ponds	1782	Eckington	4279
Bramley	4992	Edale	1685 to 1185
Brampton	4887	Elmton	4973
Breck Farm	4276	Elsecar Resr	3899
Brightside	3789	Endcliffe Park	3285

Ewden Valley	2995 to 2195	Little Matlock Wood	3089
Eyam Moor	2278	Lodge Moor	2886
Featherbed Moss	1994	Longshaw	2679
Foolow	1976	Longstone Edge/Moor	1973
Fox House	2680	Loxley Valley	3189 to 2989
Frecheville	3983	Malin Bridge	3289
Froggatt Edge	2476	Manor Park	3786
Fulwood	3187	Margery Hill	1895
Gleadless	3885	Marsh Lane	4079
Graves Park	3582	Mickleden	1998
Greasbrough Tip	4294	Middleton Moor	2074
Great Hollins Wood	3192	Middlewood	3192
Great Hucklow	1777	Midhope Resr	2299
Greenmoor	2799	Midhope Moor	1998
Grenoside	3294	Midhopestones	2399
Greno Wood	3296	Miller's Dale	1373 to 1772
Grimesthorpe	3889	Millhouses	3283
Grindleford	2477	Monsal Dale	1871
Hackenthorpe	4283	Morehall Resr	2795
Hallam Moor	2486	Mosborough	4280
Handsworth	4086	Moscar	2187
Harthill Resr	4880	Moss Valley	3780 to 4180
Hassop	2272	Nether Edge	3384
Hathersage	2381	Norfolk Park	3686
Heeley	3585	Norton	3582
Herringthorpe Park	4592	Norwood	4681
High Moor	4680	Old Brampton	3371
High Storrs	3184	Old Denaby	4999
Hillsborough	3390	Old Whittington	3874
Holbrook	4481	Orgreave	4286
Holmesfield	3277	Oughtibridge	3083
Hooton Roberts	4797	Owler Bar	2978
Hope Valley	1982 to 1683	Padley Gorge	2578
Houndkirk Moor	2981	Parkway	3887
Howden Resr	1792	Peak Forest	1179
Hunter's Bar	3385	Pebley Pond	4879
Jordanthorpe	3581	Peter Dale	1275
Killamarsh	4581	Pike Low	2097
Kilnhurst Flash	4597	Pilsley	2471
Kinder Scout	1088	Poolsbrook	4374
Ladybower Resr	1986	Porter Valley	3084 to 3285
Lane Top	3691	Ramsley Moor	2975
Langsett Moor	1799	Ramsley Resr	2874
Langsett Resr	2099	Ravenfield	4995
Leash Fen	2973	Rawmarsh	4496
Limb Valley	3083	Redmires Resr	2585
Linacre Resr	3372	Renishaw	4378
Little Don Valley	1899	Ringinglow	2683
Little London Dam	3484	Rivelin Dams	2786

Rivelin Hagg	3087	Tor Farm	2279
Rivelin Valley	2886 to 3188	Totley Moss	2779
River Doe Lea	4572 to 4670	Treeton Dyke	4386
River Noe	2182 to 1684	Troway	3979
Ronksley Moor	1595	Ughill	2590
Rotherham	4293	Ulley Resr	4687
Rother Valley C.P.	4582	Underbank Resr	2499
Sheaf Valley	3483 to 3280	Unstone	3777
Sheffield City Centre	3587	Upper Derwent	1695 to 1596
Shirebrook	4184	Upper Rivelin	2687
Shirecliffe	3490	Wadsley	3190
Shiregreen	3792	Walkley	3388
Shuttlewood	4672	Walton Dam	3670
Stanage Edge	2285	Wardlow	1874
Stannington	3088	Wath Wood	4399
Staveley	4374	Wentworth	4096
Staveley S.F.	4476	Westend	1493
Stocksbridge	2798	Weston Park	3387
Stoke Hall	2376	Wharncliffe Chase	3196
Stoney Middleton	2275	Wharncliffe Wood	2997 to 3194
Strines	2291	Whiteley Woods	3085
Swallownest	4585	Whiston	4589
Swinden Plantation	1800	Whittington	3874
Swinton	4498	Whitwell	5278
Taddington	1471	Wincobank	3891
Tankersley	3499	Winnats Pass	1382
Thorpe Hesley	3795	Wisewood	3290
Thrybergh Banks	4695	Woodhead	1089
Thrybergh Resr	4795	Woodhouse	4184
Thundercliffe Grange	3893	Woodlands Valley	1588
Thurcroft	4988	Woolley Woods	3892
Tideswell	1575	Wortley	3099
Tinsley Park	3989	Wye Dale	1072
Tinsley S.F.	4091	Wyming Brook	2786
Todwick	4984		

Appendix 10

Sheffield Bird Study Group

The Sheffield Bird Study Group was formed in 1972 to provide local birdwatchers with greater opportunities to play an active part in the study and conservation of birds. The initial membership of 30 grew to 83 within a year and 220 by 1983. The organisation is administered by a committee, elected annually, with four officers - Chairman, Secretary, Treasurer and Recorder. As the post of Recorder developed, it was expanded into a Recording Team of three, the other members helping in areas such as liaison with other societies and conservation bodies, handling sensitive issues and production of the annual Bird Report.

The main activities of the Group are fieldwork, conservation, indoor meetings and field outings. A popular Junior Section holds meetings specifically for younger members. There is also a Photographic Section (run jointly with the Sorby Natural History Society) which meets monthly to discuss the technical aspects of bird photography and view recent slides. The Group publishes the *Sheffield Bird Report,* **The Magpie,** (an occasional journal containing ornithological articles of local interest), and a bimonthly Bulletin which has been produced continuously since January 1974 and includes news, records and articles by members.

Fieldwork

The Group organises specific surveys of local birds. Species studied have included Heron, Kestrel, Collared Dove, Swift, House Martin, Magpie, Rook and Starling. There have been more general surveys of garden birds and birds in the Sheffield parks. Two more ambitious projects extending over a number of years have been the *Atlas* of breeding birds (1975-80) and the *Atlas* of winter birds (1981/82-83/84). The recent emphasis in both recording and survey work has been the accumulation of data on habitats rather than on individual species.

Members are encouraged to participate in national projects such as wildfowl counts, the Common Bird Census and most notably the Waterways Bird Survey which was pioneered by the Group in 1973. Individual projects are also undertaken by members, and include migration studies, gull roost counts, and specific investigations on Goshawk, Sparrowhawk, Moorhen, Curlew, Lapwing and Kingfisher.

Conservation

The Conservation Sub-committee endeavours to maintain a close watch on local developments which might affect bird populations and their habitats. Action is taken where it is both necessary and practicable. The Sub-committee maintains a close liaison with County conservation bodies and the various advisory committees, and is represented on several of these. Major activities include protection of rare breeding birds, notably Peregrine and Goshawk, establishment of local reserves and responsibility for accumulating data on important ornithological habitats.

Meetings

Indoor meetings are held in the Arts Tower of Sheffield University, Western Bank at 7.15 pm. on the second Wednesday of every month excluding August. An attempt is made to cater for all ornithological tastes: members are kept abreast of local bird records, given help with identification problems, presented with survey news and informed of local events. The main part of each meeting is given over to an illustrated talk by a well-known local or national ornithologist. Informal discussions often continue in a nearby hostelry after the meeting.

Field meetings, both local and further afield, complement the indoor meetings. Assistance with bird identification is willingly given to those who require it.

Membership of the Group is open to anyone, whether beginner or expert, who is interested in birds. Application forms are available from:- Mrs H.J. Barton (Membership Secretary)

74 High Storrs Road   Sheffield S11 7LE

Bibliography

1. RAY, J. (ed.) 1678. **The Ornithology of Francis Willughby**.

2. SPALDING, D. A. E. 1967. The principal localities studied by naturalists in the Sheffield area. Pt. 3 (H-L). **Sorby Record** 2, (4):1-15.

3. MOLINEUX, C. 1892. A register of birds shot by the Rev. Francis Gisborne, Rector of Staveley (1759-1821), duly recorded by himself, from the year 1761-1784. **Derbys. Archaeological Soc.** 14: 176-216.

4. ALLIS, T. 1844. **Report on the Birds of Yorkshire**. Brit. Assoc. Advt. Sci.

5. NELSON, T. H. 1907. **The Birds of Yorkshire**. 2 vols. London: Brown.

6. MORRIS, F. O. 1857. **History of British birds**. 1:313. London.

7. WHITLOCK, F. B. 1893. **The Birds of Derbyshire**. London.

8. DIXON, C. 1900. **Amongst the Birds of Northern Shires**. London.

9. WITHERBY, H. F. *et al* 1938-41. **The Handbook of British Birds**. 5 vols. London: Witherby.

10. SEEBOHM, H. 1883-85. **A History of British Birds**. London: Porter.

11. SEEBOHM, H. 1882. **Siberia in Asia**. London: Murray.

12. PATTEN, C. J. 1910. 'Aves' in **Handbook & Guide to Sheffield**. Brit. Assoc. Advt. Sci.:455-68.

13. WHITTAKER, A. 1929. Notes on the birds of the Sheffield district. **Proc. Sorby Scient. Soc.** 1:16-33.

14. CHISLETT, R. 1952. **Yorkshire Birds**. London.

15. CHISLETT, R. 1933. **Northward Ho for Birds!**. London: Country Life.

16. WILSON, D. R. 1958. The birds of the Sheffield area. **Sorby Record** 1,(1):54-62.

17. WILSON, D. R. 1959. The birds of the Sheffield area, 1957-58. **Sorby Record** 1,(2):41-45.

18. HAWLEY, R. G. 1968. 'Birds' in **The Natural History of the Sheffield District**. Sorby N.H.S.:39-44.

19. SHARROCK, J. T. R. 1976. **The Atlas of Breeding Birds in Britain and Ireland**. Tring:B.T.O., I.W.C.

20. FROST, R. A. 1978 **Birds of Derbyshire**. Hartington: Moorland.

21. SMITH, A. H. V. 1974 **The Birds of the Sheffield Area**. Sheffield.

22. HERRINGSHAW, D. & FROST, R. A. 1981. **Birdwatching in the Sheffield Area and the Peak District**. Sheffield.

23. ANDERSON, P. and SHIMWELL, D. 1981. **Wildflowers and other Plants of the Peak District - an Ecological Study**. Ashbourne:Moorland.

24. FULLER, R. J. 1982. **Bird Habitats in Britain**. Calton:Poyser.

25a. WARD, J. H. 1963. Hierarchial grouping to optimise an objective function. **Journ. of the Am. Stat. Assoc.** 58:236-244.

25b. BRAY, J. R. & CURTIS, J. T. 1957. An ordination of the upland forest community of southern Wisconsin. **Ecological Monographs**. 27:325-349.

26. ALERSTAM, T. & ULFSTRAND, S. 1972. Radar and field observations of diurnal bird migration in South Sweden, Autumn 1921. **Ornis Scand.**. 3 : 99-139.

27. AXELL, H. E. *et al* 1962. Migration at Minsmere, seen and unseen. **Bird Notes**. 30:181-186.

28. EAGLE-CLARKE, W. 1912. **Studies in Bird Migration**. London.

29. EVANS, P. R. 1966. An approach to the analysis of visible migration and a comparison with radar observations. **Ardea**. 54:14-44.

30. LACK, D. 1965. **Enjoying Ornithology**. Methuen, London.

31. SNOW, D, 1953. Visible Migration in the British Isles :a review. **Ibis**. 95:242-270.

32. CHANDLER, R. J. 1981. Influxes into Britain and Ireland of Red-necked Grebes and other waterbirds during winter 1978-79. **British Birds**. 74:55-81.

33. FRANCIS, I. S. 1981. Winter wildfowl in the Sheffield area 1973-1978. **Magpie**. 2:3-25.

34. HUGHES, S. W. M., BACON, P. & FLEGG, J. J. M. 1979. The 1975 census of the Great-crested Grebe in Britain. **Bird Study**. 25:245.

35. COULSON, J. C. and BRAZENDALE, M. G. 1968. Movements of Cormorants ringed in the British Isles and evidence of colony specific dispersal. **British Birds**. 61:1-21.

36. COULSON, J. C. 1961. Movements and seasonal variations in mortality of Shags and Cormorants ringed on the Farne Islands, Northumberland **British Birds**. 54:223.

37. POTTS, G. R. 1969. The influence of eruptive movements, age, population size and other factors on the survival of the Shag. **Journ. Anim. Ecol.** 38.

38. REYNOLDS, C.M. 1979. The Heronries census:1972-1977 population changes and a review. **Bird Study**. 26:7-12.

39. COLEMAN, A. E. and MINTON, C. D. T. 1980. Mortality of Mute Swan progeny in an area of Staffordshire. **Wildfowl**. 31:22-28.

40. CRAMP, S. and SIMMONS, K. E. L. (eds) 1977-83. **The Birds of the Western Palaearctic**. Vol.I-III. Oxford: O.U.P.

41. MINTON, C. D. T. 1971. Mute Swan Flocks. **Wildfowl**. 22:71-88.

42. OGILVIE, M.A. 1969. Bewick's Swans in Britain and Ireland. **British Birds**. 62:505-522.

43. ATKINSON-WILLES, G. L. 1981. The numerical distribution and the conservation requirements of swans in North-west Europe. **Proc. Second Internl. Swan Symp. Sapparo, Japan Feb. 1980**. :40-48.

44. ATKINSON-WILLES, G. L. 1963. **Wildfowl in Great Britain**. London:H.M.S.O.

45. WALLACE, I. 1981. **Birdwatching in the Seventies**. London:MacMillan.

46. FRANCIS, I. S. 1984. The movement of grey geese over Sheffield 1970-1979. **Magpie**. 3:34-38.

47. OGILVIE, M. A. & BOYD, H. 1976. The numbers of Pink-footed Geese and Greylag Geese wintering in Britain: observations 1969-1975 and predictions 1976-1980. **Wildfowl**. 27:63-76.

48. OGILVIE, M. A. 1977. The numbers of Canada Geese in Britain. 1976. **Wildfowl**. 28:27-34.

49. GARNETT, M. G. H. 1980. Moorland breeding and moulting of Canada Geese in Yorkshire. **Bird Study**. 27:219-226.

50. WALKER, A. F. G. 1970. The moult migration of Yorkshire Canada Geese. **Wildfowl**. 21:99-104.

51. BARRY-THOMAS, C. 1977. The mortality of Yorkshire Canada Geese. **Wildfowl**. 28:35-47.

52. ROGERS, M. J. 1982. Ruddy Shelducks in Britain 1965-1979. **British Birds**. 75:446-455.

53. GLAVES, D. J. and GRIEVE, A. in press. The status of Shelduck in the southern Pennines. **Naturalist**.

54. ALLEN, R. M. and RUTTER, G. 1958. The moult migration of Shelduck from Cheshire in 1957. **British Birds**. 51:272-274.

55. ELTRINGHAM, S. K. and BOYD, H. 1963. The moult migration of the Shelduck to Bridgwater Bay, Somerset. **British Birds**. 56:433-444.

56. OWEN, M. and WILLIAMS, G. 1970. Winter distribution and habitat requirements of Wigeon in Britain. **Wildfowl**. 27:83-90.

57. RHODES, R. J. 1978. Changes in status of some birds in the Doncaster district since 1965. Suppl. **Lapwing**. 10.

58. SALMON, D. G. 1980-82. Wildfowl and wader counts 1979-1982. Wildfowl Trust.

59. OGILVIE, M. A. 1975. **Ducks of Britain and Europe**. Calton: Poyser.

60. YARKER, B. and ATKINSON-WILLES, G. L. 1971. The numerical distribution of some British breeding ducks. **Wildfowl**. 22:63-70.

61. MARCHANT, J. H. and HYDE, P. A. 1980. Aspects of the distribution of riparian birds on waterways in Britain and Ireland. **Bird Study**. 27:183-202.

62. SMITH, A. H. V. 1977. The Tufted Duck at Redmires Reservoirs. **Magpie**. 1:55-63.

63. HAWKER, D. M. 1970. Common Scoters inland. **British Birds**. 63:382-383.

64. KEY, R. 1983. Common Scoters in Derbyshire. **Derbys. Bird Rep.**. 1982:60-61.

65. SPENCER, K. G. 1969. Overland migration of the Common Scoter. **British Birds**. 62:332-333.

66. NILSSON, L, 1969. The migration of the Goldeneye in North-west Europe. **Wildfowl**. 20:112-118.

67. MEEK, E. R. and LITTLE, B. 1977. Ringing studies of Goosanders in Northumberland. **British Birds**. 70:273-285.

68. MEEK, E. R. and LITTLE, B. 1977. The spread of the Goosander in Britain and Ireland. **British Birds**. 70:229-237.

69. VINNICOMBE, K. E. and CHANDLER, R. J. 1982. Movements of Ruddy Ducks during the hard winter of 1978-79. **British Birds**. 75:1-11.

70. PARSLOW, J. 1973. **Breeding birds of Britain and Ireland**. Berkhamsted:Poyser.

71. HORNBUCKLE, J. 1980. Roosting Hen Harriers - winter 1979/80. **Derbys. Bird Rep.** 1979:9.

72. HERRINGSHAW, D. and GOSNEY, D. 1977. Recent changes in status of some birds in the Sheffield area. **Magpie**. 1:7-18.

73. MARQUISS, M. & NEWTON, I. 1982. The Goshawk in Britain. **British Birds**. 75:243-260.

74. PRESST, I. 1965. An enquiry into the recent breeding status of some of the smaller birds of prey and crows in Britain. **Bird Study**. 12:196-221.

75. HAWLEY, R. G. 1965. Enquiry into the status of four common birds of prey. **Sorby Rec.** 2,(2):59-61.

76. NEWTON, I. 1979. **Population Ecology of Raptors**. Berkhamsted:Poyser.

77. DRESSER, H. E. 1871-81. **A history of the birds of Europe**. 8 vols.

78. NEWTON, I., ROBSON, J. E. and YALDEN, D. W. 1981. Decline of the Merlin in the Peak District. **Bird Study**. 28:225-234.

79. ROWAN, W. 1922. Observations on the breeding habits of the Merlin. **British Birds.** 15:227-8.

80. FROST, R. A. 1980. Hobbies on Beeley Moor. **Derbys. Bird Rep.** 1979:7-8.

81. RATCLIFFE, D. A. 1980. **The Peregrine.** Calton: Poyser.

82a. YALDEN, D. W. 1972. The Red Grouse in the Peak District. **Naturalist.** 922:89-102.

82b. ANDERSON, P. and YALDEN, D. W. 1981. Increased sheep numbers and loss of heather moorland in the Peak District, England. **Biol. Cons.** 20:195-213.

83a. YALDEN, D. W. 1979. An estimate of the number of Red Grouse in the Peak District. **Naturalist.** 104:5-8.

83b. PHILIPS, J., YALDEN, D. W. and TALLIS, J. 1981. **Peak District Moorland Erosion Study: Phase 1 Report:** 200-203. Bakewell: Peak Park.

84. KITCHEN, A. 1979. The decline of the Black Grouse in Derbyshire (part 5). **Derbys. Bird Rep.** 1978:6.

85. LOVENBURY, G. A., WATERHOUSE, M. & YALDEN, D W. 1978. The status of Black Grouse in the Peak District. 103:3-14.

86. YALDEN, D. W. 1979. Decline of the Black Grouse in Derbyshire - critical comments. **Derbys. Bird Rep.** 1978:7-9.

87. CADBURY, C. J. 1980. The status and habitat of the Corncrake in Britain, 1978-1979. **Bird Study.** 27:203-218.

88. HORNBUCKLE, J. 1981. Some aspects of the breeding biology of the Moorhen **Magpie.** 2:46-56.

89. FROST, R. A. 1980. The first breeding occurrences of the Ringed Plover in Derbyshire. **Derbys. Bird Rep. 1979.** :10.

90. YALDEN, D. W. 1974. The status of Golden Plover and Dunlin in the Peak District. **Naturalist.** 93:81-91.

91. YALDEN, D. W. 1983. Golden Plover, Dunlin and recreational pressure on the moorlands. **Derbys. Bird Rep.** 1982 :62-63.

92. CAMBELL, L. H. 1982. **Peak District 1981. Report of the Survey for the R.S.P.B. Conservation Planning Department.** (unpub. R.S.P.B. Report).

93. WILLIAMSON, K. 1968. Bird Communities in the Malham Tarn region of the Pennines. **Field Studies** 2:651-668.

94. HOLLAND, P. K., ROBSON, J. E. and YALDEN, D.W. 1982. The status and distribution of the Common Sandpiper in the Peak District. **Naturalist** 107:77-86.

95. HOLLAND, P. K., ROBSON, J. E. and YALDEN, D.W. 1982. Breeding biology of the Common Sandpiper in the Peak District. **Bird Study** 29:99-110.

96. HUTCHINSON, C. D. and NEATH, B. 1978. Little Gulls in Britain and Ireland. **British Birds** 71:563-582.

97. CLARKSON, K. 1977. Gulls in the Sheffield area - their status, distribution, numbers and movement. **Magpie** 1:42-54.

98. BANNERMAN, D. A. 1953-63. **The Birds of the British Isles** (12 vols). Edinburgh: Oliver & Boyd.

99. VERNON, J. D. R. 1969. Spring migration of Common Gull in Britain and Ireland. **Bird Study** 16:101-107.

100. BARNES, J. A. G. 1961. The winter status of the Lesser Black-backed Gull 1959-1960. **Bird Study** 8:127-147.

101. MARSHALL, D. S. 1981. A study of a winter gull roost at Langsett Reservoir. **Magpie** 2:34-40.

102. HICKLING, R. A. O. 1984. Lesser Black-backed Gull numbers at British inland roosts 1979/80. **Bird Study** 31:157-160.

103. HICKLING, R. A. O. 1977. The inland wintering of gulls in Britain and Ireland. **Bird Study** 24:79-88.

104. BOWES, A., LACK, P. C. and FLETCHER, M. R. 1984. Wintering gulls in Britain, January 1983. **Bird Study** 31:161-170.

105. DEAN, A. R. and DEAN, B. R. 1976. Glaucous and Iceland Gulls in the West Midlands. **British Birds** 69:179-180.

106. KEY, R. 1981. Glaucous and Iceland gull occurrences in Derbyshire. **Derbys. Bird Rep.** 1980:57-59.

107. RHODES, R. J. 1967. **Birds of the Doncaster district**. Doncaster.

108. COULSON, J. C. 1983. The changing status of the Kittiwake in the British Isles 1969-1979. **Bird Study** 30:9-16.

109. UNDERWOOD, L. A. and STOVE, T. J. 1984. Massive wreck of seabirds in eastern Britain, 1984. **Bird Study** 31:79-88.

110. MARCHANT, J. H. 1983. Bird population changes for the years 1981-1982. **Bird Study** 30:127-133.

111. HUDSON, R. 1965. The spread of the Collared Dove in Britain and Ireland. **British Birds** 58:105-109.

112. HUDSON, R. 1972. Collared Doves in Britain and Ireland. **British Birds** 65:139-155.

113. HERRINGSHAW, D. and GOSNEY, D. 1974. The Short-eared Owl on the Sheffield moors in 1972-73. **Naturalist** 928:35-36.

114. TAYLES, K. V. 1981. Short-eared Owl hiding prey. **Magpie** 2:66.

115. GRIBBLE, F. C. 1983. Nightjars in Britain and Ireland in 1981. **Bird Study** 30:165-176.

116. HORNBUCKLE, J. 1984. Survey of Swifts breeding in the Sheffield area. **Magpie** 3:29-33.

117. RICHARDSON, P. W. 1979. A survey of breeding Swifts in Northamptonshire in 1978. **Northants. Bird Rep.** 1978:7-19.

118. HORNBUCKLE, J. 1977. Observations on Kingfisher behaviour. **Magpie** 1:64-69.

119. NOLAN, P. 1975. Report of the Garden Bird Survey. **Sheff. Bird Rep.** 1974.

120. SMITH, A. H. V. 1977. Birds of the parks, open spaces and woodlands within the city of Sheffield. **Magpie** 1:19-32.

121. MAWSON, G. P. and CRABTREE, A. 1981. House Martins in the Sheffield area, 1977. **Magpie** 2:26-33.

122. MAWSON, G. P. 1979. House Martin breeding population in the Dronfield district. **Derbys. Bird Rep.** 1978:10-13.

123. TAYLOR, K. and MARCHANT, J. H. 1983. Population changes for waterways birds, 1981-1982. **Bird Study** 130:121-126.

124. CRABTREE, A. and MAWSON, G. P. 1980. Ringing and recoveries in the Sheffield area. **Sorby Rec. Sp. Ser. 2**.

307

125. SHOOTER, P. 1970. The Dipper population of Derbyshire, 1958-68. **British Birds** 63:158-163.

126. MEAD, C.C. 1984. Sand Martin slump. **BTO News** 133:1.

127. FROST, R. A., HERRINGSHAW, D. and McKAY, C. R. 1982. Note on apparent bigamy by Black Redstart. **British Birds** 75:89-90.

128. ALSOP, D. 1975. The Ring Ouzel in Derbyshire. **Derbys. Bird Rep.** 1974:10-14.

129. FROST, R. A. and SHOOTER, P. 1983. Fieldfares breeding in the Peak District. **British Birds** 76:62-65.

130. RODGERS, H. C. 1975. The extension of the breeding range of the Nuthatch in Derbyshire. **Derbys. Bird Rep.** 1974:7-9.

131. FISHER, D. J. 1982. Report on roving tit flocks project. **British Birds** 75:370-374.

132. HORNBUCKLE, J. 1981. Behaviour, food and voice of a Great Grey Shrike. **Magpie** 2:57-60.

133. CARR, L. 1960. The Magpie in Sheffield, 1946. **Sorby Record** 1 (3):25.

134. ROBERTS, P. 1977. Magpies in Sheffield - an interim report of a survey of the breeding population, 1976. **Magpie** 1:4-6.

135. CLARKSON, K. 1984. The breeding and feeding ecology of the Magpie. **PhD thesis** (unpub.).

136. GOSNEY, D. 1977. Rookeries in the Sheffield area 1965-1975. **Magpie** 1:33-41.

137. SAGE, B. L. and VERNON, J. D. R. 1978. The 1975 national survey of Rookeries. **Bird Study** 25:64-86.

138. HOLYOAK, D. T. and RATCLIFFE, D. A. 1968. The distribution of the Raven in Britain and Ireland. **British Birds** 58:105-139.

139. SPENCER, R. and HUDSON, R. 1978. Report on bird ringing for 1977. **Ringing and Migration** 2:57.

140. FRANCIS, I. 1984. Starling roosts in the Sheffield area 1979-1980. **Magpie** 3:4-14.

141. HORNBUCKLE, J. 1984. Summering male Brambling attempting to mate with female Chaffinch. **Derbys. Bird Rep.** 1983:62-63.

142. BODDY, M. and SELLERS, R. M. 1983. Orientated movements by Greenfinch in southern Britain. **Ringing and Migration** 4:129-138.

143. ORFORD, N. 1973. Breeding distribution of the Twite in central Britain. **Bird Study** 20:50-62, 121-126.

144. LUNN, J. 1985. Parrot Crossbill - a new species for the Barnsley area. **Barnsley Bird Rep.** 1983:45-46.

145. HAYHOW, S. J. 1984. The status of the Corn Bunting in the Sheffield area. **Magpie** 3:22-28.

146. MacDONALD, J. D. 1953. Black-browed Albatross in Derbyshire. **British Birds** 46:110-111, 307-310.

Index

This includes all bird species and major sub-species on the Sheffield list but excludes the escapes listed in Appendix 5 and the pages relating to Appendix 1. Scientific equivalents to English names are given in Appendix 1.

Numbers in bold type refer to the first page of the entry in the systematic list.

310

311